Record of Works by Winslow Homer

Spanierman Gallery, llc

City University of New York Ph.D. Program in Art History

The Lloyd Goodrich and Edith Havens Goodrich

Whitney Museum of American Art

Record of Works by

Volume III

1877 to March 1881

Winslow Homer

LLOYD GOODRICH

Edited and expanded by

ABIGAIL BOOTH GERDTS

SPANIERMAN GALLERY, LLC, NEW YORK

Illustration of Nos. 661, No. 757, and No. 872
are from photographs provided by the New-York
Historical Society, New York; the courtesy of
the Historical Society's assistance is appreciated.

Published in the United States of America in 2008 by
Spanierman Gallery, LLC
45 East 58th Street
New York, NY 10022
www.spanierman.com

Library of Congress Control Number: 2005924965

ISBN 0-945936-88-5

Design: Marcus Ratliff
Composition: Amy Pyle
Photography: Light Blue Studio
Lithography: Meridian Printing

Contents

William Rudolph O'Donovan (1844–1920)
Winslow Homer
bronze, 12 x 6 x 4½ (30.480 x 15.240 x 11.430)

There is ample circumstantial evidence of O'Donovan's personal association with Homer: In the autumn
of 1877 the sculptor was among the founders of the Tile Club where he went by the appellation "the
O'Donoghue," and from 1878 into 1881, had his studio in the Tenth Street Studio Building.

This diminutive portrait bust of Homer was shown—probably for the first time—at the Century
Association's monthly exhibition, 10 March 1877. The following spring O'Donovan was represented
in the annual exhibition of the National Academy of Design by several of his portrait sculptures of
artist-friends, including this of Homer. It is likely the original plaster was the object on display on
both occasions.

Examples of this bust are held in the collections of the Pennsylvania Academy of the Fine Arts,
Philadelphia; the Metropolitan Museum of Art, New York; the Brooklyn Museum, Brooklyn, NY, and
the Corcoran Gallery of Art, Washington, DC. The Pennsylvania Academy borrowed the original plaster
from Thomas Eakins in 1911 in order to make its cast; it carries the incised inscription: O Donovan / 1876.
(The plaster is now lost.)

Summary Biography 1877 – March 1881

THAT WINSLOW HOMER's art and attitude changed in the later years of the 1870s is widely recognized. The change is readily inferred from the visual evidence of his work and occasional, perhaps exaggerated, comment in the contemporary press. Its cause or causes can only be speculated upon, as no documentation such as revelatory entries in a diary or volume of correspondence survives.

Speculative construction of Homer's state of mind in this period looks only to his emotional life for explication of his artistic choices and interpretation of his behavior. The conventional conclusion—widely, but mistakenly, accepted as fact—is that Homer's malaise resulted entirely from romantic and/or sexual frustration. Mysterious women (or an adolescent male) for whom he supposedly yearned are everywhere seen in the bland features of figure models.[1]

But Homer was a grown man, not a school boy. Like any mature, rational individual he may not be defined by a single, unwavering motivation; the fabric of life is an accumulation of choices and pressures. While creating Winslow Homer as the hero of a tragic romance may be entertaining, it is not a reasoned historical assessment.

Many circumstances and incidents shaped Homer's life; most of these can never be known. However, an overlooked, and likely compelling, motivation for his behavior at any point in his life, but particularly in these late years of the 1870s, would be his perception of his achievement in his profession. Homer's first priorities were consistently the exercise of his gift and the career built upon it. His sense of the future of what he called "the business" would largely dictate the course of his life.

As Homer entered the fortieth decade of his life he could see himself as professionally successful—but not distinguished; his work generally noticed and liked by critics—but not fully admired or respected. He was making his living by his art but only by constant attention to its marketing; financial security seemed out of reach. A man ambitious to attain reputation as well as the comfortable life style of his social peers, which Homer was, would have good reason to be dissatisfied as he surveyed his professional prospects.

The celebrated sale late in December 1876 of John Taylor Johnson great collection may have put the spur to Homer's growing professional discontent. His *Prisoners from the Front* (No. 1:282)—a decade-old painting which critics frequently cited as superior to almost anything he subsequently produced—sold for $1,800, a significantly higher amount than his current work could command.

The frustrations in his own career would not have been the only troubling aspect of his professional environment. The New York art world was changing. Any comfortable sense of community among artists was being eroded by the tensions between the "new men" largely distinguished by their French training, and the older generation who defended "American" aesthetic values. The schism would become manifest in the founding of the Society of American Artist in rivalry to the National Academy of Design.

Also, as the sheer number of artists and the distinctions among their skills and styles increased, so did competition for patronage, and enmity among colleagues. Factions of the National Academy, which in the early nineteenth century offered almost the sole opportunity for American artists to promote their work, tried to use the authority of the Academy to impose restraints on members' opportunities to contribute to exhibitions not open to all.[2]

Some of the more successful artists (usually members of the Academy) formed short-term associations to organize and control sales of their own work even though such sales undercut the Academy's monopoly on "fresh" material. Such associations and sales surely contributed to the innovation which burgeoned in the later 1870s: dealer-galleries interested in representing contemporary American artists. This new option to market work through an agent would profoundly alter Homer's life pattern.

Homer had pursued a conventional path to advancement when he entered upon his profession. Although already a quite accomplished graphic artist, he had taken classes at the Academy School; he consistently submitted work to the Academy's annual exhibitions; and having early attained election to full Academician, he continued regularly contributing to its exhibitions; he attended all Academy meetings, served on its Council and committees, and expressed himself willing to accept the post of permanent instructor in the Academy School. Homer joined and engaged with the Artists Fund Society, The Palette, and the Century Association. He submitted his work seemingly at every exhibition opportunity. Then after something over fifteen years of active and positive participation in the New York art scene, the professional structures he had supported began to become fractious; friends were on opposite sides of controversies; and he was being characterized by critics as among the "older"—and by inference—obsolete members of his profession.

From about 1877 through 1880, Homer may be seen to be gradually disengaging from his accustomed professional patterns, and with characteristic focus and deliberation to be preparing for a major redirection of his life and practice. This he initiated in the spring of 1881 with his departure from New York for an extended retreat on the northeastern coast of England.

9 January: Art Students' League exhibition: shows unidentified work/s.

11–13 January: Union League Club exhibition; shows one painting.

13 January: Century Association exhibition; shows one painting.

16 January: Attended the New York Artists' Fund Society reception.[3]

c. 22–c. 26 January: has a painting for auction at Schenck.

22 January: American Society of Painters in Water Colors annual exhibition opens; shows five watercolors. (See commentary No. 612.) The catalogue of this exhibition, the Society's tenth annual, is the first to include Homer on the listing of its members.

c. 26–c. 31 January: has an unidentified painting for auction at Leavitt.

3 February: Century Association exhibition; shows two paintings.

5–9 February: has three painting for auction at Schenck.

8–10 February: Union League Club exhibition; shows one painting.

16–21 February: has a painting for auction at Schenck.

24 February: forty-first birthday.

26 February–2 March: has a painting for auction at Kurtz.

March: "Many of our most prominent artists are now contributing sketches for a truly magnificent album, which will be disposed of at the fair to be opened at Tammany Hall on the third of the next month, for the benefit of St. Ann's Roman Catholic Church. This album will doubtless attract great attention from the eminence of the artists represented and the consequent value of the work as well as the novelty of the experiment in connection with a fair. Sketches in oil and water colors illustrating the special characteristics of style and mode of treatment are furnished by the following [44 named] artists: J. H. Beard, J. G. Brown, David Johnson, . . . D. Huntington, A. Parton, Winslow Homer, Wm. McGrath, Arthur Quartley . . . ."[4]

10 March: Century Association exhibition; shows one painting, *The Cotton Pickers* (2:No. 602), which is immediately sold to an English visitor, and is taken out of the country.

c. 19–23 March: has a painting for auction at Schenck.

2–6 April: has an unidentified painting for auction at Schenck.

3 April: National Academy of Design annual exhibition opens; exhibits two paintings.

11 April: Attended Art Students' League monthly reception.[5]

12–14 April: Union League Club exhibition; shows one painting.

28 April: leaves on a trip to the South: "I have received your letter and the blocks. If July will do for the drawings I will do them. I leave tomorrow for Norfolk Va. I am sorry it should have happened so. If you should want the blocks (which I have not opened) send word to Mr. E. W. Perry and he will return them to you." (letter of 27 April [1877] to Andrew Anthony)[6]

For Homer to travel well into unaccustomed territory for the purpose of developing paintings—as he had in 1862 and 1863 when he went into the field to obtain visual stimulus for painting on the Civil War—indicates calculated intention to restructure his art. This trip South came just over a month following the critical success of *Cotton Pickers*, which suggests he may have put that painting forward as a conscious test of the appeal of the subject matter. Homer's audience was used to his gentle scenes of children and pretty women enjoying the pastimes of the country and seaside resorts. His paintings of Southern African-Americans introduced a new and unexpected gravity into his work.

2 May: Boston Art Club, *Second Exhibition for 1877* opens; shows one painting.

by May 31: "Mr. Winslow Homer is again in his studio after a month's sojourn in Virginia. He has brought back several new pictures"[7]

2 June: Century Association exhibition; shows three oil, and two watercolor paintings. (The oils were the final results of his excursions to the South and exploration of the theme of the American peasant, former slaves: *A Visit from the Old Mistress* (2:No. 602), *Sunday Morning in Virginia* (No. 620), and *Dressing for the Carnival* (No. 619); the watercolors were *Backgammon* (No. 614), and probably *The New Novel* (No. 612).

June: Society of American Artists is founded by Wyatt Eaton, Helena de Kay Gilder, Augustus St. Gaudens, Walter Shirlaw, and Louis C. Tiffany, with Frederick Dielman, Francis Lathrop, Olin Warner, Robert Swain Gifford, Homer Dodge Martin, Samuel Colman, Julian Alden Weir, John Henry Dolph, John La Farge, Thomas Moran, William Sartain, Will H. Low, Robert Minor, Alexander Wyant, George Inness, Alfred Wordsworth Thompson, and Albert Pinkham Ryder.[8]

by 19 June: "Mr. Winslow Homer, the artist, has taken the studio formerly occupied by the late Mr. J. Beaufain Irving in the Tenth street building."[9] (Homer had occupied rooms in the Tenth Street Studio since 1872; thus this was a move within the building.)

19–23 June: has unidentified work/s for auction at Barker.

mid June into August: Homer's whereabouts are unaccounted for. He may have spent some time with his parents who were likely summering in Prout's Neck, Maine. Then as was his habit, returned to upstate New York, for both work and the hunting and fishing. One thing that does not seem to have occupied his time and attention was work in watercolor. If the *New York Herald*'s report late in September that Homer returned from his summer absence with a "portfolio full of color sketches,"[10] was accurate than it was either put aside or served other purposes than developing watercolors for exhibition. Homer's focus in the 1877–1878 season was painting in oil, and probably mastering the techniques of glazing ceramics.

1 October: "Winslow Homer has returned from a summer in the Adirondacks"[11]

6 October: Century Association exhibition; shows one painting.

11 October: Homer is among artists present at the Union League Club's reception to open the first monthly exhibition of the season, and has one painting in the exhibition.[12]

autumn: Homer is one of the initiating members of Tile Club. (Its loose organization hardly entitled early participants to be called "founders.") Ostensibly the club was formed by men—most, but not all, artists—interested in pursuing decorative painting. However, tile-making was clearly an entertaining excuse for a weekly social assembly. By rule, membership was kept convivially small, twelve being the optimum number. Other first members were: Edwin Austen Abbey, R. Swain Gifford, William Mackay Laffin, William R. O'Donovan (who sculpted a bust of Homer), Walter Paris, Arthur Quartley, Charles. S. Reinhart, Earl Shinn, F. Hopkinson Smith, Edward Wimbridge, and Julian Alden Weir. Four men whose talents were musical were included as honorary members. Each member had a pseudonym; Homer's was the "Obtuse Bard." Meetings rotated from studio to studio on Wednesdays; it was the weekly host's responsibility to provide blank tiles, painting materials, beer and tobacco. In return the host kept all the evening's tiles.

Several of Homer's tiles probably done in the casual context of those Wednesday evening parties survive. (See No. 645, No. 645.5, and No. 646.) However most of his tiles are clearly the product of serious work done in daylight and without social distraction. His tile schemes are too complex and ambitious to be merely the exercise of a passing enthusiasm. There are indications Homer entertained the idea of manufacturing and marketing sets of tiles applicable to architectural decoration.[13]

Homer's use of the fancy dress shepherdess costume in a number of well developed drawings is a conspicuous departure from the sort of topical genre he had favored, and likely parallels formation of the Tile Club, rather than results from it. This whole episode is another example of Homer testing out new expressive (and marketable) forms.

3 November: Century Association exhibition; shows one painting.

1 December: Century Association exhibition; shows two paintings.

3–15 December: Brooklyn Art Association exhibition; shows one painting.

4 December: Art Students' League exhibition; shows one painting.

December: Lotos Club exhibition; shows one painting.

21 December: has one painting in the Union League Club's special exhibition in honor of the visit to the Club of President and Mrs. Rutherford B. Hayes.

1878

Homer is not listed in New York City Directory for the year ending 1 May 1878, but no Homer with a first name falling alphabetically beyond "Julius" is listed, suggesting all New Yorkers of that surname whose first initial placed them in the latter half of the alphabet were accidentally lost that year. He reappears in the listings of 1879 and 1880 still at the Tenth Street Studio Building, and there is no reason to question he was resident there in 1878.

[**26 January**]: Utica [NY] Art Association exhibition opens: shows one painting.

28 January–1 February: has a painting for auction by Leavitt; the sale is on display at Kurtz Gallery.

30 January: has two paintings for auction at Leavitt.

4 February: American Society of Painters in Water Colors annual exhibition opens, without any examples of Winslow Homer's work.

> Perhaps no contributions have had quite so much *éclat* this year as the absence of certain contributions. The always-unexpected Mr. Homer, so certain to do something that nobody could have anticipated and that no inferior artist could do, this season does nothing. He produced last year some powerful effects of the blotchy order, some abrupt eulogiums of Japanese fan-painting, some cries of irreconcilable color, that excited the liveliest attention of the public. We believe that none of those who so readily celebrated the originality of these striking works expressed their gratitude by acquisition, and the leader of the invading school has withdrawn into his tent to ponder on the bad faith of the champions of bric-à-brac. Certain foreign contributors, however, have planted the standards and the disturbed colors of the orientalists, and the Exhibition does not quite lack the peculiar and stimulating accent which it was the wont of Mr. Homer to confer on the yearly display.[14]

The *Nation's* reviewer had no way to know—and subsequent generations who have seized on his remarks as an early symptom of Homer withdrawing into a black temper have not recognized—that he had done nothing substantial in watercolor since the Society's exhibition in 1877, and consequently had nothing fresh to put into its 1878 exhibition. It was the summer of 1878 before Homer got back into steady exercise of the medium. The idea that he didn't participate in the 1878 Society exhibition because his 1877 contributions had failed to sell from the show sounds a bit mean-spirited. Homer was fully accustomed to his work attracting attention, and failing to sell. However, that his move to raise the stature of his watercolors from "sketches from nature" to serious paintings, demonstrated in his contributions to the 1877 exhibition had proved commercially unproductive, could explain his temporary turn away from the medium.

14 February: The *Evening Post* reports "Mr. Winslow Homer is drawing on wood sketches of his paintings entitled *Song of the Lark* [2:No. 600] and *Hooking Melons* [*The Watermelon Boys*, 2:No. 595], which will be engraved for Appletons' *Art Journal*." George W. Sheldon's *Journal* article on Homer and Frederick Bridgman was not published until August.

Both illustrated paintings were works of 1876, yet Homer put both into the National Academy *Annual* of 1878 which opened in April, probably to take advantage of the publicity they would enjoy from the publication—had it come out during the exhibition.[15]

22–26 February: has unidentified work/s for auction at Edward Brown.

24 February: forty-second birthday.

3 March: Century Association exhibition; shows one painting.

5 March: Art Students' League exhibition of original drawings for illustrations lent by Mr. Parsons, art director of *Harper's Weekly*, including work/s by Homer.

6 March–5 April: The Society of American Artists first annual exhibition is mounted at the Kurtz Gallery.

11–13 March: has a painting for auction at D. A. Mathews.

2 April: National Academy of Design annual exhibition opens; shows three paintings from 1876, two from 1877, and one tile. The majority of the critics gave short and frequently dismissive notice to the group, although occasionally there was a kind word for *In the Field* (*The Song of the Lark*, 2:No. 600) which had received the best hanging position. Then late in the run of the exhibition "C. C." delivered his opinion at length in the *New-York Daily Tribune*. ("C. C." may be presumed to be Clarence Cook, the *Tribune*'s regular critic.)

> Winslow Homer sends six pictures to the exhibition but no one of them will add to reputation, and only one—"In a Field,"—will be considered as at all worthy of him. For an artist who has done such clever things as Mr. Homer, and who has always found the public more than ready to welcome him, it looks like trifling both with himself and with his friends when he sends such things as are hung in the corridor on either side the door of the south room [*Fresh Morning*, No. 622 and *Two Guides*, No. 625]. The subjects of some of these are mean; those of all of them are uninteresting; and the execution is as vapid as the theme. It may be that the public does not deserve respectful treatment, but it is not in the interest of art for artists to deal with the public on that theory. We have no intention to intrude our advice upon the artists, but we may at least be allowed to speak in self-defence. Mr. Winslow Homer was recognized on his first appearance before the public, as an artist of uncommon merit. He furnished a good illustration of the quickness with which our public spies out merit The critics had nothing to do with finding out his worth; in his case, as always, they simply seconded the public's motion. What has come over this artist of late years that he sulks in his tent, and seems to take pleasure in painting as badly as he can! His bad painting, it must be confessed, is very bad, But the reason why it is so bad is because we see plainly how good it might have been had the artist chosen to put himself into

his work, and not played at chuck-farthing with his talent. The "In the Field," south room, is saved from condemnation by a bright morning sky sown with cirrus cloud, and there is some pleasant sentiment in this picture which we are glad to welcome. A few years ago, however, we should not have had to thank Mr. Homer for such a scrap of cold comfort as this.[16]

"C.C.'s" complaint that Homer "sulks in his tent" sounds suspiciously like the *Nation*'s scornful characterization a few months earlier of Homer's failure to participate in the watercolor Society's annual exhibition as having "withdrawn into his tent" because his contributions to the 1877 show had not sold. Either Cook borrowed the literary figure from a colleague, or he also authored the *Nation* article.

6 April: Century Association exhibition; shows two paintings.

29 April–3 May: has one or two paintings for auction at Barker.

1 May: *Exposition Universelle de 1878* opens in Paris. Homer was represented in the American section by *A Visit from the Old Mistress* (2:No. 603) and *Sunday Morning in Virginia* (No. 620), which presumably were his own submissions, and by *The Country School* (2:No. 388) of 1871, and *Snap the Whip* (2:No. 419) of 1872, lent by John H. Sherwood, presumably at the request of the selection committee.

2 May: "The Tile Club, whose meetings during the past season at the studio of Mr. Walter Paris have been very enjoyable to the artists members, will conclude the series tomorrow evening by a dinner at the studio of Winslow Homer. On Saturday, from ten A.M. to six P.M., the tiles painted during the season will be on exhibition in the latter studio."[17]

8 May: is present at the annual meeting of the National Academy of Design. The sole purpose of the Academy's annual meetings was institutional business, and were the only occasions on which the full membership convened. The principal activities of the meetings were election of officers and committees for the coming year, and election of new associate members, and elevation of qualified Associates to full standing as Academicians. After twenty-two years of consistent participation in Academy activities, this 1878 meeting is the last Homer attends. He continues to contribute paintings to its exhibitions over the next decade, but other than that, there is no evidence of his taking any interest in the organization.

If the New York press' descriptions of the atmosphere in the professional community of artists is believed, the meeting was marked by organizational and personal animosities. The *Daily Tribune* report was the most candid of several notices.

It was anticipated among the artists that there would be a stormy time in the National Academy of Design on the occasion of the annual election yesterday, as some of the names that were up for election as Academicians or Associates last year and were rejected then, causing considerable feeling, were again to be brought up. A number of new men also had been proposed, many of them members of the Society of American Artists, against whom and whose work opposition had been manifested by some of the old Academicians.

The only successful candidates of the fourteen Associates nominated for advancement to Academician were the inoffensive landscapist, Horace Wolcott Robbins, and Robert Swain Gifford, a founder of the Society of American Artists. Louis Comfort Tiffany and John Henry Dolph, also founders of the Society were among those not advanced that year.

Of the twenty-three men nominated for associate membership only Benjamin Porter, William O'Donovan, and Walter Shirlaw—president of the Society of American Artists— received the necessary percentage of votes. (Shirlaw resigned his election in 1879). Among those rejected were William Sartain, Julian Alden Weir, Arthur Quartley, and Robert Minor from the membership of the Society, and Homer's acquaintances Edwin A. Abbey and Roswell Shurtleff.

The *Tribune* story continued with particular mention of one of Homer's closest friends ". . . . There was also a report that dissatisfaction existed against one of the oldest and most prominent officials of the Academy, and that efforts would be made to prevent his reelection. By some this was believed to refer to E. Wood Perry . . . . Four members of the Council, T. W. Wood, George H. Hall and C. Calverly were reelected, and H. A. Loop, Jervis McEntee and Worthington Whittredge were chosen in place of E. Wood Perry, W. L. Sonntag and James D. Smillie"[18]

early May: "Mr. Winslow Homer, feeling a little under the weather, will soon go into the country on a fishing excursion of a week or two."[19]

c. 27–29 May: exhibition and sale at C. F. Libbie's auction room, Boston., of eighty-four "Original Water Color and Charcoal Sketches from Nature by Winslow Homer, N. A."

> Mr. Winslow Homer's Drawings and Sketches, on exhibition at Mr. C. F. Libbie's auction room, 13 Beacon street, and to be sold there tomorrow afternoon, would produce a sensation in London or Paris, said a leading Boston painter yesterday. There are eighty-four in pencil, crayon, charcoal and watercolor, embracing bits of army life, and life (especially child-life) at the seashore and in the country, all as American and Yankee in character as the "stars and stripes," but without a particle of vulgar forcing of that idea.[20]

This is the earliest of a series of large sales Homer organized in the three years leading up to his departure for England in the spring of 1881.

In these later years of the 1870s Homer appears to have begun to cultivate Boston exhibition and sale opportunities. The known instances of his showing there are rare before May 1877 when he contributed a painting to a Boston Art Club exhibition. A year later he mounted this major exhibition and sale at the Libbie auction house. No detailed record of the works in this sale survives. It is worth noting, however, that several Bostonians are the earliest known owners of caches of Homer drawings and watercolors from the 1870s.[21]

Homer apparently established a relationship with the Doll & Richards gallery at about this time; the gallery sold a painting for him in July 1878 and were showing several more that autumn. Late in November 1878 the Leonard & Co. auction house had something from Homer. *A Visit from the Old Mistress* and *Sunday Morning in Virginia*, paintings which had gained celebrity from their reception at the Paris Exposition of 1878, made their first domestic public appearance at the Boston Museum of Fine Arts in the *Exhibition of Contemporary Art* organized by the Boston Art Club, Boston Society of Architects, and Schools at the Museum of Fine Arts that opened in April 1879. Homer's newly strengthened Boston connection would culminate in Doll & Richards' one-man exhibition of more than 100 drawings and watercolors resulting from his 1880 summer working in Gloucester.

1 June: Century Association exhibition; shows a fireplace surround formed of tiles recorded as "Pastoral;" presumably this was *Shepherd and Shepherdess* (No. 654).

c. 9–12 June: has an unidentified painting for auction at Barker.

c. 26–28 June: *Inviting a Shot* (2:No. 260), a work of 1864, is in an auction at Barker. It is questionable whether Homer was its consignor.

June: "Winslow Homer is at Cornwall, on the Hudson."[22]

1 July: Doll & Richards, Boston, records its sale of *Autumn* (No. 640). This is the earliest documented occasion of the gallery's agency on behalf of Homer. The painting is sold for $300; the gallery noted that the $11 cost for putting the frame in order was to be charged to Homer.

5 July: inscribed date on the drawing of *The Card Game* (No. 664) being played on the porch of John Orr's boarding house in Mountainville, New York.[23]

It is conventional to assume Homer found the subjects of virtually all his drawings and watercolors from the late 1870s which feature children and young men and women in country settings at Houghton Farm, the Mountainville home of Lawson Valentine. Certainly, the Farm and its native inhabitants (both two- and four-footed), obviously sketched on site, are frequent subjects in drawings and watercolors of 1878, reflecting not only a visit that summer, but that it was devoted to work. However, Homer routinely ranged around New England and New York State in his summer travels in these years. Neither he nor his country subjects may be confined to a single setting.

summer: apparently visited in the neighborhood of Belmont, Massachusetts, where a number of relatives and old friends lived. See the drawings and watercolor featuring the Waverley Oaks, No. 737, No. 738, and No. 739.

August: G. W. Sheldon's "American Painters. Winslow Homer and F. A. Bridgman" is published.[24]

August: has two illustrations published in *Scribner's Monthly* accompanying an article: Rowland E. Robinson, "Glimpses of New England Farm Life." (See No. 661 and No. 662.)

3 September: Louisville Industrial Exposition opens; shows one painting.

September: "Winslow Homer is in that indefinite locality known as 'up the Hudson'"[25]

10 October "Leeds," and **15 October**: inscribed on drawings No. 740-R and No. 740-V.

October: Doll & Richards, Boston, has three paintings on display, and presumably for sale: *At the Window* (2:No. 403) of 1872, *The Course of True Love* (2: No. 552), a lost work of 1874–1875, and *Dressing for the Carnival* (No. 619) of 1877.

2 November: Century Association exhibition; shows one oil painting, twenty-one water-color paintings, and six graphite drawings.

November: "Mr. Winslow Homer has returned from the country with a large collection of sketches and studies in water-colors, some of which were recently on exhibition at the Century Club. They are very impressive now, and give promise of exceedingly successful pictures."[26]

19 November: has unidentified work/s for auction at Leonard & Co., Boston.

3 December: Art Students' League exhibition; shows unidentified watercolors, and the tile mantelpiece decoration, "Bo-Peep and Her Sheep," presumably this was *Resting Shepherdess* (No. 651).

December: "Mr. Louis R. Menger has opened a gallery at No. 22 Dey street, for the purpose of handling the productions of foreign and American painters. It is the intention of this gentleman to make American art a specialty . . . . Mr. Menger is well known among art connoisseurs and painters generally, and judging from the number of prominent artists who have already sent in their works, we have no doubt that in time he will feel encouraged to enlarge his gallery. Among those who have contributed fine specimens are . . . Winslow Homer, and others. These paintings are all important works, and are worthy of public attention."[27]

Menger is consistently in New York City directories before and well after 1878 as a framer whose shop was at the Dey street address, but never as operating a commercial gallery. However, he seems to have turned his hand to a number of art related services. In 1880 He was the publisher of Homer's "Artotype" facsimile *A Pretty Maiden* (No. 884-b), and probably also *Yachting Girl* (No. 883-b). And when the National Academy of Design began to require submissions to its exhibition shipped from outside New York be handled by a packing and shipping agent, Menger was one of three firms named in their 1880 circular.

1879

9–11 January: has a painting for auction at Schenck.

11 January: Century Association exhibition; shows six watercolors.

[25 January]: Utica [NY] Art Association exhibition opens; shows two unidentified works: *With Your Choice*, sale priced at $500, and therefore probably an oil; and *A Pastoral* priced at $100, and therefore probably a watercolor.

7 January: Art Students' League exhibition; shows unidentified watercolors

31 January: attends the preview reception of the American Water Color Society annual exhibition.[28]

3 February: American Water Color Society annual exhibition opens; shows twenty-four watercolor paintings (of which two are lent by their owners, Mrs. Lawson Valentine and her brother-in-law, Henry Valentine) and five works in "black and white."

February: Art Students' League exhibition of original drawings for illustrations in *Scribner's* publications, including works by Homer.

12 February: Salmagundi Sketch Club exhibition; shows a "frame of pencil memoranda."

24 February: forty-third birthday.

4 March: Loan exhibition for the benefit of the Peabody Institute, and the Decorative Arts Society of Baltimore opens in that city; shows one or two oil paintings.

1 April: National Academy of Design annual exhibition opens; shows three paintings. Homer had not exhibited any of these three before. He may have finished them not long before the exhibition, but he had certainly held them for this occasion. He placed the sale price for each at $1,500., approximately double the highest amount he had previously placed on his oils. Only one of the canvases survives in its original dimensions, but given the uniform pricing of the three, it is likely they were also uniform in size. Judging by the surviving work, that size was 50 inches by 30 inches. Up to this time Homer's largest oils—which essentially equates to those he considered most significant—was a consistent 38 inches by 24 inches. (*Pitching Quoits* (2:No. 266), of 1865, is the single exception at 54 inches by 27 inches, but it was Homer's principal contribution to the annual exhibition which inaugurated the National Academy's grand new building.)

Each work presented a clearly different theme: The *Shepherdess of Houghton Farm* (No. 772) was the culmination of Homer's idealization of country youth. *Sundown* (No. 775)—which is known only from contemporary descriptions—also focused on a young woman, but one far from the fantasy pastoral world of *Shepherdess*; here, apparently, was one of Homer's idle girls prettily posed on an all-too-real beach. *Upland Cotton* (No. 776) was a reprise of the admired *Cotton Pickers* (2:No. 602).

The Shepherdess of Houghton Farm made the least impression on the critics; opinion was nearly balanced but negative comments were in the majority. *Sundown* was savaged by the critics, and soon disappeared. *Upland Cotton* was generally well-received. None of the three attracted a buyer.

It is possible to see the presentation of these three strong paintings in the principal forum of American art at the time as Homer's challenge to the New York public and press to give him unequivocal recognition as a substantial artist rather than one who did not quite realize expectations. If that was his intention, he surely was disappointed.

Between the Academy exhibition in the spring of 1879 and his departure for England just two years later, Homer exhibited few oil paintings; all but one were "old" works. It would appear Homer nearly gave up working in oil—then accepted as the medium of important art—early in 1879, and essentially did not take it up again until his return from England.[29]

1 April: has two paintings for auction at Kurtz.

22 April: Boston Art Club, Boston Society of Architects, Schools at the Museum of Fine Arts, *Exhibition of Contemporary Art* opens; shows two oils, four watercolors and one drawing.

5 May: The American Art Gallery opens; has unidentified work/s in the inaugural exhibition.

> Mr. R. E. Moore, who has had a gallery for many years on Union Square, last evening opened new rooms in the Kurtz Building on Twenty-third street and Madison square. He has associated with him Mr. Jas. F. Sutton as a special partner and his enterprise is to conduct a gallery for the permanent exhibition and sale of exclusively American paintings and works of art.[30]

> American artists have had no single central gallery where people could go with the certainty of finding pictures of all sizes and all prices. Mr. Moore, who has had experience in the selling of American pictures, is now about to try conclusions [*sic*] with the theory that what was wanted in New-York was a well-known picture centre or painting exchange. Hitherto the painters here have been forced to send their work to a number of small auction sales distributed through the course of the year for, with the exception of the one or two annual exhibitions and the occasional demand from visitors at the studios, there was no other way to rendering their wares marketable.[31]

For some years previous to this Rufus E. Moore (1839–1918) had organized large sales of contemporary American artists' work on an approximately annual schedule, holding them on the premises of various well-known auction houses. The innovation of the American Art Gallery was that, while Moore and his partner James F. Sutton (1843–1915) bought works directly from artists, the Gallery also served like a cooperative. Artists could display paintings for an extended period of time; if sold, Moore and Sutton received a commission. Thus, the Gallery was to be a venue for a continuous display of contemporary American work. The earliest Homer is known to have been associated with one of Moore's auctions was May 1873.[32]

8–10 May: Union League Club exhibition; shows at least one unidentified watercolor.

c. 12–17 May: Leavitt auction to benefit the family of T. C. Grannis (1851–1878), painter and art critic; Homer contributed an unidentified drawing.

c. 12–17 May: has unidentified work/s for auction at Barker.

summer: "Winslow Homer does not as yet care to tell his summer resort."[33]

"Of Mr. Winslow Homer's movements in summer-time no person however intimate is ever supposed to have the secret, and the present season is not made an exception."[34]

Homer seems surely to have spent time in and around West Townsend, Massachusetts, in the north central part of the state, very near the New Hampshire border. Martha French Homer, Charles S. Homer, Jr.'s wife, came from West Townsend, where her family was prominent; the Charles Homer's summer retreat was the fairly grand French house in West Townsend. At about this time Homer is said to have lived with Dr. Henry B. Boynton in West Townsend for six summertime weeks while his broken arm healed. The year-date of this extended stay is not established, but seems likely to have been 1879.

Richard N. Smith, author of a history of Townsend commissioned by its historical society, states unequivocally that Homer spent the whole summer of 1879 in the town, but does not identify a source which would allow him to be so positive.[35]

Gordon Hendricks accepted that Homer had spent time in West Townsend and found the subject of at least one painting there, but he had no doubt it had been the summer of 1878. He rested this conclusion primarily on an unfounded assumption that the group of men Homer sketched in *The Card Game* (No. 664) were playing in the shade of the Charles Homers's West Townsend porch. Hendricks further supported his conclusion by describing (but not reproducing) an unlocated letter written by Elizabeth Preston of New Ipswich, New Hampshire, a cousin of Martha Homer. According to Hendricks, Mrs. Preston dated the letter 6 July 1878, the day following the date inscribed on *The Card Game*, and mentioned Homer then being a guest in her home.[36]

While 1879 seems the more likely dating for a substantial stay in and around West Townsend, given Homer's habit of rambling during the summer, it is reasonable that he visited the town in both 1878 and 1879.(See No. 769, No. 771, and No. 864.)

Helen Cooper, in her entry on *The Swing* (No. 826) in the Worcester Museum's catalogue of its collection of American watercolors, agrees that Homer visited West Townsend in the summer of 1879, and further states: "This stay resulted in a series of *plein air* watercolors of rural subjects of men and boys plowing and little girls picking apples or berries, lying in the grass, or playing on swings."[37] Cooper thus assumes virtually all Homer's works on paper from No. 777 through No. 858 were done in West Townsend and of subjects found there.

However, Homer may be surely placed visiting in the Boston area—that is, well east of West Townsend—in the summer of 1879. Adelaide Cole Chase, the daughter of Homer's friend, J. Foxworth Cole, recalled posing for the drawing simply titled *Girl* (No. 845). The Cole home was in Winchester, Massachusetts. While Mrs. Chase was not asked about any other works from that summer, she may be recognized in several of them.

4 October: Century Association exhibition; shows one paintings.

before 9 October: "The studio of Mr. Winslow Homer presents an almost deserted appearance as its owner has only today entered it, but having been 'all around' during the summer the results of his work in peculiarly individual treatment will soon become apparent."[38]

1 November: Century Association exhibition; shows one painting, and "Wedding Cards, twenty-eight sketches in black and white."

6 December: Century Association exhibition; shows one painting.

7–10 December: A preliminary exhibition and auction of "Original Water Color and Charcoal Sketches from Nature by Winslow Homer, N. A." is held at Wm. A. Butters and Co., Wabash Avenue, Chicago. Like the first of his major sale events in these years, held at Libbie's auction room in Boston in May 1878, Homer took a large collection well beyond New York, probably with the idea of reaching a buying audience for whom his work would have the advantage of novelty. No record is known by which any of the works in the group may be positively identified. However, several owners and dealers told Lloyd Goodrich that their Homers emanated from this sale; others with early histories of ownership in Chicago and the near mid-West are likely to have been acquired on that occasion. Homer probably sent recent product, that is, works dating from 1878 and 1879. However, a few earlier works may have been included.

6–18 December: John H. Sherwood's collection is auctioned—for the second time. Three of Homer's more important painting from 1871, 1872, and 1875 are included: *The Country School* (2:No. 388), *Snap the Whip* (2:No. 419), and *Weaning the Calf* (2:No. 593). The lengthy pre-auction exhibition was held in the galleries of the National Academy building. On this try, unlike Sherwood's 1873 sale, the Homers find real buyers.

9–13 December: Springfield (Massachusetts) Art Association first artists' exhibition; shows two paintings.

1880

8–10 January: Union League Club exhibition; shows two paintings.

10 January: Century Association exhibition; shows one painting.

c. 12–16 January: has a painting for auction at D. A. Mathews.

24 January: attends s Tile Club dinner in honor of "some guests from Boston."[39]

2 February: American Water Color Society annual exhibition opens; Homer does not show. The exhibition remains on view to 1 March.

c. 2–c. 6 February: has a painting for auction at D. A. Mathews.

7 February: Century Association exhibition; shows two watercolors.

17 February: Gill's Art Galleries annual exhibition opens in Springfield, Massachusetts; shows one painting.

c. 22–c. 26 February: has four paintings for auction at D. A. Mathews.

24 February: forty-fourth birthday.

3–4 March: auctions seventy-one watercolors and drawings and one oil sketch at D. A. Mathews. This is the third in the series of large sales Homer organized in the three years leading up to his departure for England in the spring of 1881. It takes place a few days following the close of the American Water Color Society's annual exhibition, in which Homer had not participated. Having held sales in Boston and Chicago—well beyond observation of an audience familiar with his work—this gave New York the chance to demonstrate its regard for it. In discussing the Water Color Society's *Annual* within its summary of the 1880 season *Scribner's* gave particular attention to Homer's unconventional choices.

> The Water-Colors. Water-colors retained their hold on the public and the affections of artists; and although several names of note were wanting to make the exhibition complete, new aspirants were abundantly present. For example Mr. Winslow Homer, who is always surprising his admirers, chose to stay away from the exhibition altogether this year, although he showed last year a greater number of pictures than any other painter. Instead of hazarding again his reputation as a water-colorist after the success of last year, he had the inspiration to doubt the fickle public and prefer a sale of his own, in which it is said that good prices were obtained"[40]

The massing of Homer's watercolors at this Mathews sale elicited perhaps the most expansive notice from the New York press Homer had received since the debut of *Prisoners from the Front* in 1866. More importantly, all of the coverage was laudatory. Apparently the press could be less rigorous in expressing critical opinions when comparison of artists was not an issue, and the exhibition forum was not so prestigious as the institutional annuals. Support of the local economy may also have had a part in shaping its positive attitude. Whatever the cause, the effect was to encourage tangible appreciation of Homer's work. The *World* was especially lavish in its discussion of Homer's general attainments, and in individual works and in praise of all.[41] A number of sources also followed up the reviews with reports of the financial success of the sale; the latest, and perhaps most reliable was that of the *American Art Review* which stated it brought Homer $1,037.[42]

11–13 March: Union League Club exhibition; shows one painting.

20 March: "Winslow Homer designs relinquishing his studio at a date not far distant, and continuing his work in private."[43]

30 March: National Academy of Design annual exhibition opens; exhibits four paintings. Three date from 1876 and 1877; a fourth is unidentified, but probably dated no later than 1879.

1 April: A summer-long exhibition of paintings loaned from New York private collections opens at the Metropolitan Museum of Art. Lawson Valentine lends *Army Teamsters* (1:No. 283) of 1866, and Robert Lenox Kennedy lends *Prisoners at the Front* (1:No. 282), also of 1866. *Prisoners* is not again seen on public display until 1947.

3 April: Century Association exhibition; shows three works identified only as "Fac simile," and valued at two dollars each. There is no record or press reference which identifies these objects, but it is a safe assumption that they were the photographically reproduced *Yachting Girl* (No. 883-b), *A Pretty Maiden* (No. 884-b) and a similar but unidentified subject. Surviving examples of these prints are made unique by Homer's hand-brushed touches of opaque white watercolor. Like Homer's excursion in tile-making, this experiment with a method of multiplying his works, while enhancing the value of each by making it individual, seems another example of his exploring ways to extend simultaneously his expressive and commercial opportunities.[44]

April: has an illustration published in *Scribner's Monthly* accompanying an article: Edward Payson Roe, "Success With Small Fruits." (See No. 821.)

April: G. W. Sheldon's "Sketches and Studies. II. The Portfolios of A. H. Thayer, William M. Chase, Winslow Homer, and Peter Moran" is published.[45]

3 May: Steele MacKaye, Homer's cousin, dates the formal invitation to a theatrical performance to take place 1 June, as a benefit for the English actor, Henry Beckett. The invitation announces that the benefit is intended "as an expression of the good-will of your American friends . . . indebted for the many delightful hours you have afforded them during the past eleven years of your labours here." Besides MacKaye, it is signed by F. Hopkinson Smith, Robert Swain Gifford, Julian Alden Weir, William Merritt Chase, Arthur Quartly, and Winslow Homer.[46]

12 May: "The National Academy of Design held its annual business meeting yesterday afternoon, and its annual dinner in the evening. The business meeting was duller than usual; the dinner brighter. Thirty-eight academicians were present, namely, Messrs. . . . . Conspicuous for their absence were Messrs. Wyant, Page, Martin, Magrath, D. Johnson, Inness, W. Homer, Hicks, Sanford Gifford, Durand, Cropsey, F. E. Church, Chapman, Casilear, Calverly, and H. K. Brown.[47]

June: has an illustration published in *Scribner's Monthly* accompanying an article: Clarence Cook, "Spring Hereabouts." (See No. 872.)

before 15 June: "Mr. Gilbert Gaul is occupying Mr. Winslow Homer's late studio in the Tenth street building."[48] Homer had removed to the Benedick building on Washington Square.

That this new apartment house was designed to accommodate bachelors only was clearly signaled by its being named for the hero of Shakespeare's *Much Ado About Nothing*. Thirty-three apartments were contained in its lower five floors, with its sixth and top floor formed of four artists' studios. Rents ranged from $350 to $550 a year when it opened in the fall of 1879. It was addressed by entrances at 79 and 80 Washington Square East. Although its residents came from a mix of professions, it was known as an artists' building.[49] In addition to Homer, painters who gave the building as their address in one or more National Academy exhibition catalogue between 1880 and 1884 were Henry Alexander, William Verplanck Birney, William Gedney Bunce, George Maynard, Albert Pinkham Ryder, John Twachtman, Charles F. Ulrich, and Julian Alden Weir. The sculptor Olin Warner also lived in the Benedict in this period, as did William R. Mead whose architectural firm had designed the building.

Homer shared an apartment in the Benedict with Samuel Thorndyke Preston. There is no way to know whether they were equal partners in leasing the space, and moved in together; or Preston joined Homer sometime between 1880 and 1881; or possibly that Preston first took over the space to hold it for Homer when he went abroad in March 1881. It should be noted, however, that the formal portrait photographs of the main room (reproduced on pages 26–29) were Preston's property which suggests he had a vested interest in the place.

Certainly Homer and Preston were acquainted before taking up residence in the Benedict. Preston was related to Mrs. Charles S. Homer, Jr. He is first credited as resident in New York in the City Directory for the year ending 1 May 1878; his address was then 36 Washington Square West, the home of Mr. and Mrs. Charles S. Homer, Jr. The Prestons lived in New Ipswich, New Hampshire, near Martha French Homer's native town, West Townsend, Massachusetts—where Homer visited in 1879, and possibly in other years.

In the Directories of 1879, 1880, and 1881 Preston is referenced only by his business, "skins," and its address, 89 Gold Street. Homer was still in the Tenth Street Studio Building in March 1880, as he was listed with that address in the National Academy *Annual* catalogue. However, he was living at the Benedict by the time the United States Census of 1880 noted his existence. He was out of the country fairly early in 1881, and thus out of that year's New York City Directory. The first Directory to include Preston's home address, was that for the year ending 1 May 1882: it was given as the Benedict. Although Homer was still in England when the 1882 Directory was compiled, his name is included, also as resident of the Benedict, probably because Preston took care he was recognized. Homer continues to be at the Benedict address into 1884, and Preston into 1887.

summer: The undoubted association of Homer's watercolors and drawings of 1880 and his lengthy stay in Gloucester, Massachusetts, has led to the assumption that Gloucester is the scene of all his work of this summer. However, A small group of seaside subjects dating from 1880 are quite distinct in terrain and coloration from the character of acknowledged Gloucester subjects. These visual distinctions coupled with the "Field Point, Greenwich, Conn." identification given one of Homer's submissions to the American Water Color Society annual exhibition of 1881, indicate he spent some of the warm months of 1880 at work along the western shore of Long Island Sound. (See No. 900 through No. 911.) His whereabouts in the month of June are not otherwise account for, and the atmosphere of this works is appropriate to early summer.

July and August: is in Gloucester, Massachusetts. *Sailboat and Fourth of July Fireworks* (No. 1001) is inscribed "July 4 1880;" *William B. Astor's Yacht* (No. 993) and *Sunset at Gloucester* (No. 994) are both inscribed "Gloucester Aug 25th 1880."

That this summer Homer chose to live with the light house keeper on Ten Pound Island in Gloucester harbor, rather than in a hotel in town as he had in 1873, is widely interpreted to be a demonstration of a tortured soul seeking isolation from the commonplace intrusions of near neighbors. It might be remembered however, that Ten Pound Island is very small, and a short, easy rowboat ride from downtown Gloucester, not the bleak, storm-beaten rock pile far off the coast that its name conjures in imagination. Homer's choice of residence may be more reasonably accounted to the fact that the light house keeper's wife, Mrs. Octavius A. Merrill, was a Preston and therefore a cousin of Homer's sister-in-law. It is likely this connection provided Homer with an opportunity to get his room and board on favorable terms, and surely at less expense than living at a hotel.

c. 1 September: "Winslow Homer was back in town last week from Gloucester, Mass., where he made many studies. He has gone to Mountainville, back of Cornwall."[50]

13 September: "Winslow Homer, the eminent New York figure painter, who has been passing the summer down this way studying his favorite New England types of seaside urchins and country maidens, was in town yesterday, on his way home, with a portfolio bursting with sketches."[51] Homer may have been in Boston to meet with Doll & Richards on business preliminary to the exhibition the gallery would have in December. He could have been on his way to the Cornwall area in New York State, rather than on his way home to New York City.

November: "Mr. Winslow Homer has brought to [New York] from the coast of Massachusetts, near Cape Cod, one hundred and twenty-five water color drawings of scenes in that region, and will soon exhibit the works in a Boston gallery. From a technical point of view, without reference to the designs, the pictures are the most skillful ever produced by the artist, and as for the designs these testify anew to the freshness and vigor of his intellectual methods. It is to be regretted that Mr. Homer is not to address himself to the larger audiences of the metropolis. New York would appreciate this fine collection of water colors."[52]

One of two views of the principal room in the Benedick building apartment shared by Winslow Homer and Samuel Thorndyck Preston beginning in mid-1880. The photographs were made no earlier than 1883; their mounts are labeled by the photography studio: Pach Bro's / 841 Broadway, N. Y. Not all the paintings and drawings which may be seen clearly in the photographs are by Homer. The Homers which may be identified here are (reading around the walls from left to right): No. 884; No. 877; No. 624; and No. 864.

The photograph was given to Lloyd Goodrich in 1937 by Samuel T. Preston's niece, Mrs. William Preston of New Ipswich, NH.

One of two views of the principal room in the Benedick building apartment shared by Winslow Homer and Samuel Thorndyck Preston beginning in mid-1880. The photographs were made no earlier than 1883; their mounts are labeled by the photography studio: Pach Bro's / 841 Broadway, N. Y. Not all the paintings and drawings which may be seen clearly in the photographs are by Homer. The Homers which may be identified here are (reading around the walls from left to right): No. 880; No. 687; No. 942; and 4:No. 1173, *The Incoming Tide*, a watercolor of 1883.

A figure of a seated man in a further room is obscured by a large potted plant, introduced in dark green watercolor, apparently by the photography studio, and for the purpose of suppressing this human element. The gentleman is conspicuously long-legged, and therefore is unlikely to be Winslow Homer.

The photograph was given to Lloyd Goodrich in 1937 by Samuel T. Preston's niece, Mrs. William Preston of New Ipswich, NH.

6 November: Century Association exhibition; shows one oil painting; and forty-three of his "latest water colors" and drawings; seven were sold.[53]

November: G. W. Sheldon's third article featuring Homer, "Sketches and Studies. VII. The Portfolios of R. Swain Gifford, Winslow Homer, Arthur Quartley, and A. T. Bricher," is published.[54]

7 December: Brooklyn Art Association exhibition opens; shows one painting.

8–24 December: Doll & Richards, Boston, presents an exhibition of 112 watercolors and drawings by Homer, and serves as agent in their sale. This is the fourth and final of Homer's large commercial ventures staged in the three years leading up to his departure for England. This occasion has a major distinction from the previous three: it is mounted on Homer's behalf by a dealer. Instead of the brief showing preliminary to the compressed purchasing opportunity of an auction—his customary sale venue up to this point—works remain on display for an extended time, all during which sales might be made. And Homer did not have to attend personally to practical aspects of such an event. He could be far away, and still keep "the business" up and running. Doll & Richards' recorded $1,755 in gross sales from this exhibition; the firm's commission—also noted was $351.

December: has one illustration published in *Art Interchange*. (See No. 787.) Homer's drawing was presented independent of any literary context, but accompanied by editorial comment.

> A chat about the different artists who have contributed to this Holiday number is so eminently *apropos* that we make no apology for its insertion. . . . Of Winslow Homer, the artist of "Bossy," it is hard to know what not to say. Ranking, as he does, among the foremost and most original of American painters, he commands the admiration of all critics. Few men would introduce such lines in a picture as appear in "Bossy," and not one in a thousand would dare to concentrate attention, as here, all in one corner. This, however, is characteristic of the man; for he is *posé* in the extreme, and affects eccentricities of manner that border upon gross rudeness. To visit him in his studio, is literally bearding a lion in his den; for Mr. Homer's strength as an artist is only equalled by his roughness when he does not happen to be just in the humor of being approached.[55]

1881

6–12 January: The Kirby Gallery auctions unidentified watercolors by Homer in a sale said to be of "Three private collection, the property of well-known connoisseurs of this city and Brooklyn."[56]

8 January: Century Association exhibition; shows an unidentified *Study*.

23 January: American Water Color Society annual exhibition opens; shows twenty-three watercolor paintings (of which one is lent by its owner, General Francis W. Palfrey of Boston. Judging from the titles given in the Society's catalogue these were mostly, if not all, watercolors done the previous summer in Gloucester, and, of course, were selected from works not already sold from the exhibitions at the Century Association in November 1880, and at Doll & Richards in December.

Not having participated in the Society's annual exhibition the previous year may have had some bearing on the generally harsh critical reception his representation received in 1881. However his greater fault seems to have been perceived to be his failure to repeat his own past performance.

> Mr. Winslow Homer has spent two or three years, perhaps more, in securing to himself the affectionate interest of every lover of the genuinely out-of-door work of our American landscape painters. The breezy freshness and wholesomeness of his shepherdesses, his country lasses and his bright-eyed children of the fields and hillsides have made the deepest impression. Ensuing as they did after many years of [in]different performance, and being distinctly natural, unaffected and original, they excited no little expectation of what was to come. This expectation Mr. Homer has gratified by retiring wholly within himself and refusing, from that grim and misanthropical seclusion to afford any explanation. The contributions that he sends to this exhibition are almost as eccentric as those of Mr. Currier and for the most part have had severe justice meted out to them by the Spartans on the Hanging Committee. It is a disappointment, but he is worth the waiting for.[57]

4 February: Gill's Art Galleries annual exhibition opens in Springfield, Massachusetts; shows two paintings.

24 February: forty-fifth birthday.

5 March: Century Association exhibition; shows one painting.

8–19 March: Brooklyn Art Association watercolor exhibition; shows unidentified paintings. As was customary, the Association's early spring watercolor exhibition included a number of works transferred from the Water Color Society's annual exhibition which had closed shortly before.

15 March: sails from New York for Liverpool on the "Parthia."[58]

1. It was Lloyd Goodrich who first carried into publication the story of Homer having loved and lost. Mrs. Charles Homer, Jr. may safely be presumed to be the source of the tale briefly told in his 1944 Homer monograph: "It may have been with one of these girls [in watercolors of the 1870s] that Homer had the love affair of his life. Because of his reticence the whole story will never be known, except that it ended unhappily because he did not have the income to marry. In later years there was one painting [2:No. 611] that he always kept on an easel in his studio . . . 'Shall I Tell Your Fortune?' Family legend is that this was the girl. It was probably she who also appears, seated on the beach, in *High Tide* [2:364].": Goodrich 1944, 56–57.

Jean Gould expanded the legend into a popular book-length fairy tale, based on the supposition that all Homer's art was autobiographical documentation of the constant companionship of an unnamed woman. It is Gould who promoted the Hurley, New York, school teacher, seen in paintings of the early 1870s, the probable heroine of her story, allowing her to stretch its date range to the maximum: Gould, *Winslow Homer: A Portrait* (New York: Dodd, Mead & Company, 1962).

Philip Beam, who relied heavily on the oral history of Homer provided by Charles L. Homer, made a valiant effort to put the love-sick artist story in its proper place—which was Mrs. Charles S. Homer, Jr.'s imagination: Beam, *Winslow Homer at Prout's Neck* (Boston: Little Brown and Company, 1966), 191–92. However, the myth and its enticing interpretive possibilities gained new momentum early in the 1980s.

Henry Adams made a major contribution to the tenacious appeal of the legend of failed romance with a series of increasingly fervid articles extrapolating Homer's sexual preferences and aberrations from the painting quaintly identified by Mrs. Homer as "always" on his easel, *Shall I Tell Your Fortune?*: See 2:No. 611.

Copies of the only surviving examples of Homer's correspondence with a member of the opposite sex not of his family were given to Lloyd Goodrich in 1974. This small group of brief notes survived because their recipient, Helena de Kay (later Mrs. Richard Gilder) came from one of those families who saved all their letters. Despite the fact that there is nothing with which to compare them for evidence of anything in their tone or content which would elevate them above the commonplace, they immediately were endowed with the character of love letters. Unfortunately, it again was Goodrich who unleashed this idea in a conversation with Helen Cooper, who proposed in her study of Homer's watercolors that the models of 2: No. 567, 2: No. 568, 2: No. 608, 2: No. 609, No. 612, and No. 613 were the same woman, and that "lingering attention given to individual features and details of dress is, in a sense, an act of love. Homer clearly cared for her in some way." In a footnote Cooper linked this opinion with Goodrich's musing on a possible relationship between Homer and de Kay—thus planting the delicious, but unsupported, suggestion that de Kay was Homer's frequent subject in the years immediately *after* her marriage: Cooper, *Winslow Homer Watercolors* (New Haven: Yale University Press, 1986), 43, 51.

The imaginary love affair has since been taken up and embellished by Sarah Burns. Burns finds in the correspondence between Homer and Helena de Kay a seemingly inexhaustible source of authority for theories of their unconsummated liaison having tragically blighted his life. While she creates visually untenable references to, or presence of de Kay, in a number of Homers works from as early as 1868, it is the so-called portrait of de Kay which has particularly engaged her invention: See 2:No. 328, 2:No. 386, and 2:No. 392.

No other Homer scholar has given as much weight to the effect on Homer's work in the 1870s of an indefinable "profoundly harmful emotional wound" than Nicolai Cikovsky, Jr. His perception of the darkening of Homer's temperament and art is more nuanced than other Homer analysts; it allows for more than a single cause. He sees political disillusionment as one among several: "the ideas and ideals that inspired and guided his early art—the possibility of making an original, national art suited to the 'conditions of American life' and 'common life of democratic man'—were now hopelessly out of place." He also recognizes the frustration surely occasioned by the relentless complaint of art critics that his art failed to satisfy their expectations. But "a romantic disappointment the nature of which can only be guessed at, but which permanently affected his conduct" continues to be fundamental to his interpretation of Homer's work: Cikovsky, *Winslow Homer* (New York: Harry N. Abrams, 1990), 58, 71–72; Cikovsky and Kelly 1995, 102–4, 163.

2. The Academy's prohibition on work shown in the several private club monthly exhibition appearing in its annual exhibitions resulted in Sanford Gifford resigning his membership in April 1875. The official record of what probably was the escalating and contentious argument over this issue is found in the manuscript Minutes of Academy Annual and Council meetings in May 1873; January 1874; and January, March and April 1875. For demonstration of press attention to this divisive issue, see "Art Notes," *(NY) Daily Graphic*, 31 Jan. 1874; and "Fine Arts. National Academy of Design—Private View—Forty-ninth Annual Exhibition," *New-York Daily Tribune*, 9 Apr. 1874.

3. "The Artists Fund Reception," *(NY) World*, 17 Jan. 1877.

4. "Art Notes," *(NY) Evening Express*, 17 Mar. 1877.

5. "The Art Students' League," *(NY) Daily Graphic*, 12 Apr. 1877.

6. Andrew Varrick Stout Anthony (1835–1906) was a wood engraver. In 1860 he was in charge of the engraving department of the *New York Illustrated News*. From 1866 to 1886 he superintended the production of fine editions for Ticknor & Fields (later James R. Osgood & Co.), the Boston publishing house. Homer contributed illustrations to several Ticknor & Fields books of collected stories, and poetry between 1866 and 1871. After a hiatus of six years The house again put out a book with illustrations by Homer. A collection of poems by Henry Wadsworth Longfellow, *Excelsior*, was copyrighted in October 1877 and released in 1878; it included four images designed by Homer and engraved by Anthony.

7. "Art Announcements," *(NY) Evening Post*, 31 May 1877; see also "Art Gossip," *New-York Daily Tribune*, 9 June 1877.

8. Characteristically, Homer used almost every opportunity to show his work, yet he did not contribute to a Society of American Artists exhibition until its *Annual* of 1897, the year following John La Farge's election to president of the organization.

9. "Personal," *(NY) Evening Post*, 19 June 1877.

10. "Studio Notes," *New York Herald*, 24 Sept. 1877.

11. "Fine Arts," *New York Herald*, 1 Oct. 1877; see also "Reopening the Studios," *New-York Daily Tribune*, 13 Oct. 1877.

12. "Art at the Union League," *New York Herald*, 12 Oct. 1877.

13. The most thorough history and discussion of the Tile Club is Ronald G. Pisano's *The Tile Club and the Aesthetic Movement in America*, published in 1999 by Harry N. Abrams in conjunction with the exhibition of the same title organized by the Museums at Stony Brook, New York.

Tile Club gatherings were not limited to evenings in New York; members also assembled for extended excursions—for sketching and fun, apparently with emphasis on the latter—up the Hudson valley, and to the further reaches of Long Island. Although Homer was once said to have gone along on one of these trips ("The Summer Vacation. Where the Artists Are and What They Are Doing," *(NY) Evening Post*, 14 July 1879), the report was contradicted by the more detailed account including a list of participants ("Art on a Canal Boat. The Merry and Venturesome 'Tilers' Recount Some Perils and Pastimes of an Adventurous Undertaking in Search of Fuel for the Fires of Genius," *(NY) Evening Post*, 16 July 1879.)

The Club quickly became more attentive to amusement than to art. It survived into the late 1880s, and while Homer may well have attended its evening gatherings, there is no indication he remained a devoted member once attention to the creation of tiles waned. His pursuit of the medium apparently was exhausted within 1879.

14. "Fine Arts. Eleventh Exhibition of the American Water-Color Society. I," *The Nation* 26 (14 Feb. 1878): 120.

15. "Art Notes," *(NY) Evening Post*, 14 Feb. 1878.

16. C[larence] C[ook] "Fine Arts. National Academy of Design. Fifty-third Annual Exhibition. V," *New-York Daily Tribune*, 11 May 1878.

17. "Fine Arts. The Tile Club," *New York Herald*, 1 May 1878; see also "The Tile Club Exhibition," *New York Herald*, 6 May 1878.

18. "Many Artists Disappointed. Results of the Academy Election. Only Two Academicians and Three Associates Elected," *New-York Daily Tribune*, 9 May 1878; see also "Annual Meeting of the National Academy," *New York Herald*, 6 May 1878; "Book and Art Notes. The Annual Meeting of the Academy of Design," *New York Commercial Advertiser*, 9 May 1878.

19. "Art and Artists," *New York Evening Mail* 7 May 1878.

20. *(Boston) Daily Evening Transcript* 28 May 1878; see also "Mr. Winslow Homer's Sketches," *Boston Daily Advertiser*, 28 May 1878.

21. For example, William Crowninshield Rogers owned six Homers dating from 1874 to 1876, including *The Busy Bee* (2:No. 589), *Woman and Elephant* (2:No. 608), and *Woman Peeling a Lemon* (2:No. 609); William S. Eaton owned four from the same date range, including *Backgammon* (No. 614); William Townsend was the first owner of *Blackboard* (No. 613).

22. "Fine Arts. Away for the Summer," *New York Herald*, 24 June 1878.

23. Linda Ayres's essay, "Lawson Valentine, Houghton Farm, and Winslow Homer," published in 1990 by the Art Museum, Princeton University, in *Winslow Homer in the 1870s: Selections from the Valentine-Pulsifer*

Collection, the catalogue of the exhibition of a group of works then recently acquired by a private collector, is the most extensive discussion of Homer's association with Houghton Farm. It quickly became the source of authority on the subject, and has been relied upon since that time. Given the circumstances occasioning the exhibition, and the narrow focus of the publication, it is not surprising that the conventional assumptions on Homer's relationship with Lawson Valentine were accepted unquestioningly as reliable fact and elaborated upon. Along with repeating the unsupported traditions of Homer's stays with the Valentines in 1874 and 1876, Ayres assumes Homer passed most if not all the summer of 1878 as a guest of the Valentines, "producing about fifty watercolors in addition to a large number of drawings and oil studies. These works provide a travel guide to Lawson Valentine's property" (22). Her belief that any sheep Homer drew and painted in 1878 was Lawson Valentine's property allows her to bracket his stay at Houghton Farm with drawings dated 5 July (No. 664) and 15 October 1878 (No. 740-R). The drawing on the reverse of No. 740-R is also inscribed with an October 1878 date, and the place Homer made the drawing: Leeds, New York.

24. [George William Sheldon] "American Painters. Winslow Homer and F. A. Bridgman," *The Art Journal* (New York) 4 (Aug. 1878): 225–27.

25. "Art Matters," *(NY) Evening Telegram*, 18 Sept. 1878.

26. "Art Notes," *(NY) Evening Post*, 11 Nov. 1878. The *(NY) Daily Graphic* of 7 November—four days earlier than the *Post*—notes that Homer "is once more in his studio."

27. "A New Art Gallery," *New York Commercial Advertiser*, 11 Dec. 1878.

28. "The American Watercolorists," *(NY) Evening Post*, 1 Feb. 1879.

29. The *New-York Daily Tribune* reported, 18 March 1879, that the ship carrying the American exhibition from the *Exposition Universelle de 1878* had just arrived in New York harbor, thus *A Visit from the Old Mistress* (2:No. 603) and *Sunday Morning in Virginia* (No. 620) were not available to Homer in time for the Academy annual exhibition of 1879. He sent them to the *Exhibition of Contemporary Art* in Boston which opened in April 1879; to Springfield, Massachusetts, for an exhibition which opened in December 1879; to the January 1880 monthly exhibition at the Union League Club; and finally to the National Academy's annual exhibition of 1880. Homer completed his 1880 Academy submission with *Camp Fire* (No. 627) of 1877; and the unidentified *Summer* (no. 865) which reminded the *New-York Times* critic "of the water colors for which Mr. Homer received so much praise two years ago."

The three paintings Homer showed at the Academy *Annual* of 1879, *The Shepherdess of Houghton Farm*, *Sundown*, and *Upland Cotton*, reappeared at successive Century Association monthly exhibitions in October, November, and December 1879. *Upland Cotton* went to Brooklyn for exhibition in December 1880. *The Shepherdess of Houghton Farm* was at Gill's in Springfield in February 1881, with the 1879 *Peach Blossoms* (No. 767). The identity of the *Shepherdess* shown at the Century in January 1880 is unconfirmed, but likely was No. 770, a work of 1879.

Homer's one oil which may have been executed in later 1879 or early 1880 is *By the Sea Side* (No. 874), introduced at Gill's Art Galleries, Springfield, in February 1880.

The one oil surely completed while Homer was in England is *Hark! The Lark* (4:No. 1101), which he submitted to the Royal Academy's annual exhibition of 1882, and presumably created with that destination in mind.

30. "The American Art Gallery," *(NY) World*, 6 May 1879.

31. "The American Art Gallery. Opening of Mr. Moore's Display under Pleasant Auspices," *New-York Daily Tribune*, 7 May 1879.

32. In 1882 the American Art Gallery mutated into the American Art Association, a less focussed operation. The Association continued to show and represent American art, but also exhibited, bought, and sold European work, and, with increasing frequency held auctions. By the end of the century it was wholly an auction house—and the direct ancestor of the present day Sotheby's in New York.

33. "Studio Notes," *Art Interchange* 2 (14 May 1879): 84.

34. "Summer Haunts of Artists," *Art Amateur* 1 (Aug. 1879): 50. In its enthusiasm for keeping track of the city's artists, the New York press also could overreach. According to the article "The Summer Vacation. Where the Artists Are and What They Are Doing," in the *(NY) Evening Post* of 14 July 1879, "Mr. Winslow Homer is off with the Tile Club." However the *Post* story, "Art on a Canal Boat. The Merry and Venturesome 'Tilers' Recount Some Perils and Pastimes of an Adventurous Undertaking in Search of Fuel for the Fires of Genius," which appeared two days later, and apparently was written by a "Tiler," does not include Homer in listing the company who made an excursion to Lake Champlain from 28 June to 14 July.

35. Richard N. Smith, *Divinity and Dust: A History of Townsend, Massachusetts* (Lancaster, MA: privately printed, 1978), 39.

36. Hendricks 1979, 138

37. Helen Cooper, in Susan E. Strickler, ed., *American Traditions in Watercolor: The Worcester Art Museum Collection* (New York: Abbeville Press, 1987), 84.

38. "Bits of Art Gossip about the Artists," *(NY) World* 9 Oct. 1879.

39. "The members of the Tile Club, of this city gave a dinner on Saturday afternoon to some guests from Boston and to themselves in Mr. W. M. Chase's studio, in Tenth street, and held a reception which was attended by all the prominent artists of New York in the evening at Mr. Sarony's rooms in Union Square." "A Dinner of the Tile Club, How Art Can be Made to Increase the Pleasures of Digestion," *(NY) Evening Post*, 26 Jan. 1880.

40. "The Art Season," *Scribner's Monthly* 20 (June 1880): 313.

41. "Water-Colors by Winslow Homer," *(NY) World* 4 Mar. 1880; see also "Fine Arts," *(NY) Evening Post*, 26 Feb. 1880; "Art Notes. Winslow Homer's Water Colors, &c," *New York Commercial Advertiser*, 2 Mar. 1880; "Fine Arts," *(NY) Evening Post*, 3 Mar. 1880

42. "The collection of 72 watercolors, etc. which Mr. Winslow Homer offered for sale by auction at the Mathew's Auction Rooms, on March 4in, realized $1,037,—the prices obtained for individual works varying from $5.50 to $50 each. The drawings ranged in size from 8 by 10 to 16 x 22 inches, and were mostly rapid, but careful sketches." "Exhibitions and Sales," *American Art Review* 1, (1880): 269.

43. Quoted by Charles Brock in his "Chronology" in Cikovsky and Kelly 1995, 395, cited as "20 March 1880 *Andrews' American Queen*."

44. For a clear, condensed explanation of the process, and its commercial applications, published in Homer's time, see "The New Process of Reproduction Fac-Similes of Paintings, Etchings, &c.," *New York Herald*, 23 Jan. 1876.

45. [George William Sheldon] "Sketches and Studies. II. The Portfolios of A. H. Thayer, William M. Chase, Winslow Homer, and Peter Moran," *The Art Journal* (New York) 6 (Apr. 1880): 105-9.

46. Percy MacKaye, *Epoch: the Life of Steele MacKaye, Genius of the Theatre, In Relation to His Times & Contemporaries. A Memoir by His Son* (New York: Boni & Liveright, 1927), 353–54.

47. "The Academy of Design," *(NY) Evening Post*, 13 May 1880

48. "Artists' Calendar," *(NY) Evening Post*, 15 June 1880. Gaul was not just a short-term sub-leasee. The 26 February 1881 issue of the *New York Herald* reported on "The Tenth Street Studio Reception," noting "In the studio of Gilbert Gaul where Winslow Homer formerly painted, will be found his two Academy paintings."

49. Christopher Gray, "Bachelors as Artists in Residence," *New York Times*, 27 Apr. 1997.

50. "Home Notes," *New York Herald*, 6 Sept. 1880.

51. "Art Notes," *(Boston) Daily Evening Transcript*, 14 Sept. 1880; see also, Greta, "Boston Correspondence," *The Art Amateur* 3 (Oct. 1880): 95.

52. "Fine Arts," *(NY) Evening Post*, 4 Nov. 1880.

53. "Fine Arts," *(NY) Evening Post*, 11 Nov. 1880; "Exhibitions and Sales," *American Art Review* 2, part 1 (1881): 84.

54. [George William Sheldon] "Sketches and Studies. VII. The Portfolios of R. Swain Gifford, Winslow Homer, Arthur Quartley, and A. T. Bricher," *The Art Journal* (New York) 6 (Nov. 1880): 325–27.

55. "The Studio. Art Interchange Artists," *Art Interchange* 5 (22 Dec. 1880): 129.

56. "Fine Paintings at Auction," *New York Evening Mail*, 6 Jan. 1881.

57. "The American Watercolor Society," *(NY) Sun*, 23 Jan. 1881.

58. The fallibility of the New York press is demonstrated by a report in the 16 March 1881 *Evening Post* of the meeting of a committee comprised of Daniel Huntington, James D. Smillie, Edward Gay, Alfred Howland, James C. Nicoll, Thomas Hovenden, George Inness and Winslow Homer "to arrange for a reception to Mr. F. A. Bridgman, the exhibition of whose pictures at the American Art Gallery has been a leading art event of the season. Mr. Bridgman will soon return to Paris." The *Post* amplified its coverage the next day in announcing that the event was to take place "at Sarony's art rooms on the evening of the 24th of March." (The *American Art Review* 2, part 1 (1881): 257 repeated all this information.) However, in reporting on the reception on 25 March 1881, the day after it took place, the *New-York Times* omitted Homer and Inness in naming the committee doing Bridgman honor. That Homer had left the country before arrangements were even begun was not commented upon, but the *Times* noted Inness had expressed his objection to being mistakenly named in the *Post*'s story, as he did not want to be counted among admirers of Bridgman.

Record of Works

1877 – March 1881

612

The New Novel

1877

Book

Watercolor, 9½ × 20⁷⁄₁₆ (24.130 × 51.913)
Inscribed lr: Homer 1877

Museum of Fine Arts, Springfield, MA, the Horace
P. Wright Collection, 46.D11

ABG: The fourth occasion of Homer's participation
in the annual exhibition of the American Society
of Painters in Water Colors was also his first as a
member of the organization. This recognition of
commitment to professional practice of the medium
may have had some bearing on the marked change
in the character of his submission to the exhibition.

Homer's first appearance in the Society's annual
exhibitions in 1874 was conspicuously self-effacing;
it was with five pairs of "Leaves from a Sketchbook"—which were not for sale. Only one of these
"leaves" can now be surely identified, *Longing* or
Waiting for Dad (2:No. 475), a work from his 1873
stay in Gloucester, Massachusetts. As Homer used
that summer in Gloucester to develop mastery of
watercolor as a painting medium, it may be supposed
most if not all the remaining nine "leaves" are
among the Gloucester subject watercolors from
1873 which have survived.

In 1875 Homer sent thirty-four works to the
Society's *Annual*, of which seven were noted as in
"Black and White" and may be supposed to have
been line or wash drawings. All thirty-four were
for sale, and a fair number of them attracted buyers.

This commanding showing was a mix of subjects
from Gloucester in 1873, and "souvenirs" of his
1874 summer visits in the Adirondacks and East
Hampton on Long Island. Homer's contribution
to the Society's 1876 exhibition was not so prodigal;
he showed fourteen works, of which five were noted
as in "Black and White." Their subjects again
reflected Homer's whereabouts the previous summer.
All Homer's surviving watercolors from 1873, 1874,
and 1875, with just two exceptions, are of closely
similar size, an unimposing 9 to 10 by 13 to 14 inches
(or smaller); all are bucolic in theme; the majority
feature children.

Just four watercolor paintings survive from 1876:
A Woman with a Rose (2:No. 606); *Woman Sewing*
(2:No. 607); *Woman and Elephant* (2:No. 608); and
Woman Peeling a Lemon or *Lemon* (2:No. 609). In
contrast to Homer's previous work in watercolor, these
all focus on solitary figures of young, urbane women.
However, his choice of sheet size for *A Woman with
a Rose*, *Woman Sewing*, and *Woman and Elephant*
remained the modest scale which was then his
standard. But in *Lemon* he swelled the maximum
dimension of the support to nearly 20 inches.

It was *Lemon* with four paintings finished just
in time for the late January opening of the 1877
annual exhibition of the American Society of
Painters in Water Colors which comprised Homer's
representation in the show. The four works dated
1877 were titled by Homer *Book* (No. 612), *Blackboard*
(No. 613), *Backgammon* (No. 614), and *Rattlesnake*
(see No. 615). *Rattlesnake* seems to have quite literally
been the "odd man—or, rather, boy—out" of the
group, excepting probably in being as large or larger
than the four feminine subjects. Homer's choice

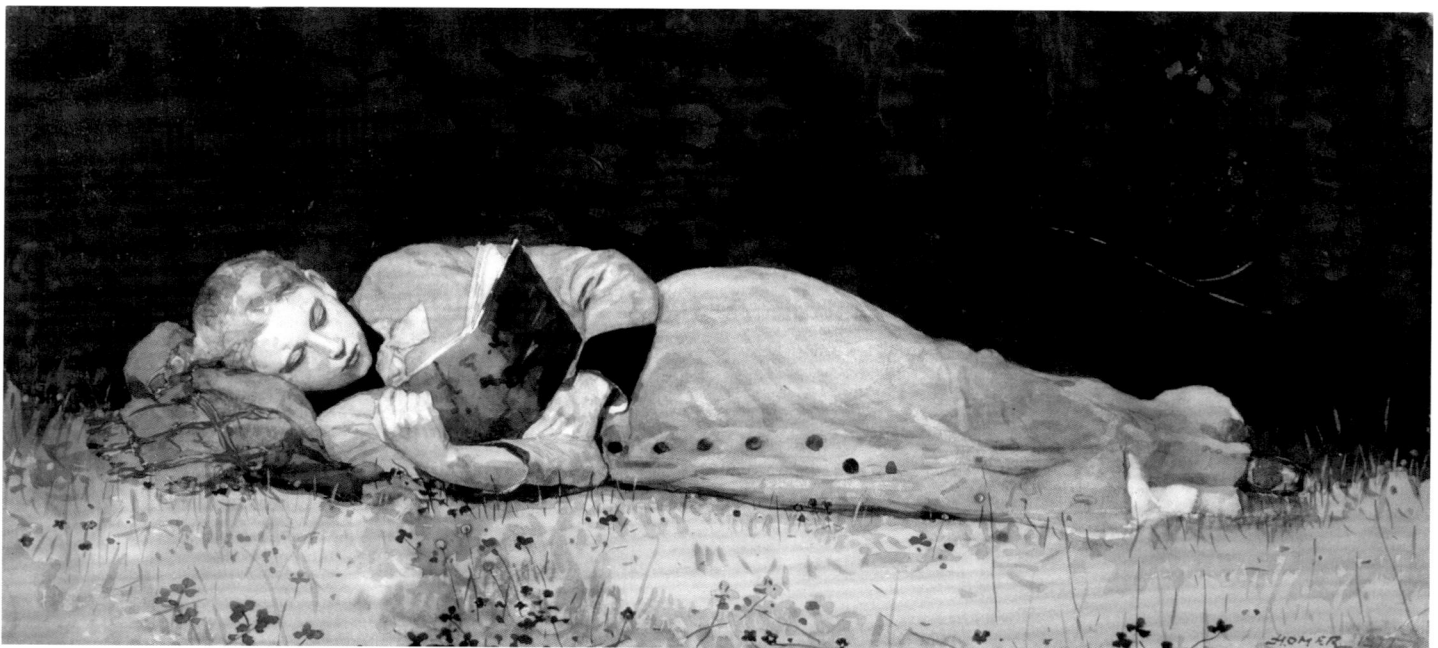

No. 612. The New Novel

see color illustration, p. 404

of these terse, oblique titles was a departure from his usual practice, and may have been intended to distance the five paintings from narrative associations.

The four images of women formed a suite, a concept which, in itself, signals a significant change in Homer's perception of the qualities of the watercolor medium. The four are not only cohesive in theme and in their liberal dimensions, but also in the subtly abstracted, decorative character of composition and use of color. The figures and faces of the subjects are generic but each painting has a close harmony of color particular to it, established by the subjects' costumes and surroundings. The color schemes even extend to the hair color of each subject: This reader rather flamboyantly dressed in orange is red-haired; the ladies seated on a red sofa playing a game are red-heads; the russet details in the dress of the lady peeling a lemon are picked up in the wood of the stool on which she sits and in her hair color; but the school teacher's light brown hair is nearly the same color as the wall behind her blackboard and blends—rather than contrasts—with the cool grays and blues of her costume. (Such consistency in the clothing and coloring of figure subjects is also seen in *A Woman with a Rose*, *Woman Sewing*, and *Woman and Elephant*.)

Homer's change in attitude toward the uses of the medium is also demonstrated in the prices he set on the five paintings. Where in 1874 he had not put his "leaves" to the test of the market, in 1875 he assigned prices ranging from $30 to $75, with one work at $100; the average being $60. In 1876 the range was $25 to $75, with two works priced at $100 each, and two at $125 each; the average was $70. But in 1877, the smallest of Homer's five paintings, *Lemon*, could be had for $100; the slightly larger *Blackboard* was $125; *Book* and *Backgammon* were $250, each; *Rattlesnake* could be acquired for a comparatively hefty $350. The increase in market valuation not only reflected the larger size of the works, their greater degree of detail and finish, and probably also the more "serious," grown-up nature of their subject matter in comparison to the country and seaside children's amusements which characterized so much of his previous work in watercolor.

It was March 1877 before Homer would read a reaction to his representation which recognized its character and departure from his previous work. Susan Carter writing in the *Art Journal* gave much of her article to his contribution. It must have gratified him to read: "Several artists, . . . though fully as good as before have advanced but little; but others have made decided progress and their pictures impress the spectator very fully with the conviction that they have come near realising their own standard of excellence. At the head of these pictures, which are inspiriting to those who have watched our Art-progress, are the works of Mr. Winslow Homer." She went on to expand on the qualities of the body

of his works in the exhibition, singling out *Lemon* for special attention, and before ending her review returned to appreciation of Homer's contribution.

Walking through the north room, filled with paintings among the best of those in the exhibition, and admiring the pictures of Berne, Bellecour, Mrs. Stillman, and others, our eye was again caught and held by one called "Book," by Mr. Homer, representing a young woman lying easily, and in a natural pose, reading from an open volume, with a rich and agreeable palette of colour, composed of greens cool and warm, yellows of peculiar shades, composing textured material positive and charming, and this combination was keyed and emphasized by deep, dark blues and iron-colour. This picture and the one above-described [*Lemon*] are but two of several paintings sent by Mr. Homer, all of which show, in our judgment a marked advance.

The New York newspaper reviewers, with less leisure to prepare their articles, seemed almost inadvertently to recognize Homer's representation in the 1877 Society of Painters in Water Color exhibition as somewhat out of the ordinary, and to comment on it as a unit, with two works selected for individual notice. *Book* was consistently chosen, and consistently received positive comment; the critics had various preferences and reasons for the second work each singled out for comment

The *Daily Graphic* noted "Winslow Homer's works, of which there are several in the present exhibition, are quite unmistakable always. The artist's clear-cut outlines and bold coloring are conspicuously shown in his 'Blackboard' and in the figure of a girl stretched at full length." The *Times* was much more cursory in its review of the show, taking up the pictures in order of their hanging, coming to " . . . a characteristically bold picture of a girl and book, by Winslow Homer (No. 42)" in passing around the North Room, and noting only that "The girl lies at full length, clothed in a dress to match her hair."

The reviewer for the *Evening Express* thought "One of the best things that Winslow Homer has done in a long time is a small picture which he quaintly calls 'Book.' It represents a girl reclining upon the grass reading a book. The whole composition is simplicity itself, but the color and the feeling of out doors are thoroughly admirable."

The *Evening Post* took up Homer's representation as a group—and was decidedly put off by it.

Mr. Winslow Homer is fond of experiments, and is nothing if not Mr. Winslow Homer. Four out of his five pictures are figures of young women, and we notice that the hands and feet are enormous and coarse, and that three of the faces display large, sickly, dirty, faint green patches No other young women in the room (nor any old women, either) have such patches. As for ourselves we never saw the like of them either on canvas or epidermis. There is but a trace of them on the schoolmistress at the 'Blackboard' (122), in some respects by far the best of his contributions . . . . It is only fair to say, however, that the reader of the "Book" (42) lies very easy and comfortable on her side (patches and all), and displays in her countenance the nonchalance of every other woman that Mr. Homer has ever painted.

The periodical *Scribner's Monthly*'s review did not come out until April; it borrowed the somewhat sour literalism of the *Post*'s vision, but found overriding merit in the group.

There are not so many Winslow Homers on exhibition this year as usual; but they are all good in their way, even the bad ones: no, not all—the "Rattlesnake" (198) is beyond redemption villainous. "Backgammon" (396) not only has no background—that we might endure as an artist's whim—but it is a poor joke to paint the girls' cheeks green. The cheeks of "Lemon" (280) are equally unpleasant. But in the "Book" (42), and in the "Blackboard" (122), Homer is himself again—one of the few American painters of originality and force.

Were there any doubt that the work known as *The New Novel* is the *Book* shown in the American Society of Painters in Water Color 1877 annual exhibition, its repeated description in the press reviews of the exhibition confirms the identity of the Springfield Museum's watercolor.

There is no equivalent documentation that the painting listed as *Girl Reading* in the Century Association register of its June 1877 exhibition is *The New Novel*. However, its presentation in immediate company with *Backgammon* is a persuasive circumstance: the two paintings were identified as watercolors, numbered 36 and 35, respectively, and were Homer's only contributions to this last monthly event of the 1876–1877 season.

The next—and last—appearance of the watercolor before the mid-twentieth century occurred a year following the Century exhibition, when it was up for auction at the Barker Art Galleries. On 30 April 1878 the *(NY) World* reported its inclusion in the sale.

Nearly a hundred paintings in oil and water colors, many of them belong to Mr. W. H. Beard, the artist, and many contributed by various other painters, are on exhibition at the rooms of Barker & Co. . . . . Many of the other pictures are familiar ones to New York gallery visitors. For example, Mr. Winslow Homer's crisp and pretty water-color, "The Latest Novel," was in the [American Society of Painters in Water Color] exhibition a year ago.

The *World* followed up a few days later: "The Sale of William H. Beard's studio pictures, together with examples of the work of several other artists, in the auction rooms of Barker & Co., yesterday was attended largely by dealers. The bidding was slow and the offers small . . . . Winslow Homer — 'Farmer's Daughter' [$] 33." It is possible Homer had more than one work in this Barker auction, but given the press's haphazard way with titles in this period, the *World*'s *Farmer's Daughter* reported sold was probably the work which had caught its attention during the auction preview.

PROVENANCE
Otto Heinigke, New York, nd; Otto Heinigke, New York, his son, by 1892; Mrs. Cornelius J. Sullivan, New York, by 1935; (Parke-Bernet Galleries, Dec. 6–7, 1939, sale 150, no. 196); Francesco von Mendelssohn, 1939 [?]; (Newhouse Galleries, c. 1946)

EXHIBITIONS
American Society of Painters in Water Colors, New York, *Tenth Annual Exhibition*, 22 Jan.–4 Mar. 1877, no. 42 (as *Book*); Century Association, New York, 2 June 1877, no. 36 (as *Girl Reading*) [?]; Barker Art Galleries, New York, [auction], 29 Apr.–3 May 1878 (as *The Latest Novel*); NGA 1958/MFA, Boston, 1959, no. 90/84; University of Arizona 1963, no. 127; Albright-Knox 1966, no. 8; Farnsworth 1970, no. 27; Baltimore 1978, no. 3; Bowdoin 1983, no. 4; NGA 1986, no. 30; NGA 1995, no. 84; AI Chicago 2008

LITERATURE
"Pictures at the Academy. The Exhibition of the American Society of Painters in Water Colors," *(NY) Daily Graphic*, 22 Jan. 1877; "Exhibition of Water-Colors. Reception of the American Society of Painters in Water-Colors," *New-York Times*, 22 Jan. 1877; "Art Matters. The Water Color Exhibition," *(NY) Evening Express*, 22 Jan. 1877; "The Painters in Water Colors. Pictures by American Artists in the Exhibition," *(NY) Evening Post*, 13 Feb. 1877; S[usan] N. C[arter], "The Tenth New York Water-Colour Exhibition," *(NY) Art Journal* 3 (Mar. 1877): 95; "The Old Cabinet," *Scribner's Monthly* 13 (Apr. 1877): 866; "Mr. Beard's 'Studio Pictures,'," *(NY) World*, 30 Apr. 1878; "Mr. Beard's Pictures. Some Notable Works Going for Prices That Discourage Art," *(NY) World*, 3 May 1878; National Gallery of Art, Helen A. Cooper, *Winslow Homer Watercolors* (Washington, DC, 1986), 38–41; Cikovsky and Kelly 1995, 154

613
Blackboard

1877

The Schoolteacher

Watercolor, 19¾ × 12¾ (50.165 × 32.385)
Inscribed cr, on blackboard: Homer '77

National Gallery of Art, Washington, DC, (partial
and promised) gift of Jo Ann and Julian Ganz, Jr.,
in honor of the 50th anniversary of the National
Gallery of Art, 1990.60.1

ABG: See commentary No. 612.

Blackboard enjoyed the favor of the New York *Daily
Graphic* and *Evening Post* reviewers of the American
Society of Painters in Water Colors 1877 *Annual*, but
their notices were cursory, and without description.
However, it was the only one of Homer's five paintings
in the exhibition which engaged the full attention
and admiration of the critic for the *New-York Times*

> No. 122. "Blackboard." Why is it that one always
> remembers Mr. Homer's things! In the first place,
> (we hazard to answer) because he always has
> something to say, and, in the second, because he
> tells the truth as far as to him [it] lies to see it,
> without hesitation or remorse. This unusually
> rigid schoolmarm, pointing to the blackboard,
> must give Mr. Homer's powerfully organized
> senses an agreeable rasping. She is so still and
> individual, so true.

The figures chalked on the *Blackboard*, and
thus the lesson being taught by the "schoolmarm,"
remained a mystery until Nicolai Cikovsky, Jr.
recognized them as the forms peculiar to the method
of drawing instruction widely used in public schools
in the 1870s. In establishing a context for *Blackboard*
Cikovsky notes that drawing was a legally mandated
part of the published school curriculum in Massachusetts where Walter Smith, who developed the
method demonstrated in Homer's painting, had been
appointed state director of art education in 1871.

No reference has come to light which might
document Homer having again exhibited *Blackboard*
or put it at auction in New York following its early
1877 debut in the watercolor Society's *Annual*. An
explanation is suggested by its ownership by three
successive generations of the Townsend family of
Boston. Among Homer's several major fund-raising
enterprises in the later 1870s was the 29 May 1878
sale by the Boston auctioneer, Charles F. Libbie, of
more than eighty works. No list of the contents of
this sale is known to survive. However, it is possible
to extrapolate identification of some of what went
on the block that day from the holdings of several
Boston collectors. For example: Six drawings and

No. 613. Blackboard   see color illustration, p. 405

watercolors by Homer, dated 1874, 1875, and 1876,
decended to William Crowninshield Rogers's son,
who dispersed them in the 1920s. William S. Eaton's
son recalled for LG his father having brought home
his four Homers (all dating from the mid-1870s)
on the same day, having acquired them at an auction
"downtown." Rogers owned *Woman and Elephant*
(2:No. 608) and *Lemon* (2:No. 609); Eaton owned
Backgammon (No. 614). It is reasonable to speculate
that William Townsend may have acquired
Blackboard from the same source as that from which
his neighbors got their Homer watercolors.

PROVENANCE
William Townsend, Boston, nd; Rose Townsend and
Elizabeth Townsend, Boston, his nieces, by bequest,
nd; Thomas H. Townsend, Boston, their cousin,

and William Townsend's great-nephew, by bequest, c. 1975; (Vose Galleries of Boston, 1977); Jo Ann and Julian Ganz, Los Angeles, 1977

EHIBITIONS
American Society of Painters in Water Colors, New York, *Tenth Annual Exhibition*, 22 Jan.– 4 Mar. 1877, no. 122; NGA 1986, no. 31; NGA 1995, no. 85; Nelson-Atkins 2001 (Nelson-Atkins, only); NGA 2005

LITERATURE
"Exhibition of Water-Colors. Reception of the American Society of Painters in Water-Colors," *New-York Times*, 22 Jan. 1877; "Pictures at the Academy. The Exhibition of the American Society of Painters in Water Colors," *(NY) Daily Graphic*, 22 Jan. 1877; "The Painters in Water Colors. Pictures by American Artists in the Exhibition," *(NY) Evening Post*, 13 Feb. 1877; "The Old Cabinet," *Scribner's Monthly* 13 (Apr. 1877): 866; Nicolai Cikovsky, Jr., "Winslow Homer's *School Time*: 'A Picture Thoroughly National,'" in John Wilmerding, ed., *Essays in Honor of Paul Mellon, Collector and Benefactor* (Washington, DC: National Gallery of Art, 1986), 57–59; National Gallery of Art, Helen A. Cooper, *Winslow Homer Watercolors* (Washington, DC, 1986), 38–41; National Gallery of Art, "Winslow Homer: *Blackboard*," by Nicolai Cikovsky, Jr., in *Art for the Nation: Gifts in Honor of the 50th Anniversary of the National Gallery of Art* (Washington, DC, 1991), 172; Cikovsky and Kelly 1995, 154–55

614

Backgammon

1877

An Afternoon Chat
Watercolor, 17¹³⁄₁₆ × 22³⁄₁₆ (45.245 × 56.358)
Inscribed cr, intersected: Homer 1877

The Fine Arts Museums of San Francisco, gift of Mr. and Mrs. John D. Rockefeller 3rd, 1993.35.15

ABG: See commentary No. 612.

Of Homer's four images of young women introduced at the 1877 exhibition of the American Society of Painters in Water Color, *Backgammon* was not only the largest in size—to accommodate two figures— but also the one most overtly stylized. If he did not truly convert from Western conventions and standards of naturalistic illusionism, yet Homer made a forthright statement of admiration for Eastern (specifically, Japanese) abstraction in the composition and detailing of this painting. The total elimination of a container of physical space for the ladies and their delicate sofa; the contradictory rendering of that sofa as partly two-dimensional and partly three-dimensional; the Japanese fan placed at the exact center of the composition; and finally the inscription of his name and date in colophon all demonstrate Homer's knowledge, as well as control of new forms.

The painting seems to have posed a dilemma for the critics: they admired it almost grudgingly, and, yet could not comprehend its challenge to physical realities. The New York *Evening Express* noted

> "Backgammon," is still more simple [than *Book*], representing two women playing the game, which give the picture its title. The color is strong, but Mr. Homer has made no background to the figures, placing them boldly on the pure white paper, and, to still further add to the boldness of the work, the sofa upon which the two women are sitting has but two legs, which, to say the least, must be uncomfortable to the backgammon players.

The *New York Commercial Advertiser* commentator also mistook the painting's sophistication for eccentricity.

> Winslow Homer has a quaint study and one which shows his strong personal characteristics in his "Backgammon," which hangs in the corridor. Two young ladies seated upon a shawl covered sofa are deeply interested in a game of backgammon. The sofa has no hind legs and it is difficult to understand how it is upheld with its load of youth and beauty. Homer is eccentric in his ideas, and having seen the country milkmaids seat themselves at their evening's work on a bench balanced on a single leg, evidently deems four legs a superfluous number for a sofa, and has adopted two instead.

Perhaps the reviewer for *Scribner's Monthly*'s reaction was the most obtuse: "There are not so many Winslow Homers on exhibition this year as usual; but they are all good in their way, even the bad ones . . . . 'Backgammon' (396) not only has no background—that we might endure as an artist's whim—but it is a poor joke to paint the girls' cheeks green."

Backgammon was the only one of Homer's five works in the 1877 Society of Painters in Water Color *Annual* to be illustrated in the exhibition catalogue. Like all the other illustrations in the catalogue, this was a thumbnail-sized line drawing equivalent of the painting; there is no indication Homer had any hand in its execution.

The women's fashionable costumes may have been part of Homer's studio equipment. The bodice worn by the lady on the left is also worn by the figure on the right in the 1875 oil known as *Rab and the Girls* (2:No. 570), and the figure in the watercolor *Woman*

No. 614. Backgammon

see color illustration, p. 406

Peeling a Lemon (2:No. 609) of 1876, and the oil *Butterflies* (No. 641) of 1878.

In the spring of 1878 Homer sent more than eighty works to the Boston auctioneer, Charles F. Libbie. The sale took place 29 May. No list of its contents is known to survive. William S. Eaton's son recalled for LG his father having brought home *Backgammon* and three other Homers (all dating from the mid-1870s) on the same day, having acquired them at an auction "downtown." It is likely Mr. Eaton made his acquisitions at the May 1878 Libbie sale.

PROVENANCE
(unidentified auction, Boston, c. 1878); William S. Eaton, Boston, c. 1878; Francis S. Eaton, Boston, his son, by 1926; (William Macbeth, Inc., c. 1950); Charles D. Lang, Baltimore, c. 1950; (Milch Galleries, 1955); William J. Poplack, Detroit, 1956; (Hirschl & Adler Galleries, c. 1959); Blanchette F. Hooker Rockefeller (Mrs. John D. Rockefeller 3rd), New York, 1960

EXHIBITIONS
American Society of Painters in Water Colors, New York, *Tenth Annual Exhibition*, 22 Jan.–4 Mar. 1877, no. 396; Century Association, New York, 2 June 1877, no. 35; MFA, Boston, 1936; NE Museums 1936; NGA 1995, no. 87; Nelson-Atkins 2001

LITERATURE
"Art Matters. The Water Color Exhibition," *(NY) Evening Express*, 22 Jan. 1877; "Display of Water-Colors," *New-York Times*, 28 Jan. 1877; "Water Colors. Success of the Exhibition—Review of Some of the Pictures," *New York Commercial Advertiser*, 21 Feb. 1877; "The Old Cabinet," *Scribner's Monthly* 13 (Apr. 1877): 866; The Fine Arts Museums of San Francisco, "Backgammon," by Marc Simpson with the assistance of Patricia Junker, in *The Rockefeller Collection of American Art* (San Francisco, CA, 1994), 194–95; Cikovsky and Kelly 1995, 157

615

Snake in the Grass

[1877]

Rattlesnake

Watercolor, 13½ × 6¼ (34.290 × 15.875) sight
Inscribed lr: W H

Private collection

ABG: See commentary No. 612.

Of the five watercolors Homer submitted to the annual exhibition of the American Society of Painters in Water Colors in 1877 only *Rattlesnake* presents a puzzle of identification. Direct mention of it in press coverage of the exhibition is scant and so scathing as to suggest why the painting was generally passed over by the majority of critics. All the New York *Times* had to say was "Winslow Homer exhibits in [no.] 198 'Rattlesnake,' as indifferent a piece of work as we remember to have seen from his studio." *Scribner's Monthly*'s reviewer was equally brief, but not so restrained: "There are not so many Winslow Homers on exhibition this year as usual; but they are all good in their way, even the bad ones: no, not all—the 'Rattlesnake' (198) is beyond redemption villainous." Unfortunately neither of these writers chose to elaborate, and thus provide some details describing the subject. The New York *Evening Post* did inadvertently make the point that the sex of the principle actor in the work was opposite to those in Homer's other submissions: "Four out of [Homer's] five pictures are figures of young women."

The clear focus of attention in each of the four paintings of young women is the young women; the attributes alluded to in the paintings' titles are decidedly subordinate elements. It is, therefore, reasonable to speculate that the subject of *Rattlesnake* was a male shown in some passing engagement with a snake. Certainly, the image of this small watercolor known as *Snake in the Grass* approximates this hypothesis.

In recording his examination of *Snake in the Grass* LG noted that it is "highly finished, and rather deep in color, like such pictures as *The Trysting Place* (2:No. 568) or *Portrait of a Lady* (2:No. 567). It is a curiously naive picture in its subject, but very able in execution. Evidently [Homer] took great pains with it."

The high degree of finish and appropriate subject matter would seem to be ample support of an identification of *Snake in the Grass* as the *Rattlesnake* shown in the 1877 exhibition. However, the present small size of *Snake in the Grass* calls that conclusion into question. Homer could well have included one work in his submission for the exhibition which was not designed on the liberal dimensions of *Lemon*

No. 615. Snake in the Grass

(2:No. 609), *Book* (No. 612), *Blackboard* (No. 613), and *Backgammon* (No. 614). But the $350 price set on *Rattlesnake*, substantially greater than the amounts named for those four watercolors—$100, $250, $125, and $250, respectively—is the inverse of the relative size of *Snake in the Grass* in comparison with the others. To justify the high value Homer placed on *Rattlesnake*, it should have at least held its own with the smallest of his works in the 1877 exhibition, that is, to have been not less than 20 inches in one dimension.

As it is presently known, *Snake in the Grass* appears to be missing a vital component: the snake of the title. The ready stick in the boy's hand, his clenched fist, and the intensity of his gaze downward to his right, suggests the object of his attention was once part of the scene. Also, that the snake was referenced in the work's title when it was exhibited in 1904, suggests the reptile was then still in evidence.

There are indications the sheet has been cut down. Homer was not given to such abrupt truncation as has befallen the stick in the boy's right hand. Also the figure seems disproportionately large for the sheet-space he occupies. And while there is no doubt that the painting is Homer's work, the initialling now at the lower right edge of the work has the appearance of being a later addition by another hand, a reasonable substitution if Homer's inscription were lost in trimming the sheet.

The sheet may have been trimmed significantly at the left side, in order to get a possibly disquieting image of a snake out of sight, but how extensively the work may have been reduced from its original dimensions cannot be determined. It is also possible parts of the composition have only been obstructed by strategic matting. When LG examined *Snake in the Grass* in the mid-1930s he could only take the measurements of the area visible within the mat aperture, and apparently found nothing worthy of notice about the size or character of its matting and framing.

Homer does not seem to have put *Rattlesnake* out for exhibition again after its inauspicious debut at the Society of Painters in Water Colors *Annual* of 1877. It was probably *Rattlesnake* which was one of more then seventy drawings and watercolors auctioned for him by Daniel Mathews in March 1880. The New York *Evening Post* gave the preview of the sale the most extensive publicity, and among its long listing of subjects of the works to be seen and sold was one showing a boy "boldly slaughtering snakes [*sic*] (No. 54)."

James Craig Nicoll (1847–1918) owned *Snake in the Grass* by 1904, when he lent it for exhibition at the Louisiana Purchase Exposition. Whether *Rattlesnake* and *Snake in the Grass* are the same work must remain an open question, but if they were, then Nicoll may have made his acquisition from the Mathews sale.

Nicoll was especially active in the American Society of Painters in Water Color, having participated in its founding. He served as its secretary 1870–1879—within which period *Rattlesnake* was in the Society's annual exhibition. He was treasurer of the Society from 1881 into 1888, and its president from 1904 into 1910. Nicoll occupied rooms in the Tenth Street Studio Building from 1870 to the end of his life.

PROVENANCE
(Daniel A. Mathews Art Gallery, 4 Mar. 1880, Homer sale, no. 54) [?]; James Craig Nicoll, New York, before 1904; Emily Nicoll, New York, his daughter, by bequest, 1918; (Milch Galleries, 1919); Warren P. King, Willoughby, OH, 1919; Mrs. Warren P. King, Willoughby, OH, nd

EXHIBITIONS
American Society of Painters in Water Colors, New York, *Tenth Annual Exhibition*, 22 Jan.–4 Mar. 1877, no. 198 (as *Rattlesnake*) [?]); Mathews 1880, no. 54 [?]; *Universal Exposition* (*The Louisiana Purchase Exposition*), Saint Louis, 30 Apr.–31 Oct. 1904, no. 1139

LITERATURE
"Exhibition of Water-Colors. Reception of the American Society of Painters in Water-Colors," *New-York Times*, 22 Jan. 1877; "The Painters in Water Colors. Pictures by American Artists in the Exhibition," *(NY) Evening Post*, 13 Feb. 1877; "The Old Cabinet," *Scribner's Monthly* 13 (Apr. 1877): 866; "Fine Arts," *(NY) Evening Post*, 3 Mar. 1880

616

Girl with Checker Board
[1877]

Graphite, watercolor, 8 × 5¾ (20.320 × 14.605)
Inscribed ll: W. H.
Cincinnati Art Museum, Isreal and Caroline Wilson Fund, 1924.477

No. 616. Girl with Checker Board

616.5

Arrival of the French Ambassador in Madrid

[1876–1877]

Oil

Unlocated

ABG: By the middle of the decade of the 1870s Homer was clearly exploring new figure subject themes and contexts. One of these is such a conspicuous anomaly it seems incredible: historical genre.

In February 1877 the *New York Commercial Advertiser* noted, in reporting on an upcoming Schenck auction, "W. Homer [sends] . . . a cabinet canvas illustrating a middle age cavalcade, the finish of which is superb." The next day's *New York Herald* noted that "Mr. Schenck has seldom had a better collection of pictures on exhibition than is now to be seen in his gallery, and which will be offered for sale on Thursday and Friday afernoons. . . . Among the most attractive pictures is . . . 'The Robin's Note,' by Winslow Homer, who has two other pictures in this collection; 'The Arrival of the French Ambassador in Madrid,' a carefully painted picture, in a new style for Mr. Homer, and 'The Farmer's Boy,' a large canvas in his best known manner." The *Daily Graphic* also named the painting as a work by Winslow Homer in its report of the forthcoming sale.

That three newspapers documented such a startling juxtaposition of artist and subject could be discredited as repetition of an egregious mistake made by the Schenck organization. However, the coupling of Homer's name and the same unlikely subject matter recurred seven months later. Late in August the *Herald* listed the group of paintings gathered up from New York sources over the previous week for shipment to Saint Louis for that city's annual *Exposition* which would open in September. Among them was "'The Old Cavalier' by Winslow Homer." This may have been a different example of Homer adventuring in costumed fantasy, but it is more likely a careless reference to *The French Ambassador*.

The most compelling argument in support of the existence of such a subject having come from the hand and imagination of Winslow Homer is the Century Association record of *Reception of the French Ambassador* being one of two paintings he contributed to its monthly exhibition of December 1877. There can be no question of a miss-match of artist and object at the Century where the exhibitions were relatively small assemblies of members' work. Immediately following its appearance at the Century Homer sent the painting to the annual exhibition organized by the Utica, New York, Art Association; the exhibition catalogue noted *Receiving the French Ambassador* as for sale for $150, Apparently it did not find a buyer. The Utica show ran through February 1878. By the second week of March the New York *Evening Post* reported: "Mr. Daniel A. Mathews, auctioneer, has returned to Liberty street and opened art rooms at No. 51 where there is now on exhibition, free, a collection of more than one hundred oil paintings by American and foreign artists, which will be sold by auction this afternoon and to-morrow afternoon at 3:15 o'clock. . . . To-morrow afternoon some of the pictures to be offered are . . . Winslow Homer's 'Landing of the Spanish Ambassador' . . ."

(It is more rational to suppose the *Post*'s reporter confused the nationalities of the principal actor and his *mise-en-scène* than that Homer had begun a series on the diplomatic corps of Medieval Europe.)

Nothing further is known of this intriguing canvas, nor is there any evidence Homer ventured again into such exotic narrative territory. It may be noted, however, that Homer introduced the French Rococo fancy dress shepherd and shepherdess costumes into his work at just this time.

EXHIBITIONS

Schenck Art Gallery, New York, [auction], 5–9 Feb. 1877; Century Association, New York, 1 Dec. 1877, no. 2 (as *Reception of the French Ambassador*); Utica (New York) Art Association, *Paintings Exhibition*, 26 Jan.–26 Feb. 1878, no. 230 (as *Receiving the French Ambassador*); Daniel A. Mathews Art Gallery, New York, [auction], c. 8–13 Mar. 1878 (as *Landing of the Spanish Ambassador*)

LITERATURE

"Mr. Schenck's Art Gallery," *New York Commercial Advertiser*, 6 Feb. 1877; "Art Matters. On Exhibition," *New York Herald*, 7 Feb. 1877; "Art Notes," *(NY) Daily Graphic*, 7 Feb. 1877; "Fine Arts," *New York Herald*, 27 Aug. 1877; "Fine Arts. The Mathews Sale," *New York Evening Mail*, 11 Mar. 1878; "The Mathews Art Rooms," *(NY) Evening Post*, 12 Mar. 1878; "Pictures To Be Sold," *New York Herald*, 12 Mar. 1878

617

Twilight at Leeds, N. Y.

[1877]

Landscape

Lithograph crayon, 10 × 14 (25.400 × 35.560)
Inscribed lr: W. H.

Private collection

This drawing was the source for the 2¼ by 3 inch
illustration of no. 406 *Landscape* (2:No. 598) in
the catalogue of the National Academy of Design's
Annual of 1877, and in the handbook for the
exhibition prepared by "Nemo," *Academy Sketches,
Exhibition of 1877*, published by G. P. Putnam's Sons.
The illustrations were specifically identified in the
opening pages of the Academy catalogue as having
been "produced by the Photo-plate Engraving Co.,
and with the exception of six marked *, are *fac-similies of drawings made by the artists*." As the illustration
of *Landscape* was not among the asterisked six, it may
be presumed Homer executed this drawing himself,
and with its photographic reproduction in mind.

PROVENANCE
Maj. George Clendon, Glens Falls, NY, nd; Mrs.
Cutler DeLong, Glens Falls, NY, his daughter, 1908;
Mrs. Helen DeLong Bush, Glens Falles, NY, her
daughter, 1926; Howard C. Bush, Alexandria, VA,
her son, by gift, c. 1945; Isabel K. Bush (Mrs.
Howard C. Bush), Alexandria, VA, by bequest, nd

618

Answering the Horn

[1877]

[Lithograph crayon]
Inscribed lr: W. H.

Unlocated

ABG: In addition to *Twilight at Leeds* (2:No. 598),
Answering the Horn (2:No. 599) was among the
limited selection from the National Academy of
Design annual exhibition of 1877 to be illustrated
in its official catalogue, and in *Academy Sketches,
Exhibition of 1877*, a handbook published by G. P.
Putnam's Sons. According to the definition—provided
in the Academy's catalogue—of the character of
the illustrations, the 3 by 1¾ inch illustration of
Answering the Horn was a photographic reduction
of an image drawn by Homer. Such drawings, made
solely to serve as sources for photo-reproduction,
commonly were retained by the publisher of the
work they illustrated; in this case it is likely Putnam's
kept the 110 drawings used for *Academy Sketches*.
Unlike his drawing for *Twilight at Leeds* (No. 617),
Homer's drawing for *Answering the Horn* seems not
to have survived.

No. 617. Twilight at Leeds, N. Y.

619

Dressing for the Carnival

1877

The Carnival

Oil, 20 × 30 (50.800 × 76.200)
Inscribed lr: Winslow Homer N. A. / 1877

The Metropolitan Museum of Art, Amelia B.
Lazarus Fund, 22.220

LG's first opportunity to examine this work thoroughly was when it was on loan from the Metropolitan Museum to his Homer centennial exhibition mounted by the Whitney Museum of American Art late in 1936. At that time he noted that the back of the original canvas was exposed, and carried the inscription, "Reichard Co." in oversized script written in white chalk or paint. This marking suggests that at some time Homer placed *Dressing for the Carnival* with the New York dealer, Gustav Reichard. Homer's close association with Reichard dates from about 1885, by which time *Dressing for the Carnival* was a relic of Homer's earlier career. However, Reichard, having been with William Schaus for many years, had gone into business for himself late in 1876—with considerable attendant publicity. Homer tested the agency approach to marketing in Boston in 1878 by placing several paintings, including *Dressing for the Carnival*, with Doll & Richards; he might have tried New York, and Reichard, at about the same time.

ABG: Just when Homer first went South, and where he found the African-American subjects of four paintings of 1876 and 1877, is a popular subject for conjecture. (For discussion of some options see commentary 2:No. 602.) However, that he went on a painting trip to Virginia for the month of May 1877 is documented.

In a letter of 27 April 1877 to the wood engraver, Andrew Anthony, Homer explained that because he was leaving the next day for Norfolk, Virginia, it would be July before he could deliver the illustrations (probably for the book *Excelsior*) that were under discussion. On 31 May 1877 the New York *Evening Post* reported, "Mr. Winslow Homer is again in his studio after a month's sojourn in Virginia. He has brought back several new pictures." Whether *A Visit from the Old Mistress* (2:No. 603), *Sunday Morning in Virginia* (No. 620), and *Dressing for the Carnival* had literally been brought back from this spring 1877 trip to Virginia is open to question, but the *Post* reporter might reasonably have jumped to this conclusion, having seen Homer working on them a few days before he introduced the three at the Century Association's monthly exhibition.

The Cotton Pickers (2:No. 602) had debuted at the Century in March 1877. It and *A Visit from the Old Mistress* were inscribed by Homer with the date 1876. *Sunday Morning in Virginia*, although dated 1877, may be presumed to have been conceived and probably begun in tandem with *A Visit* in the previous year. *Dressing for the Carnival*, also dated 1877, is so distinctively different in scenery, subject, and palette from the other three surely Virginia subjects, it is tempting to think it was the focus of, if not the sole reason for Homer's return to the South in the spring of 1877. It could have been blocked out on a canvas before that trip, or have been only an idea in the spring of 1877. The exceptional success of *The Cotton Pickers* in March might have spurred Homer to bring unfinished canvases, and unrealized ideas on related themes to completion and exhibition before the 1876–1877 season ended and *The Cotton Pickers* began to fade from memory.

Although from early in 1877 the Century had barred the press from its exhibitions, the *Evening Post*, which among New York newspapers was the most consistent in reporting on these events, continued to find ways to publish critiques of the club's exhibitions. Its coverage of Homer's contribution to the June 1877 presentation was extensive, but did not provide descriptive detail.

> The last monthly reception of the Century Club this season will be held this evening. A large attendance of members and guests, and a notable display of pictures are expected. In addition to Mr. Le Clear's fine portrait of Mr. George Bancroft, which we noticed yesterday, three studies of Virginian negro life will be exhibited by Mr. Winslow Homer, which will not fail to please. Though scarcely more than sketched, they are very rich and true in color effects, very successful in the representation of typical "darkies" of the days of bondage, and altogether original in design and handling. Mr. Homer's recently painted "Cotton Pickers," the unusual merits of which have already been indicated in the Evening Post, was one of the first trophies of his purpose to "carry the war into Africa;" and these latest works of his show very plainly that that purpose is a happy and fruitful one. The same reasons that made "Uncle Tom's Cabin" a successful book bring success to good sketches of negro life on canvas.

Gordon Hendricks decided that the work identified in the Century's registration record of the 2 June 1877 exhibition as "Sketch—4th July in Virginia" was "evidently" a study for *Dressing for the Carnival*, and not the painting itself. Hendricks based his conclusion on his casual—and mistaken—assumption: that "the artist always called [the painting] *The Carnival* and not *The Fourth of July* .... [and] Homer would not have called the Fourth a 'carnival.'"

No. 619. Dressing for the Carnival

see color illustration, p. 407

A week after the Century exhibition the *New-York Daily Tribune* singled out *Dressing for the Carnival* for attention in catching up its readers on "Art Gossip."

The fruits of one trip away from New-York are already visible at the studio of Mr. Winslow Homer, who has been spending a few weeks in the South, and is just home. A number of sketches of colored life on the plantations have been brought back. One is a group representing a scene on the day, which in New-York and in the vicinity of Tompkins-square would be termed by the boys "ragamuffin day." The central figures in the group are dressed in carnival attire, giving a chance for the employment of primary colors and lively effects.

Nicolai Cikovksy has identified "ragamuffin day" by relating it to one of Homer's own designs for a wood engraving: "The Fourth of July in Tompkins Square, New York—'The Sogers Are Coming!',", published in *Harper's Weekly* 11 July 1868. This tends to support belief that the work styled "Sketch—4th July in Virginia" at the Century is the same canvas as *Dressing for the Carnival*, and that Hendricks's imagined preliminary study did not exist.

That the painting was on view and for sale in Boston in the early autumn of 1878, in company with *At the Window* (2:No. 403) and *Corn Husking* (2:No. 540), is known from a clipping in one of the scrapbooks in the Homer family archive now in possession of the Bowdoin College Museum of Art. The clipping is headed "Fine Arts. Mr. Winslow Homer's Pictures," but is otherwise unidentified.

At Doll & Richards's gallery, on an easel down stairs, is a large study in color, by Mr. Winslow Homer, of New York, which he calls *Getting Ready for the Carnival*. It represents several negroes of the plantation order, evidently a family group, the head of the family being engaged in rigging himself up in colors that would have shamed Joseph of old—a yellow garment focusing the light in a brilliant manner, and sending the dusky faces very decidedly into shadow. While the paterfamilias thus monopolizes the general share of attention, the oldest son is also showing his hand in the foolishness with a fair show of success, though his choice of colors has evidently been made at second-hand. The wife and mother of the dusky group seems to be having a voice in the direction of proceedings—as the wife and mother usually does, whether black or white, and (with a pipe in her mouth) she is at present first-lieutenant, if not acting-captain. A little pickaninny who has evidently not seen more than two Summers, however hot they may have been, stands by in a bashful way, half pleased and half frightened at what is going on; one from a neighboring plantation looks over the fence, and farther away are just descried the rude Southern houses and southern foliage. Mr. Homer has not only succeeded in making a picture full of bright color and vivacious life, but he has shown that it is not necessary to ransack studios and scrape the old world for bizarre and picturesque subjects or characters. The South especially is full of unused material. Southern characteristics could be very profitably studied for a time in the Winter, and less of the painting of painted-out localities in the North indulged in for a while.

Mary Ann Calo has pointed out that the figure of the little girl at the left in *Dressing for the Carnival* "who has evidently not seen more than two Summers" reappears ten years later in one of Homer's illustrations for the four-volume work, *Battles and Leaders of the Civil War*. (See *Waiting for His Breakfast* 4:No. 1369.) Calo believes the repeated use of this figure and another from *A Visit from the Old Mistress* in an illustration for a book on the Civil War, suggests Homer used sketches made when he was in Virginia during the War for these paintings done in 1876 and 1877 as well as the illustration. It is equally possible, however, that sketches he made on his visits South in the mid-1870s, served for the paintings which were an immediate result, then proved useful again in 1887, especially for the one subject by Homer in *Battles and Leaders* that is set in a domestic, rather than military context.

Homer put *Uncle Ned at Home* (2:No. 488) and *Dressing for the Carnival* up for auction in New York in April 1879. *Dressing for the Carnival* attracted the greater attention on this occasion, yet it failed to find a buyer. *Uncle Ned at Home*, on the other hand was reported to have sold. This report is unreliable, but Thomas B. Clarke was surely *Uncle Ned*'s owner not long after this sale, probably by direct purchase from Homer.

That thirteen years later Clarke initiated pursuit of *Dressing for the Carnival* may be inferred from Homer's letter to him of 23 April 1892.

I have two darkey pictures one of which you refer to - "Dressing for the Carnival." The other [is] the companion to the one Mr. W. T. Evans has,

"A Visit from the Old Mistress." I always thought that Mr. Evans should have it—its the same size and was exhibited in Paris with his "Sunday Morning in Va." He paid me 400 & I would sell this to him for $500. The other darkey picture that was at the Club, $750. I will sell the two for $1,000.

An abbreviated reference to "the Club" in correspondence with Thomas B. Clarke should mean the Union League Club, with which Clarke was conspicuously associated. However, the only known appearance of *Dressing for the Carnival* in a club exhibition is at the Century Association in June 1877. Yet it is possible *Dressing for the Carnival* had hung at the Union League Club. Press reports of the Club's January 1880 exhibition mentioned only *A Visit from the Old Mistress* and *Sunday Morning in Virginia* as representing Homer among the approximately sixty paintings in the display. They were highlighted for having just "returned to New York after a visit to Paris." *Dressing for the Carnival* did not enjoy the celebrity of having been included in the Paris Exposition of 1878, but it might have been coupled with the other two Southern subject paintings on this occasion, as it had been at the Century in 1877, and its presence simply not mentioned in the press coverage of the 1880 exhibition.

Clarke accepted Homer's offer of *A Visit from the Old Mistress* and *Dressing for the Carnival* discounted to $1,000 for the two, and paid him that amount under cover of a letter of 5 November 1892 in which he identified them as "'Carnival' and 'Visit to the Missus'." In his formal receipt sent to Clarke on 9 November, Homer again designated them "'A Visit from the Old Mistress' [and] 'Dressing for the Carnival'." Nonetheless, Clarke persisted in using his titles for both paintings. The sole exception was that *Dressing for the Carnival* was allowed its proper title at the Columbian Exposition in Chicago in 1893.

A story specifically attached to *Dressing for the Carnival* first appeared in an article in the New York *Sun* in March 1898.

There is interest, too, in . . . "The Carnival," a bright little composition painted in Smithtown, Va., in 1877, as a salve, it seems, to the negro population.

The negroes had taken offense, it is said, at the studies [Homer] made of them, for his models were generally poorly clad, and their fellows who were much better dressed took it much to heart that he should choose such subjects. They carried a complaint to the Mayor, and gave him to understand that the sketches in question were of a kind that would reflect little honor on them, and that the artist should be notified that there were plenty of well-dressed negroes if he would but look for them. In short, there was a very strong feeling of animosity toward him so, by way of re-establishing himself in their favor, he painted this canvas, in which he represented a group of negroes in tawdry costumes of many colors, to their entire satisfaction.

Christopher Knauff repeated the story with some elaboration a few months later in his article on Homer, which, as he said, depended heavily on

the courtesy of Mr. Thomas B. Clarke... [in whose home] one entire apartment is given up to the works of Winslow Homer.... In [this] apartment . . . there hangs another fine canvas, having to do with Virginian scenes. It is entitled "The Carnival." Mr. Homer had been working at Smithtown, Va. Like many another artist, he found picturesque subjects in the people of color. He had painted them as he found them, in tatters. So they saw themselves in "The Old Mistress" and other pictures. At last the models demurred; they objected to this—that such undignified likenesses of themselves should go up to the North. Excitement ran high; they almost mobbed the painter. At length, by way of compromise, the latter agreed to paint them in their finery, as they were accustomed to deck themselves for their Christmas festivities. Here we see chosen examples, shining out in brilliant array—yellow, red, blue— great patches and bits of broad ribbon occurring in unexpected localities. So to their satisfaction, they appeared for once upon a canvas as well dressed darkeys.

Although Clarke was surely both writers' source for this story, it is reasonable to believe he, in turn, had received its essential content from Homer. As all but one of the principals in *Dressing for the Carnival* are in ordinary dress, it may be questioned how much these narratives were shaped by their authors, how much by Clarke, and possibly by Homer to conform to the stereotype of African-Americans (especially those in the South) as simple and foolish, and easily impressed by things bright or shiny.

David Park Curry has demonstrated that the extraordinary costume that is the focus of *Dressing for the Carnival* is a hybrid of African and European festival traditions, similar to the fanciful outfit associated with Jonkonnu dance ceremonies held at the Christmas season in the West Indies, and clearly descended from slaves' African cultures. Curry therefore assumes that Homer witnessed and represented the specific scene of "a dying custom: Boxing Day, the day after Christmas," noting that "during the slave-holding era, Boxing Day was one of just a few annual holidays when most slaves were excused from work. Some would dress in fancy costumes and were

allowed to go round to the 'big houses' performing and begging for little Christmas gifts and tips . . . . such Southern customs survived the Civil War and emancipation."

While the costume might have been used in Christmas observances by Homer's models, it is highly improbable Homer would have been in the South in the last week of December, away from his family with whom he ritualistically spent holidays, not to mention absenting himself from New York at the height of the season. The abundant foliage also belies a late December context for the subject.

The small American flags held by the children support both the initial titling of the painting, and Peter Wood and Karen Dalton's observation that by the 1870s African-Americans in the South had made the Fourth of July their most important celebration of the year. If Homer is believed to have required direct experience for inspiration, then Independence Day 1876 would be the probable date he witnessed the scene depicted in *Dressing for the Carnival*. Even if he is thus denied the imagination and competency to create at a distance from his subject, again, for Homer to have been in the South on the Fourth would be contrary to his custom of joining his family for significant holidays. However, the core of the tale relayed to the press by Thomas B. Clarke—that Homer's models assumed "their finery" exactly to serve his imagery—is credible as an appropriate artistic method, and antidote to presumptions that the subject of *Dressing for the Carnival* documents Homer's itinerary.

Jonkonnu, a 1997 children's book by Amy Littlesugar, uses *Dressing for the Carnival* as the device to promote some of the unsupported tales meant to enhance appreciation of Homer's personality and paintings. Its point of departure for a narrative intended to instruct the young on the evils of racism and on Winslow Homer's heroism is Thomas B. Clarke's story about the *Carnival* subjects' objection to the attire in which Homer represented them. Littlesugar stirs into her confection paraphrases of lines an *Art Amateur* critic proposed—in relation to the exhibition at the National Academy of Design in 1880 of *A Visit from the Old Mistress* and *Sunday Morning in Virginia*—to have been spoken by Homer:

"Why don't you paint one [of our] lovely girls instead of these dreadful creatures?" asked a First-Family belle when he was in Virginia, laying up his studies for his pictures. "Because these are the purtiest," he said in his gruff final way.

(Littlesugar reforms this diction to have Homer say "prettiest," presumably to prevent corruption of her readers' grasp on spelling.)

For a dramatic climax to her story, Littlesugar retells, with considerable embellishment, William Howe Downes's account of Homer's supposed confrontation with an angry citizen, who was discouraged from any speech or action by suspicion Homer was carrying concealed weapons. The illustrations by Ian Schoenherr for this work of children's fiction, similarly throw together images extrapolated from most of Homer's oils and watercolors of the 1870s that include African-American figures.

PROVENANCE
Thomas B. Clarke, New York, 1892; (American Art Association, 14–18 Feb. 1899, Clarke sale, no. 86); N. C. Matthews, Baltimore (purchased by F. R. Kaldenburg, as agent for Matthews), 1899; (unidentified dealer, after 1911); (M. O'Brien & Son, Chicago, by 1921); (C. W. Kraushaar, 1939)

EXHIBITIONS
Century Association, New York, 2 June 1877, no. 2 (as *Sketch—4th July in Virginia*); Doll & Richards, Boston, c. 15–c. 30 Sept. 1878 (as *Preparing for the Carnival*); Daniel A. Mathews Art Gallery, New York, *The American Collection of Paintings, Contributed, in Every Instance, by the Artist Represented*, 1–9 Apr. 1879, no. 107 (exhibited at the Kurtz Gallery); National Academy of Design, New York, *New York Columbian Celebration of the 400th Anniversary of the Discovery of America*, 9–22 Oct. 1892, no. 80 (as *The Carnival*); Union League Club, New York, *A Group of Paintings by American Artists Accepted for the Columbian Exposition*, 9–11 Mar. 1893, no. 5 (as *The Carnival*); Columbian Exposition 1893, no. 566 (as *Dressing for the Carnival*); Union League 1827, no. 27 (as *The Carnival*); Clarke, AAA, 1899, no. 86 (as *The Carnival*); Pennsylvania 1936, no. 10; Whitney 1936, no. 15; Carnegie 1937, no. 35; Wildenstein 1947, no. 21; NGA 1958/MFA, Boston, 1959, no. 41/36; Whitney 1973, no. 39; Menil 1988, no. 34; NGA 1995, no. 82

LITERATURE
"The Century Club," *(NY) Evening Post*, 2 June 1877; "Art Gossip," *New-York Daily Tribune*, 9 June 1877; "Fine Arts. Notes on the Pictures at the Fair. A Few New Things at the Galleries," *(Boston) Herald*, 22 Sept. 1878; "Notes. Boston," *(NY) Art Journal* 4 (Nov. 1878): 351–52; "Fine Arts. Paintings from American Studios," *New York Herald*, 3 Apr. 1879; "Auction Sale of American Pictures," *New-York Daily Tribune*, 3 Apr. 1879; "Fine Arts," *(NY) Evening Post*, 9 Jan. 1880; "Fine Arts. Art Reception at the Union League," *New York Evening Mail*, 9 Jan. 1880; "Exhibition of the Academy of Design," *Art Amateur* 2 (May 1880): 112; "Columbian Exhibition of Paintings. . . The Works of George Inness and Winslow Homer Combined," *(NY) Sun*, 7 Oct. 1892; "The Columbian Art Display. Loan Exhibition of Paintings, Sculpture nd Drawings," *New York Herald*, 8 Oct. 1892; Christopher W. Knauff, "Certain Exemplars of Art in America. IV. Elliott Daingerfield—Winslow Homer," *The Churchman* 78 (23 July 1898): 128; Downes 1911, 85–86; H[arry] B. W[ehle], "Early Paintings by Homer," *Bulletin of the Metropolitan Museum of Art* 18 (Feb. 1923): 40–41; Karen M. Adams, *Black Images in Nineteenth-Century American Painting and Literature: An Iconographic Study* (Ann Arbor, MI: University Microfilms, 1977), 132–33; Hendricks 1979, 104; Mary Ann Calo, "Winslow Homer's Visits to Virginia During Reconstruction," *American Art Journal* 12 (Winter 1980): 19–20; Natalie Spassky, *American Paintings in the Metropolitan Museum of Art, Volume II* (Princeton, NJ: Princeton University Press, 1985), 461–65; The Menil Collection, "Winslow Homer's Images of Blacks," by Peter H. Wood and Karen C. C. Dalton, in *Winslow Homer's Images of Blacks: The Civil War and the Reconstruction Years* (Houston, 1988), 100–6; David Park Curry, "Homer's *Dressing for the Carnival*," in Nicolai Cikovsky, Jr., ed., *Winslow Homer: A Symposium*, National Gallery of Art Studies in the History of Art 26, Washington, DC, 1990, 91–113; Cikovsky and Kelly 1995, 96–97, 152; Amy Littlesugar, *Jonkonnu: A Story from the Sketchbook of Winslow Homer* (New York: Philomel Books, 1997)

620

Sunday Morning in Virginia

1877

Oil, 18¼ × 24 (46.355 × 60.960)
Inscribed ul: Homer 1877; ll: Virginia 1877

Cincinnati Art Museum, John J. Emery Fund,
1924.247

Little of the correspondence Homer received has
survived, so it is unknown what in the spring of 1892
occasioned Thomas B. Clarke to inquire after a
painting which had not been seen in exhibition since
1879. However, in his reply to Clarke of 23 April
1892 Homer told him more than probably was
expected, and revealed something of his thoughts
concerning *Sunday Morning in Virginia* and *A Visit
from the Old Mistress* (2:No. 603).

I have two darkey pictures one of which you refer
to - "Dressing for the Carnival" [No. 619]. The
other, the companion to the one Mr. W. T. Evans
has, [is] "A Visit from the Old Mistress." I always
thought that Mr. Evans should have it—its the
same size and was exhibited in Paris with his
"Sunday morning in Va." He paid me 400 & I
would sell this to him for $500...."

ABG: William T. Evans amplified this story of his
aquisition of *Sunday Morning in Virginia* in a letter
to Charles de Kay, dated 15 August 189–. (The final
digit of the date has been lost in the crumbling
away of the right edge of the first page of this letter.):
"As I mentioned Saturday, I began [to] collect in
the winter of '79/80. The first painting I purchased
at the Academy was Winslow Homer's 'Sunday
Morning in Virginia,' which still holds a place in
my heart and on the line in my gallery."

Apparently the painting's hold on Evans failed to
survive the decade for it was among the substantial

No. 620. Sunday Morning in Virginia

see color illustration, p. 408

portion of his collection Evans sold in February 1900. Had he hesitated *Sunday Morning in Virginia* might have been reunited with *A Visit from the Old Mistress*, which Evans acquired in February 1901.

That Homer considered *Sunday Morning in Virginia* and *A Visit from the Old Mistress* to be pendants is demonstrated by his reference to them as companions in his letter of 23 April 1892 to Thomas B. Clarke. Their shared setting, the same interior wall of a rough cabin, used in both compositions to create a shallow stage for a frieze of figures, as well as their matching size and format, further testifies to their bond. It is likely the two paintings were conceived and commenced at about the same time, and it is the point at which Homer considered them essentially completed that is indicated by their disparate inscribed datings of 1876 and 1877. Another symptom of Homer's concept of the two as a pair is that so long as both remained in his possession, they were not exhibited singly; nor did he show *A Visit from the Old Mistress* between 1880 and 1892 when it was the only one of the two he still held.

The two paintings were introduced at the Century Association's monthly exhibition of June 1877. The Century presentations were perhaps the only venue where Homer would have had some influence on the hanging position of his contributions; it is therefore worth noting that *Sunday Morning in Virginia* was numbered "25" on this occasion and thus may have been placed to the left or just above *A Visit from the Old Mistress*, which was numbered "26." *Dressing for the Carnival*, also first shown in this Century exhibition, was numbered "2," indicating it was not associated with the other two in the hanging arrangement.

It was, as usual, a reporter for the New York *Evening Post* who had access to the works assembled for private exhibition at the Century.

The last monthly reception of the Century Club this season will be held this evening. A large attendance of members and guests, and a notable display of pictures are expected. In addition to Mr. Le Clear's fine portrait of Mr. George Bancroft, which we noticed yesterday, three studies of Virginian negro life will be exhibited by Mr. Winslow Homer, which will not fail to please. Though scarcely more than sketched, they are very rich and true in color effects, very successful in the representation of typical "darkies" of the days of bondage, and altogether original in design and handling. Mr. Homer's recently painted "Cotton Pickers," the unusual merits of which

have already been indicated in the Evening Post, was one of the first trophies of his purpose to "carry the war into Africa;" and these latest works of his show very plainly that that purpose is a happy and fruitful one. The same reasons that made "Uncle Tom's Cabin" a successful book bring success to good sketches of negro life on canvas.

Rather than hold the two paintings for the National Academy of Design's next annual exhibition, Homer apparently chose to take the opportunity to have them included in the American presentation at the Paris Exposition of 1878. It again was the *Post* which singled out for attention the two paintings that were Homer's own submission for the Paris Exposition, giving an entire article to *Sunday Morning in Virginia* and *A Visit from the Old Mistress*.

Mr. Winslow Homer is giving the finishing touches to two pictorial representations of negro life in Virginia which he expects to send to the Paris Exhibition. In one of the canvases he introduces us to the interior of a shanty where a sable girl of twelve summers or so is reading from a large Bible to a group of her kinswomen of various ages and sizes. It is Sunday morning, and what pieces of gaudy ribbon and other adornment were available have been brought into use on the persons whose swarthy faces enhance the effect by contrast. The other canvas shows us a similar interior, where a not dissimilar company are receiving a visit from an elderly, kindly-disposed gentlewoman once their owner and mistress. Mr. Homer has treated these simple themes with fidelity and freshness. His negroes are real negroes, children of the southern soil, and will not fail to interest Europeans who expended so much sympathy upon them in earlier days. The figures possess remarkable roundness and relief, and the facial expressions are distinct studies for the spectator. In subject, conception and execution these works are most refreshingly original.

It presumably was no more than a few days before this article appeared on 26 January 1878, that the *Post*'s reporter observed Homer "giving the finishing touches" to *Sunday Morning in Virginia* and *A Visit from the Old Mistress*. The two paintings had been exhibited briefly seven months earlier, to a limited but sophisticated audience of Century club members. It is unlikely either was not well developed when Homer showed them at the Century. The report given in the *New York Herald* on 3 February 1878— "Winslow Homer has on an easel, blocked in, a negro character study, 'Sunday Morning in Virginia.' Very natural so far."—is therefore open to suspicion. Yet a few days later, on 8 February, the *Daily Graphic* echoed the *Herald*—perhaps too exactly: "Winslow

Homer is at work upon a negro character study, entitled 'Sunday Morning in Virginia,' which bids fair to be one of his best pictures." The *Graphic* reporter may have visited Homer's studio, or he may have cribbed this news item from the rival paper. If these reports are taken at face value, then it suggests Homer had scraped down *Sunday Morning in Virginia* and was engaged in substantially repainting it, a notion not supported by the surface appearance of the painting. There is a strong possibility, however, that one or both reporters were confusing the title of a finished work with a work very definitely still in an early stage of development: *Upland Cotton* (No. 776). The *Graphic* had described *Upland Cotton* in a 10 January 1878 article headed "Paintings now in Progress on the Easels of Prominent Artists."

While there may have been more than a touch of irony in the *Post* writer's reference to the anticipated European response to Homer's paintings of African-Americans, his prediction proved correct: they were noticed and admired in the international critical coverage of the art exhibition part of the Exposition. They reappeared in American exhibitions with an aura of celebrity. When the two were shown in Boston in the spring of 1879, it was the opinion of the critic for the *Daily Evening Transcript* that "Winslow Homer's pictures (404 and 308) are, of course, the best things in the line of figures, clean and forcible in drawing, clear and complete in characterization and story-telling detail, yet so concentrated in composition as to be comprehended at a glance,—a worthy, indeed most flattering, representative American exhibit for the Paris Exposition."

Late the same year when the two were shown in Springfield, Massachusetts, that city's *Daily Republican* acknowledged both paintings: "The center of the eastern wall is occupied by a characteristic piece of James M. Hart which he calls "Farmington Valley," . . . . The Winslow Homers which flank this picture are genre works, but of a sort whose meanings are not obvious. It requires study to see how thoughtful the insight of character is in these negro faces, bent over the Bible." But the *Republican*'s critic then turned to *A Visit from the Old Mistress*, pronouncing it "the more important picture of the two."

Sunday Morning in Virginia and *A Visit from the Old Mistress* were reintroduced to a select New York audience at the Union League Club in January 1880, where they were again remarked in the press for their qualities, and for having been well-received in Paris.

The Springfield *Republican* critic's preference for *A Visit from the Old Mistress* foreshadowed their reception by the National Academy of Design's hanging committee when they appeared in the 1880 annual exhibition. Where Homer would surely have preferred they be hung together, and priced each equally at $600, *Sunday Morning in Virginia* was consigned to the Northwest gallery, decidedly, the Academy's back room; *A Visit from the Old Mistress* was hung in a side gallery, the East Room. This may partly explain the unequal critical attention the paintings received, but both placement and press response may have reflected a perception that *A Visit* was the superior work.

The *Art Amateur*'s was the only review of the Academy *Annual* to give substantial attention to *Sunday Morning in Virginia*.

As for Mr. Homer, it is hard to find what he has been doing for the twelve-month past; the negroes he sends are those dispatched to the Paris Exposition. In one the mistress visits her emancipated blacks, showing the contrast of lofty-toned Virginia respectability, with the crushed, rudimentary natures of the slaves defined in awkward gestures and curious waiting and expectant repose of attitude, as if attending the dawn of civilization; this abeyance of enlightenment is revealed again in the picture when the black girls, in starched Sunday aprons, sit in rigid row waiting for the church-bell to summon them to worship, along side of the centenarian negress whose whole attitude expresses a life-time of waiting, and who recalls the history of a race in her look of patience and acceptance. In all these negro pictures Mr. Homer shows an involuntary depth of observation and philosophy, making his canvases so many authentic documents; he has occasional felicities in pose, a roll of the eyeball, a sweeping or reaching animal-like gesture, which defines race distinctions as at a stroke, and constitute him the most valuable reporter we have ever had of the tropical manners implanted in our midst. The reason is, that he has observed these manners with the enthusiasm of a historian and man of imagination.

Homer probably found the setting and models for *Sunday Morning in Virginia* and *A Visit from the Old Mistress* in Virginia and in 1876. Homer's unusually specific inscription on *Sunday Morning*, "Virginia 1877," suggests it, at least, was completed at wherever in that state he set up a temporary studio, and possibly during his May 1877 stay in Virginia. But definition of a place and time from which these works spring is a popular subject for conjecture. (For discussion of some options see commentary 2:No. 602.)

Mary Ann Calo accepts that the setting of the scenes was found somewhere in Virginia, but has a unique suggestion of the time of year represented: "The figures are heavily clad to protect themselves from the discomforts of cold winter weather. In Sunday Morning in Virginia, the children are huddled together on a bench to keep warm."

PROVENANCE
William T. Evans, Montclair, NJ, 1880; (American Art Association, 31 Jan.–3 Feb. 1900, Evans sale, no. 122); James Craig Nicoll, New York, 1900; Emily Nicoll, New York, his daughter, by bequest, 1918; (Milch Galleries, 1918); (Ainslie Galleries, 1918)

EXHIBITIONS
Century Association, New York, 2 June 1877, no. 25; *Exposition Universelle de 1878*, Paris, 1 May–10 Nov. 1878, no. 61; Boston Art Club, Boston Society of Architects, Schools at the Museum of Fine Arts, *Exhibition of Contemporary Art*, 22 Apr.–24 May 1879, no. 404; Springfield (Massachusetts) Art Association, [first artists' exhibition], 9–13 Dec. 1879; Union League Club, New York, 8–10 Jan. 1880; National Academy of Design, New York, *Fifty-fifth Annual Exhibition*, 30 Mar.–29 May 1880, no. 593; Metropolitan Museum of Art, New York, *Seventh Loan Exhibition*, 1 May–15 Oct. 1883, no. 129; Palma Club Fair, Jersey City, NJ, *Art Loan Exhibition*, Nov. 1885, no. 8; Union League Club, New York, *Exhibition of Paintings*, 11 Mar. 1886, no. 9; Inter-State Industrial Exposition of Chicago, *Eighteenth Annual Exhibition*, 3 Sept.–18 Oct. 1890, no. 148; National Academy of Design, New York, *New York Columbian Celebration of the 400th Anniversary of the Discovery of America*, 9–22 Oct. 1892, no. 17; Lotos Club, New York, [thirty-six American paintings from the William T. Evans collection], Nov.–Dec. 1896; Brooklyn [Museum], [inaugural exhibition], 1 June–autumn 1897, no. 352; American Art Association, New York, *American Paintings Belonging to William T. Evans* [auction], 24 Jan.–2 Feb. 1900, no. 122; MOMA 1930, no. 5; Worcester 1944, no. 12; NGA 1958/MFA, Boston, 1959, no. 42/37; University of Arizona 1963, no. 29; NGA 1995, no. 81; Nelson-Atkins 2001

LITERATURE
"The Century Club," *(NY) Evening Post*, 2 June 1877; "Gossip of Local Art Circles . . . Paintings Now in Progress on the Easels of Prominent Artists," *(NY) Daily Graphic*, 10 Jan. 1878; "Pictures for the Paris Exhibition," *(NY) Evening Post*, 26 Jan. 1878; "Fine Arts," *New York Herald*, 3 Feb. 1878; "Art Notes," *(NY) Daily Graphic*, 8 Feb. 1878; "The Paris Exposition. English Opinion on American Pictures and Artists," *New York Herald*, 3 June 1878; "Fine Arts. L'Art on American Artists," *New York Herald*, 23 Dec. 1878; "The Art Museum Exhibition. Oil Paintings—Portraits and Landscapes," *(Boston)*

Daily Evening Transcript, 29 Apr. 1879; "Special Correspondence," *Art Interchange* 2 (30 Apr. 1879): 66; [Marianna G. Van Rensselaer], "The Exhibition of Contemporary Art in Boston: II," *American Architect and Building News* 5 (17 May 1879): 157; "The Art Show Opens. The Best Paintings in the Gallery," *Springfield (MA) Daily Republican*, 10 Dec. 1879; "Fine Arts. Art Reception at the Union League," *New York Evening Mail*, 9 Jan. 1880; "Fine Arts," *(NY) Evening Post*, 9 Jan. 1880; "Fine Arts. Pictures at the Union League," *New York Herald*, 9 Jan. 1880; "Artists and Their Work. Pictures in the Academy. The Negro in American Art—Winslow Homer—Marines by Bunce, Quartley, Edward Moran, and de Haas," *New-York Times*, 9 Apr. 1880; "Fine Arts. National Academy of Design—Fifty-Fifth Annual Exhibition—I," *The Nation* 30 (15 Apr. 1880): 295; "Fine Arts. Fifty-fifth Annual Exhibition of the National Academy of Design—Fifth Notice," *New York Herald*, 19 Apr. 1880; Strix, "Our Feuilleton. The Academy Exhibition," *(NY) Evening Express*, 24 Apr. 1880; "Exhibition of the Academy of Design," *Art Amateur* 2 (May 1880): 112; "The New York Spring Exhibitions. I. The National Academy Exhibition," *(NY) Art Journal* 6 (May 1880): 154; "'Sunday Morning in Virginia' from the painting by Winslow Homer in the National Academy of Design," *Harper's Weekly* 24 (22 May 1880): 324; S[amuel] G[reen] W[alker] Benjamin, "The Exhibitions V. National Academy of Design Fifty-fifth Exhibition. Opened March 30 closed May 29," *American Art Review* 1 (part 2. 1880): 308; "American Pictures at the Union League," *Art Interchange* 16 (27 Mar. 1886): 100; National Arts Club (NY) Papers, Archives of American Art, Smithsonian Institution, Washington, DC, film no. 4241; Mary Ann Calo, "Winslow Homer's Visits to Virginia During Reconstruction," *American Art Journal* 12 (Winter 1980): 19; The Menil Collection, "Winslow Homer's Images of Blacks," by Peter H. Wood and Karen C. C. Dalton, in *Winslow Homer's Images of Blacks: The Civil War and the Reconstruction Years* (Houston, 1988), 84–88; Cikovsky and Kelly 1995, 149; Nelson-Atkins Museum of Art, "Facing the 'New Departure'" and "Moving On," by Margaret C. Conrads, in *Winslow Homer and the Critics: Forging a National Art in the 1870s* (Kansas City, MO, 2001), 125–29, 174–77

621

Study for *In the Mountains*

[1877]

Charcoal, watercolor, 8½ × 13 (21.590 × 33.020)
sight
Inscribed ll: W H

Private collection

PROVENANCE
(Wm. A. Butters & Co., Chicago, 10 Dec. 1879,
Homer sale) [?]; Sarah Van Doren Shaw, Chicago,
1879 [?]; Howard Shaw, Chicago, her son, nd;
Silvia Shaw Judson (Mrs. Clay Judson), Chicago,
his daughter, before 1939; unidentified private
collection, c. 1961; (Butterfield & Butterfield,
San Francisco, 17 Mar. 1988, sale 3920P, no. 2512);
(Hirschl & Adler Galleries, 1988); (Sotheby's, 25
May 1994, sale 6568, no. 23)

EXHIBITIONS
Butters, Chicago, 1879 [?]

No. 621. Study for In the Mountains

622

In the Mountains

1877

Fresh Morning [?]; In the White Mountains
Oil, 23⅞ × 38⅛ (60.643 × 96.838)
Inscribed ll: Homer / 1877

Brooklyn Museum, Dick S. Ramsey Fund, 32.1648

Late in 1910, after Homer's death, William Howe Downes visited the cottage, "Kettle Cove," that Homer had built in 1901. Homer had used its walls as a sort of "open storage" facility, especially for some of his early paintings. This canvas was among those Downes noted, describing it as showing "a number of figures climbing Mount Washington," and "dating from 1869 or 1870." Downes relied for identifications on his host, Arthur Benson Homer, who demonstrated little grasp of his older brother's activities and career in the years before he began to be celebrated. By 1877, the inscribed date of this work, Homer's preference in rugged terrain had long been the Adirondack Mountains of New York State. The mistaken family tradition of placing this scene in New Hampshire was not finally put down by removing "White" from its official title until the 1960s.

The two ladies at the left also appear— minus their walking sticks—in *Beaver Mountain, Adirondacks* (No. 623).

ABG: The size and degree of finish of this painting mark it as a major work, clearly intended by Homer for some significant exhibition venue. Yet no such event has been recognized in its history—under the titling given it by Arthur B. Homer. However, there is a highly likely candidate for its true title and occasion of public debut.

Of the six works by Homer accepted for presentation in the National Academy of Design's annual exhibition of 1878, five are identified: *The Watermelon Boys* (2:No. 595); *In the Field* (2:No. 600); *Shall I Tell Your Fortune?* (2:No.611); *The Two Guides* (No. 625); and the ceramic tile, *Morning* (No. 645). The identity of the sixth, *A Fresh Morning*, has not been established—nor been the subject of speculation by historians. It did not catch the attention of contemporary critics either. The *Independent*'s reviewer of the *Annual* of 1878 noticed only that his "eyes [had] been lashed with the crudity" of *Shall I Tell Your Fortune?* and *A Fresh Morning*. The New York *World*'s was alone among the reviews of the

Annual to take substantive notice of *A Fresh Morning*, unfortunately, without mentioning any detail of the composition which would irrefutably identify it.

On each side of the corridor entrance in the main room are two more of Mr. Homer's pictures not carried as far by any means as his "In the Field," and without the really poetic feeling that goes along with all the freshness of ["In the Field"]. But "A Fresh Morning" is very accurately named, and looks more like a study from nature painted out of doors than any other picture in the exhibition, unless it be the companion, "The Guides." Both of them are Adirondack reminiscences, and it is interesting to note in them how different an impression the North Woods make upon Mr. Homer from that which they leave upon most of our artists who go a-sketching there. From no one else has a report of their breeziness, their freshness and their openness anything like this of Mr. Homer's hitherto come.

In its matching size (24 by 38 inches, Homer's standard for major works at the time), paint handling and geographical context *In the Mountains* is comfortable as a pendant to *The Two Guides*.

In 1996 David Tatham thought the site of this painting might be Mount Marcy; by 2004 he had decided Homer placed the women "hiking on Mount Hopkins near the valley," but does not explain how he had come to identify the slope so exactly. (However, a note to Teresa Carbone's entry on the painting in her 2006 catalogue of the Brooklyn Museum collection states that the Mount Hopkins location was suggested to Tatham by Mr. Robin Pell.) The argument seems irrelevant, however; the dramatic clarity of the incline, and stark division of land and sky are bold compositional choices, rather than literal representations of a specific location.

Tatham also notes "the pervasive belief that paintings of life in the wilderness ought to depict sturdy local folk rather than fashionably attired female hikers." If *In the Mountains* is *Fresh Morning*, Tatham's observation may help explain why the painting failed to engage attention on its presentation in the 1878 Academy *Annual*.

Carbone's speculation that *In the Mountains* may be the scene of a "tramp to Mount Marcy" reported to be in Homer's studio by the *New-York Daily Tribune* in mid-October 1877, collapses in light of the *New York Herald* reporter's detailed description of the painting being called "On the Trail to Marcy" when he wrote up his account of a visit to Homer made some two weeks ahead of the *Tribune*'s man: it clearly was *The Two Guides* who were on that trail to Marcy.

No. 622. In the Mountains

see color illustration, p. 410

PROVENANCE
Charles S. Homer, Jr., by bequest, 1910; Arthur B.
Homer, by gift, 1910; Charles L. Homer, by bequest,
1916; (William Macbeth, Inc., 1932)

EXHIBITIONS
National Academy of Design, New York, *Fifty-third
Annual Exhibition*, 2 Apr.–1 June 1878, no. 128 (as
A Fresh Morning) [?]; Maynard Walker 1953, no. 10
(as *In the White Mountains*); Whitney 1973, no. 41;
Reynolda House, Museum of American Art,
Winston-Salem, NC, *Winslow Homer: Early Prints
and Paintings*, 24 Sept.–28 Nov. 1999

LITERATURE
"Fine Arts," *New York Herald*, 1 Oct. 1877;
"Reopening the Studios," *New-York Daily Tribune*,
13 Oct. 1877; "Fine Arts. The Academy Exhibit. II,"
The Independent 30 (18 Apr. 1878): 9; "The Academy
Exhibition. III," *(NY) World*, 18 May 1878; Tatham
1996, 65–68; David Tatham, "Winslow Homer and
the Great Forest," in *Winslow Homer: Masterworks
from the Adirondacks* (Cooperstown, NY: Fenimore
Art Museum, 2004), np; Teresa A. Carbone,
*American Paintings in the Brooklyn Museum: Artists
Born by 1876, v. 2* (Brooklyn, NY: The Brooklyn
Museum, 2006), 652–53

623

Beaver Mountain, Adirondacks, Minerva, New York

[1877]

Oil, 12⅛ × 17⅛ (30.798 × 43.498)
Inscribed lr: Winslow Homer

The Newark (NJ) Museum, Louis B. Bamberger
Bequest Fund, 55.118

Despite the figures readily recognizable from *In the Mountains* (No. 622) and *The Two Guides* (No. 625), LG initially seriously doubted the attribution of this painting. Besides the "arbitrary, made-up" composition, he noted the poor drawing of the figures, their lack of stabilizing lower limbs, and the weak, thin paint application, especially the "meaningless collection of brush strokes of different colors, without any relation to shape or character of the plants" of the field in which they are propped.

LG's close examination of the painting was made in 1937 when it was included in the Carnegie museum's Homer centennial exhibition. Within the following year Samuel T. Preston's niece gave LG two original photographs of the interior of the main room in the apartment Homer occupied in the early 1880s, and shared with Preston. That *Beaver Mountain* is clearly visible in one of these photographs provided the necessary counterweight to the shortcomings of the painting and secured its place in the catalogue of Homer's works.

The Preston family was related to Martha French Homer, Homer's sister-in-law (not to the Homers, as is often stated); they had lived—and continued to live in New Ipswich, New Hampshire. It can be no more than speculation that the earliest known owner of the painting, the Reverend Mr. Prescott, of Boston, made connection with the painting through his summer residency in New Ipswich.

When LG examined *Beaver Mountain* the reverse of the canvas was visible. He recorded that it bore the stamp: PREPARED BY / P. DECHAUX & CO / Artists Colourmen / New York. The same stamp is found on the reverse of *Sounding Reveille* (2:No. 385), a work of about 1871. Generations of the Dechaux family were a principal source of materials for New York artists; Paul Dechaux took over the business in 1869, and altered its name to reflect that fact. It may be noted that *Beaver Mountain* is significantly

No. 623. Beaver Mountain, Adirondacks, Minerva, New York

smaller than the prominent paintings accountable to Homer's 1877 stay in the Adirondacks: *In the Mountains*, *The Two Guides*, and *The Camp Fire* (No. 627). The discrepancy between the present dimensions of *Beaver Mountain* and of *Sounding Reveille* is about one inch.

The seeming connection *Beaver Mountain*'s support makes with a work dating from around the time of Homer's first recognized stay in the Adirondacks could be used to compound the questions on dating the work. However, it is more likely Homer was using a canvas he had on hand for some time than that *Sounding Reveille* and *Beaver Mountain* have chronological proximity.

ABG: The geographical precision of the titling of this painting has no historical support, and was probably bestowed upon it in 1936 by Knoedler & Co.

Margaret Conrads and David Tatham both wrestle with the dilemma of finding Orson Phelps, the noted guide from the Keene Valley region, standing in what would be a Minerva field because the bland, symmetrical outline of Beaver Mountain is behind him. Neither considers that Homer need not have had the principal components of this composition immediately before his eyes in order to assemble this composition.

Following Tatham's lead, Conrads assumes "the two [Keene-based] guides, with Homer and his friends, probably made a special trip to the Baker farm" thus providing Homer with tableaux for reproduction in *The Two Guides* and *Beaver Mountain*. Tatham's solution is to assign a four-year window of opportunity for execution, dating *Beaver Mountain* 1874–1877. However, in his 1996 study of Homer's Adirondack subjects he discusses the painting in the context of the artist's 1874 visit to the Adirondacks, and believes "the work's chief significance is that it contained within it the seeds of two far more distinguished paintings, not only *The Two Guides* but also *In the Mountains*," which presupposes it is a significantly earlier work than those two. *Beaver Mountain* is noted in Tatham's 1996 inventory of Homer's Adirondack works under both the 1874 and 1877 headings, but with preference given to the latter year.

However, if the postal-address style of titling and interpreting this work is divorced from its features, it may be recognized as the manifestation of an idea on trial for a picture—a trial and an idea which Homer abandoned. It is irrelevant whether *Beaver Mountain* preceded the development of *In the Mountains* and *The Two Guides*, or was a possible third arrangement of the actors from those; it seems surely to have been created in 1877 in tandem with them, and to owe more to Homer's excursion to Keene Valley than to his more sustained association with the Baker Farm near Minerva.

The more interesting aspect of *Beaver Mountain* might be its suggestion Homer was trying a variation—or expansion—on the composition of related works from 1875 which placed two elaborately costumed young women in incongruously rough country setting: the watercolor *What Is It?* (2:No. 569) and oil *Over the Hills* (2:No. 570, known as *Rab and the Girls*).

It is possible—but beyond proof—that this painting was the "Adirondack study" Homer sent to the Art Students' League for one of its educational exhibitions, held in December 1877, and reported by the *New York Herald*.

> The second monthly social reunion of that admirable institution, the Art Students' League, was held at their rooms in Fifth avenue last evening . . . . the exhibition last evening was an unusual one, consisting of a number of color studies sent on invitation by various artists, and which showed admirably to the students the manner of handling of each . . . . Among the color sketches finished in various degrees were . . . an Adirondack study and a farm scene by Winslow Homer."

PROVENANCE
Rev. Mr. Prescott, Boston and New Ipswich, NH, nd; unidentified Prescott employee, by gift, nd; (William J. Kaula, Greenville, NH, c. 1935); (J. W. McBrine, Boston, 1936); (M. Knoedler & Co., 1836); (Maynard Walker Galleries, 1936); Mr. and Mrs. Leland Hayward, New York, 1936; (Babcock Galleries, 1954)

EXHIBITIONS
Carnegie 1937, no. 6; University of Arizona 1963, no. 10; The Newark (NJ) Museum, *Off the Pedestal: New Women in the Art of Homer, Chase and Sargent*, 17 Mar.–18 June 2006; McNay Art Museum, San Antonio, 26 July–15 Oct. 2006; Frick Art and Historical Center, Pittsburgh, 4 Nov. 2006–14 Jan. 2007

LITERATURE
"Art Students' League," *New York Herald*, 5 Dec. 1877; David Tatham, "*The Two Guides*: Winslow Homer at Keene Valley, Adirondacks," *American Art Journal* 20, no. 2 (1988): 22–24; Margaret C. Conrads, *American Paintings and Sculpture at the Sterling and Francine Clark Art Institute* (New York: Hudson Hills Press, 1990), 73; Tatham 1996, 60, 64, 68, 138, 139

624

Adirondack Guide

[1877]

Oil on panel, 11⅞ × 7⅝ (30.163 × 19.368)
Inscribed ll: Homer

The Hyde Collection Trust, Glens Falls, NY, given
anonymously, 1998.2

The support for this character study is a cigar box
cover. Legible parts of a paper label were still
exposed when LG examined the painting in October
1939 at the Macbeth gallery. The panel was later
cradled, thus obliterating its reverse. The name of
the purveyor of the cigars had been shredded, but its
location was clear: "Plattsburgh, N. Y." LG initially
thought it possible this work dated from Homer's
1870 stay at the Baker Farm, associating it with *An
Adirondack Lake* (2:No. 373) and its near-twin *The
Trapper* (2:No. 374). However, he concluded that
characteristics of style placed it in the mid 1870s,
with *The Two Guides* (No. 625). Although this
Guide's costume has several points in common with
the younger of *The Two Guides*, there are substantial
differences—notably the former's goatee—which
preclude their being the same man.

No. 624. Adirondack Guide

ABG: Plattsburgh is about as far north of Keene
Valley as Keene Valley is north of the Baker Farm.
The Guide's panel support would therefore seem to
put the figure closer to Keene Valley and Homer's
1877 visit there than to Minerva, but, of course, the
box of cigars could have traveled farther than Homer
had, and not necessarily on his schedule.

In 1996 David Tatham assigned this work a date
of 1892, on the basis that *The Guide*'s profile and
beard are repeated in the head of the recumbent
figure in the watercolor of that date, *Burnt Mountain*
(5:No. 1505). By 2004 Tatham thought it possible
Rufus Wallace, a guide from the Minerva area and
frequent Homer model, had posed for this study,
and dated it "ca. 1876."

(Shortly after acquiring this painting, the
Grosvenor Trading company consigned it to the
Parke-Bernet sale 859, held 9–10 April 1947, lot no.
126, where it failed to sell; the purchaser of record
was the Grosvenor company.)

PROVENANCE
Charles S. Homer, Jr., by bequest, 1910; Mrs. Charles
S. Homer, Jr., by bequest, 1917; Arthur P. and
Charles L. Homer, by bequest, 1937; (William
Macbeth, Inc., by 1940); (Babcock Galleries, 1940);
(Valentine Gallery, 1941); Mr. and Mrs. Thomas N.
Metcalf, Boston, nd; (Charles D. Childs Gallery,
Boston, 1946); (Ivan Podgoursky, 1946); (Grosvenor
Trading Corp., 1947); unidentified private collection,
nd; (Hirschl & Adler Galleries, by 1958); James H.
Couey, Jr., Tampa, FL, 1965; (Hirschl & Adler
Galleries, 1968); private collection, 1968; (Rick
Lapham, Shoreham, VT, nd); private collection,
by 1991

EXHIBITIONS
Adirondack 1959, no. 10 (as *Adirondack Guide*);
Vermont Art Center 1964, no. 17 (as *Adirondack
Guide*); Hyde 1994, no. 4 (as *Study of an Adirondack
Guide*, c. 1890); Fenimore 2004, no. 10 (as
Adirondack Guide, c. 1876)

LITERATURE
Tatham 1996, 141; David Tatham, "Winslow
Homer and the Great Forest," in *Winslow Homer:
Masterworks from the Adirondacks* (Cooperstown,
NY: Fenimore Art Museum, 2004), np

No. 625. Two Guides

see color illustration, p. 411

625

Two Guides

[1877]

Oil, 24¼ × 38¼ (61.595 × 97.155)
Inscribed ll: Winslow Homer / 187[?]

The Sterling and Francine Clark Art Institute,
Williamstown, MA, 1955.3

ABG: For many years perhaps the most compelling question about this painting was its date of execution. The last digit of the inscribed date is illegible. It seems once to have been somewhat less elusive: the catalogue for the 1898 presentation of Thomas B. Clarke's Homers and Innesses at the Union League Club dated *Two Guides* 1876. LG noted the last digit as "indistinct," but also perceived it to be a "6." The time frame within which *Two Guides* could be presumed to have been created was bounded by Homer's documented visit to the Baker Farm in late spring 1874 and return to the Adirondack region that October, and the painting's debut at the National Academy *Annual* in the spring of 1878. David Tatham in his 1988 article devoted to the painting, and Margaret Conrad's in her 1990 catalogue of the Clark Art Institute collection of American paintings, opted for "c. 1875."

In 1995, in the process of research for publication of the Homer catalogue raisonné, I recognized that the descriptions of visits to Homer's studio which appeared in the 1 October 1877 issue of the *New York Herald* and in the 13 October 1877 issue of the *New-York Daily Tribune* provided the missing link in knowledge of Homer's stays in the Adirondacks. Both reports began by noting that Homer was back from the Adirondacks and noted the resulting canvases he had in process: especially the work Homer ultimately titled *Two Guides*, and a scene of a campfire at night in the woods (*Camp Fire*, No. 627).

The *Tribune* remarked that one of the paintings Homer was working on was "a tramp to Mt. Marcy," and that it "introduces Old Phelps, one of the well-known guides of the region," but gave no further useful information. Fortunately, the *Herald* described the subject in detail—thereby giving *Two Guides* a firm date.

> Another picture which Mr. Homer is finishing is "On the Trail to Marcy." Two guides, one of whom is the well known old Phelps, pointing out the cap of Marcy, the other a stalwart young mountaineer, are coming over a mountain side. Both have with them their axes and their usual slight camp equipage. A bold breezy canvas, the figures admirable and the landscape good.

Of the five paintings Homer contributed to the 1878 annual exhibition of the National Academy of Design, only *In the Field* (2:No. 600) attracted much positive press attention. The New York *Sun* mentioned *Two Guides* as "a spirited composition." The New York *World* was a bit more expansive.

On each side of the corridor entrance in the main room are two more of Mr. Homer's pictures not carried as far by any means as his "In the Field," and without the really poetic feeling that goes along with all the freshness of [*In the Field*]. But "A Fresh Morning" is very accurately named, and looks more like a study from nature painted out of doors than any other picture in the exhibition, unless it be the companion, "The Guides." Both of them are Adirondack reminiscences, and it is interesting to note in them how different an impression the North Woods make upon Mr. Homer from that which they leave upon most of our artists who go a-sketching there. From no one else has a report of their breeziness, their freshness and their openness anything like this of Mr. Homer's hitherto come.

The indifference of its reception may have contributed to the painting not being seen or heard of over the next dozen years. When *Two Guides*—in company with *Camp Fire*—reappeared, it was for a few days in mid-February 1890 at a Union League Club, before both joined Homer's suite of Adirondack subject watercolor paintings of 1889, which had gone on exhibition at the Reichard gallery shortly before the monthly Union League event. The large group of watercolors attracted significant notice and admiration. It happened again to be a writer for the *Sun* who noticed *Two Guides*—with a warmth and understanding Homer might have hoped for in 1878. The marked change in the critical standard of "finish" in exhibition paintings is clearly reflected in the *Sun*'s remarks. The writer also provided the probable evidence that the painting had gone directly from the Reichard exhibition to a new owner, presumably, Thomas B. Clarke.

> ... of the two oil paintings included [in the Reichard exhibition] the more important was sold, and of the thirty-two water colors only a stray example or so still remains in the artist's possession. . . . One of the oils represented a camp fire at night, with a sleeping and a watching figure, and though hard in effect was most interesting from its evident veracity. The other was in every way a remarkable picture, thoroughly American, thoroughly realistic, yet thoroughly artistic, too. It showed two mountaineers traversing a rough clearing, with forest and hills beyond, and heavy wreaths of mist floating about them.

The contrast between the two men, each a characteristic type, was extremely well brought out—one short, old and bent, yet vigorous still; the other young tall, instinct with energy and with the grace of pure health in every line. The treatment was comparatively detailed, as we have come to think of landscape work of late, even the forms of the bracken growth in the foreground being clearly made out; yet it was neither hard nor lacking in breadth. It was only more complete than most painters can make it without falling into those defects. It will be a pity if we are long left to wait for another representation of the skill of one who is, without question, among the most marked and interesting personalities of our art to-day. But it is also a pity that he rates himself below his proper worth. Not only for his own sake, but for the sake of art and American artists in general, Mr. Homer ought to have asked more for these admirable water colors than $125 a piece.

After the question of dating *Two Guides*, a perceived anomaly in its setting has preoccupied students of the work. The composition of the supporting landscape is essentially identical to the roughed-in background of *Beaver Mountain, Adirondacks* (No. 623). The prominent profile of Beaver Mountain puts the scene in the area of Minerva and the Baker Farm, Homer's preferred Adirondacks destination. The two actors Homer places on this stage are "Old" Orson Phelps and Charles Monroe Holt; both men were resident in the Keene Valley, approximately thirty linear miles north of Minerva. (Phelps was an Adirondack celebrity by the time *Two Guides* was painted, and has always been associated with it by name; David Tatham brought recognition to his younger companion.)

In his 1988 article on *Two Guides* Tatham accounts for the combination of locations by proposing a four-day camping trip from the Keene Valley to the Minerva undertaken by Homer and "undoubtedly" several companions, and thus requiring the services of two guides.

In Homer's painting, the two guides stand in the midst of foliage the colors of early autumn, the time of Homer's documented presence in Keene Valley. His characterization of the guides speaks of a camping trip in the wilderness rather than a day excursion on a well-worn trail. Both men carry axes. Phelps, the volubly knowledgeable pathfinder, points and talks. Holt, the camp maker, carries a food bucket. From these clues we can posit a journey taken in October, 1874, from the Widow Beede's Cottage in Keene Valley to the Baker farm west of Minerva by Homer and one or more others, guided by Phelps and Holt. . . . Though such a trek through the wilderness remains conjectural, it offers the best explanation of the subject of Homer's painting.

That scenario, while plausible in itself, is founded on the fallacious assumption an artist requires literal experience of a subject in order to represent it. It is at least as likely that in forming this painting Homer did what artists do: create a composition from imagination, using images accumulated in memory and in sketches from a range of times and experiences.

By 1996 and the publication of his comprehensive study of Homer and the Adirondacks, Tatham had tempered his explanation for the geographical "problem" presented by the painting. Along with a reprise of the narrative he proposed in 1988, he admits an alternate theory:

> [N]othing seems to have survived to explain the origins of *The Two Guides*. Perhaps an answer can be found in the painting's chief landscape component. Homer may have set Phelps and Holt, two Keene Valley worthies, in front of Minerva's Beaver Mountain not only because of his partiality to the mountain's shape but also to link together in art for personal reasons two places that in actuality were far apart.

PROVENANCE
(Reichard & Co., 1890); Thomas B. Clarke, New York, 1890–91; (American Art Association, 14–18 Feb. 1899, Clarke sale, no. 360); Chauncy J. Blair, Chicago, 1899; Mrs. Chauncy J. Blair, Chicago, by 1915; (Scott & Fowles, 1916); Robert Sterling Clark, New York, 1916

EXHIBITIONS
National Academy of Design, New York, *Fifty-third Annual Exhibition*, 2 Apr.–1 June 1878, no. 135; Union League Club, New York, *Pictures by American Figure Painters and Persian and Indian Works of Art*, 13–15 Feb. 1890, no. 2; Reichard 1890; Clarke, PAFA, 1891, no. 84; National Academy of Design, New York, *New York Columbian Celebration of the 400th Anniversary of the Discovery of America*, 9–22 Oct. 1892, no. 86; Union League Club, New York, *A Group of Paintings by American Artists Accepted for the Columbian Exposition*, 9–11 Mar. 1893, no. 6; Columbian Exposition 1893, no. 572; Union League 1898, no. 26; Clarke, AAA, 1899, no. 360; Carnegie 1908, no. 158; Clark AI 1961; Whitney 1973, no. 36; Clark AI 1986, no. 24; NGA 1995, no. 59; Nelson-Atkins 2001 (Nelson-Atkins and High, only); Fenimore 2004, no. 2; Clark AI 2005

LITERATURE
"Fine Arts," *New York Herald*, 1 Oct. 1877; "Reopening the Studios," *New-York Daily Tribune*, 13 Oct. 1877; "The National Academy of Design. II," *(NY) Sun*, 13 Apr. 1878; "The Academy Exhibition. III," *(NY) World*, 18 May 1878; "American Painters at the Union League and in Other Galleries," *New York Commercial Advertiser*, 15 Feb. 1890; "Three Interesting Exhibitions. Pictures at the New York Athletic Club, the Salmagundi Club, and Elsewhere," *(NY) Sun*, 3 Mar. 1890; Pennsylvania Academy of the Fine Arts, *Catalogue of the Thomas B. Clarke Collection of American Pictures* (Philadelphia, 1891), 58–59; Christopher W. Knauff, "Certain Exemplars of Art in America. IV. Elliott Daingerfield—Winslow Homer," *The Churchman* 78 (23 July 1898): 123–25, 128; Downes 1911, 82–83, 178; Goodrich 1944, 57–58; David Tatham, "*The Two Guides*: Winslow Homer at Keene Valley, Adirondacks," *American Art Journal* 20, no. 2 (1988): 20–34; Margaret C. Conrads, *American Paintings and Sculpture at the Sterling and Francine Clark Art Institute* (New York: Hudson Hills Press, 1990), 73–77; Richard Patrick Roth, *The Adirondack Guide (1820–1919): Hewing Out an American Occupation* (Ann Arbor, MI: UMI Dissertation Services, 1990), 73–93; Cikovsky and Kelly 1995, 128–29; Tatham 1996, 68–75

626

Adirondack Trapper
[1877]

Oil

Unlocated

ABG: Tantalizing references to another result of Homer's 1877 visit to the Adirondacks exist, although it is likely the painting does not. The reporter from the *New York Herald* who visited Homer's studio just at the end of September 1877 paid considerable attention to *Two Guides* (No. 625) and *Camp Fire* (No. 627) in his 1 October article. He noticed a third work but apparently found it only worthy of the spare "There is also a trapper in a 'blue boat' searching along a bank for beaver signs."

Just a month later, this appears to have been the painting Homer contributed to a Palette exhibition. It may well have been the same *Herald* writer who wrote:

> The Palette Club held their opening fall loan exhibition of paintings and monthly reception last evening. The collection of paintings numbered considerably over a hundred. . . . Taking as

a starting point in the gallery Winslow Homer's *Trapper in the Adirondacks*, [in a] blue boat looking for beaver signs, we will pass around the gallery to the right, noticing the pictures which seem the most deserving of it."

Whoever the author of the brief report, he made clear his opinion that Homer's *Trapper* did not deserve notice. Less than a week later it was again the *Herald*'s man who all but ignored the painting on its appearance in the Century Association's monthly presentation for November 1877: ". . . in the center of the east wall a large and ambitious Cropsey, an English country scene. Winslow Homer's 'Adirondack Trapper Looking for Beaver Signs' hung on the same wall."

Homer apparently put the painting forward a third time at what was probably his very next opportunity, the Brooklyn Art Association December 1877 exhibition. There *Otters Signs* was for sale for $500. That he set such a substantial price on the work indicates it was not a small, inconspicuous canvas. Yet that is the last that is seen of the work and all that is known about it.

The scraps of description found in these press notices and the Brooklyn catalogue evoke the images of the wood engraving "Trapping in the Adirondacks" published in the 12 December 1870 issue of *Every Saturday*, and of the 1892 watercolor, *The Blue Boat* (5:No. 1478). The substantial gap of years between these several works precludes there being any immediate connection, and certainly a composition involving a single figure (where the illustration and the watercolor both use figures of two men) could not help but be distinctive.

EXHIBITIONS
The Palette [Club], New York, 29–31 Oct. 1877; Century Association, New York, 3 Nov. 1877, no. 18 (as *Trapper*); Brooklyn Art Association, 3–15 Dec. 1877, no. 382 (as *Otter Signs*)

LITERATURE
"Fine Arts," *New York Herald*, 1 Oct. 1877; "Art at the Palette," *New York Herald*, 30 Oct. 1877; "Art at the Century—Second Monthly Reception at the Club," *New York Herald*, 4 Nov. 1877

627
Camp Fire
[1877]

Oil, 23¾ × 38⅛ (60.325 × 96.838)
Inscribed lr: Homer '80

The Metropolitan Museum of Art, gift of Henry Keney Pomeroy, 27.181

ABG: Of the three paintings remarked upon by several New York newspaper reporters who visited Homer's studio in early autumn 1877, it was the night scene that impressed them most. The *Herald*'s account was the first to appear.

> Winslow Homer has returned from a summer in the Adirondacks and is finishing up a large picture, "Night in the Woods." Although pitch dark it is not late, and a man lies stretched under the back tent half asleep, while another sits by the fire, which leaps up into the darkness, making the surroundings more gloomy. The long waving sparks from the moss on the wood rise in great numbers above the flames from the pine fire. Around are scattered fishing tackle and implements of the chase. Above rear their heads the gaunt pines, one of which, felled half way, lies across and over the tent.

Homer clearly considered *Camp Fire* essentially completed for he lost no time in putting it before his public. It was shown at the Century Association within a week of the *Herald*'s article, and had moved on for a few days display at the Union League Club before the *Tribune*'s description of a visit to Homer's studio had appeared in print. Although old news for New York readers by the time it appeared, the *Tribune*'s account is now highly significant as further evidence that a painting long accepted as a work of 1880, as it is clearly inscribed, in fact is a work of 1877.

> Winslow Homer is back from the Adirondacks finishing two pictures of life in that region, one of a campfire at night in the woods, and the other of a tramp to Mt. Marcy. The former brings out not only a pretty good thing in the way of a bark hut in which the artist's party bivouacked—a structure hardly to be seen in the New-York woods other than in the Adirondacks region—but also a peculiarity in camp-fires which every boy and man who has ever roved the woods much has seen in his own camp-fire, but perhaps never before on canvas. In stacking up branches and logs for a rousing fire, one occasionally comes across a rare chunk of moss-covered wood which when thrown into the fire [fills] the flames above it with sparks which fly up in long, bright waving lines and lend to the fire a most fanciful charm.

No. 627. Camp Fire

see color illustration, p. 409

Not every campfire has those comet-like sparks. It is only when mossy branches are thrown in that they appear. Mr. Homer is trying to paint a campfire of this sort.

Especially as it seems to have been greeted with general approval, it is surprising that after the two brief showings in October 1877 Homer held *Camp Fire* back from exhibition for two and a half years. It did not again appear until spring 1880 at the National Academy of Design's annual exhibition. Homer's *tour de force* in representing a fire at night again led press reports to describe it in more detail than usual. The *New-York Times* review was particularly expansive.

One of [Homer's] bold flights is "Camp-fire," No. 417, in the South Room, a realistic view of a log and leaf hut in the woods, before which two Adirondack guides have kindled a fire. The wall of darkness behind the fire is skillfully indicated, not a little of the skill depending upon the way in which the boughs and briars lean forward and jut out into the light from the fire. Especially good is

a flower on a briar to the left of the hut, which has been most admirably brought out. The two men are in very natural attitudes, although they have not been studied for beauty in the pose. What is most striking about the picture—and Mr. Homer is always sure to avoid the stupidity of mediocrity even if he makes many misses—is the treatment of the sparks from the camp-fire. With a boldness which emulates Japanese draughtsmen (who sometime make lightening proceeding from a cloud in the shape of bamboos running at acute angles to each other.) Mr. Homer follows the airy trail of the sparks from his camp-fire, and gives at length and in full, against the dark background, what the eye only sees for a moment and in motion.

The brevity of the *Art Amateur*'s comment on *Camp Fire* contrasts sharply with that of the *Times*, but its writer seems no less dazzled by Homer's special effects: "The other picture by Homer is one of a hunter by a camp-fire; it is hard dense, opaque, metallic, but there is an illusion of flying sparks, darting upward in snake-like curves, which has never been painted before, and so natural that the eye is imposed on, and convinced that the sparks do fly upward."

Descriptions of the painting written in 1877 and in 1880 give no indication of any substantive changes which would have caused Homer to consider it a sufficiently reformed composition entitled to updating. If the inscribed date was present when it was shown at the Academy in 1880, it may have been Homer's politic accommodation to the Academy's insistence that works submitted for *Annuals* not have been shown in New York before, a ruling aimed directly at the club exhibitions.

It is also possible, however, that Homer did not add the "'80" following his name until 1905, when he probably carried through his promise to "overlook" the painting for Henry K. Pomeroy. Pomeroy acquired *Camp Fire* within 1899, the year of its sale by Thomas B. Clarke. The catalogue entries for the painting when Clarke showed his collection at the Pennsylvania Academy of the Fine Arts in 1891, and when he put it at auction in 1899, reference its inscription as "signed at the right," making no mention of a date. The entry style of both catalogues dictates that a date would have been included in the citation, had it been noticed. When Clarke's Homers and Innesses went on view at the Union League Club for the summer of 1898 *Camp Fire* was dated 1876 in the exhibition catalogue, which also suggests the inscription did not then include a date.

George W. Sheldon may have had his much-quoted exchange with Homer concerning his methods relatively shortly before his "Sketches and Studies. II" appeared in the April 1880 issue of the *Art Journal*—the same month *Camp Fire* was first on public view in the Academy *Annual*.

> [Homer] believes, however, that the most complete pictures are not founded upon outdoor studies. "The great compositions of the old masters," he says, "were almost all interiors. You can't control the thing out-doors." Yet he admits that it is possible, sometimes, to find a picture— a complete one—out-doors; to meet with a combination of facts so happy that a sketch of it would deserve to be called a picture—a rare case, of course, but not an impossible one. His "Adirondack Camp-Fire" is almost an example in point. He painted it out-doors; but the large tree on the left, the line of which answers to the line of one of the poles of the tent, is not in the original scene. He found it elsewhere, built a fire in front of it, observed the effect, and transformed it to the canvas. With this exception, the composition is a general transcript of the surroundings of a fire lighted one night while he was camping in the Adirondacks.

Homer was in England by the time of the next Academy *Annual*; just as his art was in the process of significant change, so were his patterns of exhibiting and marketing. That a decade passed before he again exhibited *Camp Fire* is this time not surprising. And when it did come out again, with *Two Guides* (No. 625) it was to serve as complement to Homer's extraordinary body of watercolors of Adirondack subjects painted in 1889. The two oils were displayed for a few days in mid-February 1890 at the Union League Club—where Thomas B. Clarke, who would soon own both, would have had a good chance to examine them—before they were relocated to the Reichard gallery where the exhibition of watercolors had just opened.

It is interesting to note that where the pyrotechnics of *Camp Fire* had made it more admired than *Two Guides* in 1877 and 1880, a decade later the subtleties of rendering atmosphere and character in *Two Guides* seem to have made it the favored of the two works. The New York *Sun*'s reviewer of the Reichard exhibition assumed the public would agree that *Two Guides* was the "more important."

> Of the two oil paintings [the exhibition] included the more important was sold, and of the thirty-two water colors only a stray example or so still remains in the artist's possession.... One of the oils represented a camp fire at night, with a sleeping and a watching figure, and though hard in effect was most interesting from its evident veracity. The other was in every way a remarkable picture, thoroughly American, thoroughly realistic, yet thoroughly artistic, too. It showed two mountaineers traversing a rough clearing, with forest and hills beyond ....

Clarke evidently was the purchaser of *Two Guides* from Reichard's, and its next occasion of exhibition was in the presentation of the Clarke collection at the Pennsylvania Academy of the Fine Arts in October 1891. For the time being he had passed on *Camp Fire*. It was sent to a loan exhibition of contemporary American paintings presented by the Saint Louis Museum of Fine Arts in May 1890, where it was for sale, and for the same price, $800, as it had had when shown at the National Academy in 1880. Clarke must have relented, possibly because he could negotiate a favorable reduction when *Camp Fire* returned unsold from Saint Louis, or perhaps so *Camp Fire* could rejoin *Two Guides* at the Pennsylvania Academy exhibition of his collection. Whatever the circumstances, the two paintings were reunited, and shown frequently by Clarke.

On 5 March 1905 Homer wrote Knoedler gallery:

> I met at the Century Club on Saturday night – a Mr. Pomeroy who bought at the Clarke Sale a picture [*Campfire*] by me – He tells me that it has cracked & I have asked him to send it to your store knowing that you would let me overlook it & fix it for him – It will not take more than an hours time – I will call Monday afternoon at 2.

It may be assumed Homer honored his promise to Mr. Pomeroy, and carried out a bit of conservation work on his painting in some workroom at Knoedler's. If he did add the inaccurate dating inscription at this time, it would probably have been at the request of Pomeroy. After twenty-eight years Homer might be forgiven a lapse of memory, or the whim to date the work to the year of its "official" debut.

As Natalie Spassky points out in her entry on *Camp Fire* in the Metropolitan Museum American paintings catalogue, Gordon Hendricks only added to misunderstanding with his pronouncement that "A picture discussed in the *Post* was *The Trappers* 'in a boat on a stream on the edge of the woods.' *The Trappers* must be the same as the Metropolitan's *Camp-Fire* as well as the [1878] Academy catalogue's *A Fresh Morning*." As usual Hendricks has his "facts" muddled: The quotation concerning *The Trappers* cannot be found in the source he cites, the *(NY) Evening Post* of 30 March 1878—or elsewhere; neither can an oil painting of multiple trappers be found in Homer's known oeuvre. And at the time Hendricks was writing *Camp Fire* was unquestionably accepted as a work of 1880, and thus would not have been available for exhibition in 1878. Many pages further on in his text Hendricks was clear on the accepted dating of the painting when he doubted the scene could be set in the Adirondacks because he could not place Homer in the woods of northern New York State between 1874 and 1880.

Unfortunately, a brief remark in Spassky's essay on *Camp Fire* introduced a new canard into Homer lore: "The self-absorbed seated man strongly resembles both the central figure in *Shooting the Rapids, Saguenay River* [5:No. 1761] and two watercolor portraits of the artist's brother Charles [1:No. 44 and No. 877]." The notion that Charles S. Homer, Jr. is a character in the unfinished *Shooting the Rapids* comes from Charles L. Homer's practice of "enhancing" his uncle's paintings with back-stories. The one he attached to *Shooting the Rapids* is particularly outrageous. The single feature the man riding in the center of the canoe in *Shooting the Rapids* has in common with the two early portraits—and all photographs—of Charles S. Homer is a moustache. The face of the seated man at the right in *Camp Fire* is fully illuminated in the firelight; it is clean shaven. In his 1996 discussion of the painting David Tatham enlarged Spassky's gratuitous placement of Charles in *Camp Fire* into a "family tradition."

PROVENANCE

Thomas B. Clarke, New York, 1890–91; (American Art Association, 14–18 Feb. 1899, Clarke sale, no. 239); Alexander Harrison, New York, 1899; Henry K. Pomeroy, New York, 1899

EXHIBITIONS

Century Association, New York, 6 Oct. 1877, no. 4 (as *Night in Camp*); Union League Club, New York, 11–13 Oct. 1877; National Academy of Design, New York, *Fifty-fifth Annual Exhibition*, 30 Mar.–29 May 1880, no. 417; Union League Club, New York, *Pictures by American Figure Painters and Persian and Indian Works of Art*, 13–15 Feb. 1890, no. 3 (as *Night in the Woods*); Reichard 1890; Saint Louis Museum of Fine Arts, *Exhibition of Paintings by American Artists*, May 1890, no. 239 (as *Night in the Woods*); Clarke, PAFA, 1891, no. 85; National Academy of Design, New York, *New York Columbian Celebration of the 400th Anniversary of the Discovery of America*, 9–22 Oct. 1892, no. 90; Union League Club, New York, *A Group of Paintings by American Artists Accepted for the Columbian Exposition*, 9–11 Mar. 1893, no. 7; Columbian Exposition 1893, no. 568; Union League 1898, no. 30; Clarke, AAA, 1899, no. 239; National Academy of Design, New York, *Winter Exhibition*, 10 Dec.–9 Jan. 1911, no. 213; Metropolitan 1911, no. 4; Bowdoin/Colby 1954; NGA 1958/MFA, Boston, 1959, no. 44/40; Whitney 1973, no. 44 (Whitney, only); Nelson-Atkins 2001; FAMSF/Amon Carter 2002, no. 6; Fenimore 2004, no. 3

LITERATURE

"Fine Arts," *New York Herald*, 1 Oct. 1877; "Art at the Union League. A Noteworthy Display of Paintings—The Artists Present, &c.," *New York Commercial Advertiser*, 12 Oct. 1877; "Reopening the Studios," *New-York Daily Tribune*, 13 Oct. 1877; "Artists and Their Work. Pictures in the Academy. The Negro in American Art—Winslow Homer— Marines by Bunce, Quartley, Edward Moran, and de Haas," *New-York Times*, 9 Apr. 1880; [George William Sheldon], "Sketches and Studies. II. The Portfolios of A. H. Thayer, William M. Chase, Winslow Homer, and Peter Moran," *(NY) Art Journal* 6 (Apr. 1880): 105–9. Reprinted in, G. W. Sheldon, *Hours with Art and Artists* (New York: D. Appleton and Company, 1882, 136–41; "Exhibition of the Academy of Design," *Art Amateur* 2 (May 1880): 112; "American Painters at the Union League and in other Galleries," *New York Commercial Advertiser*, 15 Feb. 1890; "Three Interesting Exhibitions. Pictures at the New York Athletic Club, the Salmagundi Club, and Elsewhere," *(NY) Sun*, 3 Mar. 1890; Pennsylvania Academy of the Fine Arts, *Catalogue of the Thomas B. Clarke Collection of American Pictures* (Philadelphia, 1891), 59; Goodrich 1944, 64–65, 66; Hendricks 1979, 137–38, 314; Natalie Spassky, *American Paintings in the Metropolitan Museum of Art, Volume II* (Princeton, NJ: Princeton University Press, 1985), 466–68; Tatham 1996, 75–80; Nelson-Atkins Museum of Art, "Moving On," by Margaret C. Conrads, in *Winslow Homer and the Critics: Forging a National Art in the 1870s* (Kansas City, MO, 2001), 177–78

628

Almira Houghton Valentine and Mary Chamberlain Valentine

1877

Oil, 22¾ × 17¾ (57.785 × 45.085)
Inscribed ll: Homer 1877

Wadsworth Atheneum, Hartford, gift of the Lawson Valentine Foundation, 1989.60

ABG: The inscription which gives this double portrait a firm dating only emerged in the course of conservation treatment done by the Wadsworth Atheneum in 1989. Without knowledge of that inscription LG had placed it as a work of c. 1878.

The only children of Lawson and Lucy Heywood Houghton Valentine were their daughters, Mary Chamberlain Valentine (1862–1899) and Almira Houghton Valentine (1854–1919), shown here at the ages of fifteen and twenty-three, respectively. In 1889 Mary married Lawrence Fraser Abbott (1859–1933), the son of her father's friend and neighbor, the Rev. Lyman Abbott.* They had no children; she died at the early age of thirty-seven.

Almira married Nathan Trowbridge Pulsifer (1851–1931) in 1880. He later was president of Valentine & Company. They had two sons: Lawson Valentine Pulsifer (1881–1957) and Harold Trowbridge Pulsifer (1886–1948). Lawson Pulsifer joined the family business in 1903, initially in the position of assistant to Charles S. Homer, Jr. Harold

No. 628. Almira Houghton Valentine and Mary Chamberlain Valentine

see color illustration, p. 412

Pulsifer had a strong interest in the Valentine legacy as patrons of the arts and leaders in agricultural research. He shared family papers with LG at an early stage of his work on Winslow Homer. Pulsifer, himself, wrote about the family association in "Winslow Homer's Paintings Shown at Prout's Neck," an article published in the *Portland (Maine) Evening Express* 23 July 1936. Eventually Harold Pulsifer donated the Valentine-Pulsifer archive to Colby College in Waterville, Maine.

Homer never demonstrated the least interest in working as a portrait painter, even as a fall-back source of income. His work as an illustrator served that practical function. He was certainly competent in the genre, and, strangely, more successful when working in graphic media or watercolor (either in monochrome wash drawing or full color) than in oil. These were done of family or intimate friends and have a spontaneity which allows full use of his skilled draughtsmanship. Homer's formal portraits in oil are this double portrait of the Valentine sisters; the portrait of their mother, Lucy Houghton Valentine (4:No. 1175); and that of Charles Prentice Howland (No. 642), the nine-year-old son of Judge Henry E. Howland.** All are cabinet portraits, as they show full-length figures at substantially less than life size. The subjects are dependents of prominent men with whom Homer had personal relationships. They are likely commissions—real or inferred—which he accepted rather than risk offending the commissioner.

The Valentine sisters are routinely said to have had lessons in painting from Homer. It is improbable Homer would have submitted to a formal schedule of "lessons" even to please a patron. It is believable, however, that one or both the sisters was an enthusiastic amateur "artist," and that Homer occasionally critiqued her work, offering advice which would have amounted to informal instruction. That he has posed Almira in the act of drawing, and Mary as her avid audience suggests artist and subjects had that community of interest.

The sisters probably posed in Homer's studio: the footstool on which they both manage to sit may be seen in *Salem* (2:No. 404) of 1872; *Woman Sewing* (2:No. 607), and *Woman and Elephant* (2:No. 608), both probably from 1876, and *Woman Peeling a Lemon* (2:No. 609), inscribed 1876, suggesting it was a fixture in Homer's Tenth Street Studio Building rooms.

Homer's portrait of their mother was not done until 1883, six years after execution of this portrait of her daughters. It seems possible it was the long-delayed completion of an intended pair of portraits representing Lawson Valentine's family. The two paintings are the same size, although by 1883 the canvas is exceptionally small for Homer. Almost inevitably, given the passage of years between the two portraits, their conception and tonality are not seamless, and they are not true pendants. Mrs. Valentine is also shown seated in an interior, but

she occupies a lighter, much more articulated space, probably a "library" in the Valentine home. It is a portrait as genre subject, in contrast to this more formal presentation of her daughters.

Given the rarity of portraiture in Homer's oeuvre, and that this example presents more than one subject, it seems the only option to be the work shown at the Century Association in March 1878. In 1881 a *Portrait Group* was again Homer's sole contribution to the Century's March exhibition, which occurred just ten days before his departure for an extended stay in England. On this occasion the portrait was noted in the Association's ledger with an insurance valuation of $1,000. Considering the timing of its exhibition and high valuation, the historical reconstruction *Captain W. F. Bartlett and Lieutenant-Colonel F. W. Palfrey at Camp Benton, MD, 1861* (No. 1015) is the more likely candidate to have been the *Portrait Group* on view in 1881.

On neither of these occasions when Homer showed a portrait at the Century was it associated with the name of a lender, who would presumably have had some immediate connection to the subjects depicted. An oversight in recording ownership by someone other than the artist is certainly possible, but would have been unusual. The void may denote that the paintings came to the Century directly from Homer's studio, and had not yet been formally accepted by their "sponsors."

*For a glimpse of this relationship, see Lyman Abbott, *Reminiscences* (Boston: Houghton Mifflin Company, 1915), 340–47.

**Homer's portrait of Homer Dodge Martin (2:No. 322) is here excluded as it was executed to fulfill Martin's obligation on election to membership in the National Academy of Design, and its form and dimensions were dictated by Academy regulations.

PROVENANCE
Lawson Valentine, New York, 1877; Lucy Houghton Valentine (Mrs. Lawson Valentine), 1891; Almira Valentine Pulsifer (Mrs. Nathan Trowbridge Pulsifer), her daughter, 1911; Harold Trowbridge Pulsifer, New York, her son, nd; Susan Nichols Pulsifer (Mrs. Harold Trowbridge Pulsifer), in trust, 1948; Alice Pulsifer Doyle (Mrs. Joseph Doyle), his niece, 1987

EXHIBITIONS
Century Association, New York, 2 Mar. 1878, no. 22 (as *Portrait Group*) [?]; Storm King 1963, no. 6; Princeton 1990, no. 7

LITERATURE
Art Museum, Princeton University, "Almira Houghton Valentine and Mary Chamberlain Valentine," by Robert Wolterstorff, in *Winslow Homer in the 1870s: Selections from the Valentine-Pulsifer Collection* (Princeton, NJ, 1990), 54–59

No. 629. Girl with Fan

629

Girl with Fan

[1877]

Charcoal, 16¾ × 7½ (42.545 × 19.050)
Inscribed ll: Homer

Private collection

ABG: Robert Leaf transcribed for LG the text of a label which had been attached to the paper covering the back of the frame on this work at the time it came into his possession: "From Thurber's Art Gallery / 210 Wabash Ave., Chicago / artistic framing a specialty / No. 2586." This label occasioned LG's speculation the drawing had been sold to Mr. Leaf's grandmother by this Gallery; it is equally possible to speculate that Thurber's had only been responsible for providing "artistic framing" for the drawing.

A work of this date and finish found in the Chicago area in the later nineteenth century also invites speculation it was part of the collection of works Homer sent to Chicago for exhibition and auction just at the close of 1879.

PROVENANCE
(Wm. A. Butters & Co., Chicago, 10 Dec. 1879, Homer sale) [?]; (Thurber Art Gallery, Chicago, nd) [?]; Julia Leary Leaf (Mrs. Wingate B. Leaf), Waterville, WI, nd; Robert W. Leaf, Oconomowoc, WI, her grandson, by bequest, c. 1929; (Hirschl & Adler Galleries, by 1963); Cecil Lipkin, Easton, PA, 1964; (Hirschl & Adler Galleries, by 1978); (Sotheby Parke-Bernet, 23 Apr. 1981, sale 4583, no. 54); (Spanierman Gallery, LLC, 1981); (Christie's, 7 Dec. 1984, sale 5794, no. 97)

EXHIBITIONS
Butters, Chicago, 1879 [?]; Vermont Art Center 1964, no. 16

630

Head of a Boy

1877

Graphite, 9⅜ × 7⅜ (23.813 × 18.733)
Inscribed ll: Winslow Homer / 1877

National Gallery of Art, Washington, DC, promised
gift of John Wilmerding, 123195

PROVENANCE
Charles Steele Brown, New York, nd; Archibald
Manning Brown, New York, his son, nd; Mrs.
Archibald Manning Brown, New York, by bequest,
nd; (Hirschl & Adler Galleries, 1976); John
Wilmerding, Princeton, NJ, 1976

No. 630. Head of a Boy

631

Shepherd

[1877]

Charcoal, chalk, 11¾ × 11½ (29.845 × 29.210)
Inscribed ll: W. H.

The Free Library of Philadelphia, Rosenthal
Collection, Print and Picture Collection

ABG: Drawings No. 631 through No. 636 introduce
a theatrical pastoral theme into Homer's work,
signalled by his dressing up his shepherds and
shepherdesses in French Rococo style fancy dress
costumes. The theme and costumes are especially
associated with the tiles he executed in 1878. Some
or all of this small group of drawings may predate
the autumn of 1877, and the formation of the Tile
Club, and be evidence of an interest Homer was
already pursuing, or they may have been done fairly
late in the year, and mark the beginning of his developing subjects appropriate to decorative ceramics.

PROVENANCE
Albert and Max Rosenthal, Philadelphia, by 1922

No. 631. Shepherd

No. 632. Shepherd and Shepherdess

632

Shepherd and Shepherdess

[1877]

Charcoal, chalk, 8⅜ × 16 (21.273 × 40.640)
Inscribed ll: Homer

Private collection

ABG: The shepherdess seen here appears to have
been Homer's source for the tile, No. 648.

See commentary No. 631.

PROVENANCE
Henry Foster Sewall, Boston, before 1890 [?]

No. 633. Shepherdess

633
Shepherdess
1877

Charcoal, 14¼ × 9½ (36.195 × 24.130)
Inscribed ll: Homer / 77

Private collection

John Calvin Stevens, a Portland architect engaged by
the Homer brothers in building or remodeling
several cottages at Prout's Neck, Maine, told Robert
Vose, Sr. he had found this drawing in an old shack
at Prout's Neck.

ABG: See commentary No. 631.

PROVENANCE
John Calvin Stevens, Portland, ME, nd; Estate of
John Calvin Stevens, 1940; (Grand Central Art
Gallery, nd); International Business Machines
Corporation, New York, 1946; (Parke-Bernet
Galleries, 16 Feb. 1960, sale 1951, no. 77); R. W.
Hompe, Villanova, PA, 1960

EXHIBITIONS
Vose 1940, no. 13

634
Shepherdess
1877

Charcoal, watercolor, 16 × 9¹⁵⁄₁₆ (40.640 × 25.243)
Inscribed ll: Homer / 1877

The Cleveland Museum of Art, gift of
Dr. J. A. Vincent, 24.489

ABG: See commentary No. 631.

PROVENANCE
Dr. J. A. Vincent, nd

No. 634. Shepherdess

No. 635. The Shepherdess

635

The Shepherdess

[1877]

Charcoal, watercolor, 15½ × 8½ (39.370 × 21.590)
Inscribed lr: Homer

Brigham Young University Art Collection, Provo, UT, purchase and gift of Mahonri M. Young estate, 880000600

ABG: See commentary No. 631.

This drawing was one of a large number of works dispersed without proper authority from the holdings of Brigham Young University in the 1960s. The circumstances under which it came into the New York art market gave every evidence of legitimacy, and the drawing moved quickly into a prominent private collection. Twenty years passed before a later generation of University administrators became aware of the losses from its art collection and sought to reclaim as many of the works as could be located. It was the collector's decision to give up the drawing to the University without challenge.

PROVENANCE
Albert Rosenthal, nd; (William Macbeth, Inc., nd); Mahonri Young, New York, by 1937

No. 636. Shepherdess

636

Shepherdess

1877

Graphite, 7⅛ × 17 (18.098 × 43.180)
Inscribed lr: Winslow Homer / 1877

Addison Gallery of American Art, Phillips Academy,
Andover, MA, 1936.46

ABG: See commentary No. 631.

PROVENANCE
(William Macbeth, Inc., nd)

EXHIBITIONS
NE Museums 1936; Whitney 1936, no. 106;
Worcester 1944, no. 87; Wildenstein 1947, no. 110
(addenda); Addison 1980; Knoedler 1986, no. 33;
Addison 1990

637

Gathering Autumn Leaves

[1877]

Oil on panel, 38¼ × 24¼ (97.155 × 61.595)

Cooper-Hewitt, National Design Museum,
Smithsonian Institution, gift of Charles Savage
Homer, Jr., 1917-14-3

ABG: The title by which this painting is known
was bestowed upon it by Charles S. Homer, Jr., or
the Doll & Richards gallery in Boston when it was
shown there in 1912.

   In December 1877, Homer contributed to the
Century Association monthly exhibition, a painting
listed in the club's records as "Autumn Leaves. single
figure." The work might have been any one of the
three extant autumn-themed figure paintings: this
work, *Woman in Autumn Woods* (No. 639), or *Autumn*
(No. 640). It is also possible some work which has
not survived would have qualified for that description.

   The Century Association exhibitions ledger
was more explicit in identifying the Homers in its
April 1878 presentation. The "Autumn Study (Boy)"
on view then is in all probability this painting.
An "Autumn Study (Girl)" by Homer was hung in
tandem with his "Boy" on this occasion; it may have
been either *Woman in Autumn Woods* or *Autumn*, or,
again, some lost canvas. That Homer seems to have
stopped work on *Gathering Autumn Leaves* just short
of completion is consistent with trial exposure of a
new work in the sheltered circumstances of a club
exhibition. It would appear he abandoned the paint-

No. 637. Gathering Autumn Leaves   see color illustration, p. 413

ing at this point, perhaps in favor of devoloping the
subject known as *Butterflies* (No. 641) to serve as the
companion to a feminine representation of Autumn.

PROVENANCE
Charles S. Homer, Jr., by bequest, 1910

EXHIBITIONS
Century Association, New York, 6 Apr. 1878, no. 34
(as *Autumn Study (Boy)*) [?]; Doll & Richards 1912,
no. 2; Carnegie 1937, no. 7; Spanierman 1966, no. 12;
Cooper-Hewitt 1972, no. 94; Whitney 1973, no. 40;
Cooper-Hewitt 2006

No. 638. In Autumn Woods

In Autumn Woods

[1877]

Watercolor, 11½ × 7½ (29.210 × 19.050)
Inscribed ll: W H

Godel & Co., Inc., New York

ABG: Although smaller and in a more ephemeral medium than *Woman in the Autumn Woods* (No. 639), which it obviously resembles, this watercolor is a finished, signed work, and may be accounted a replication, rather than a preliminary study.

At the time this work came to light its owner understood it had come into her great uncle's possession as a gift from Homer when—or because—they had been art students together. By 1870 Arthur J. Pickering (1847–1922) was a practicing portrait painter in Chicago, and was described as a student of George Peter Alexander Healy, then the leading artist in Chicago. Like so many of the provenances said to rise from intimate connection with Homer, there is no supporting evidence and little likelihood of it being other than the product of descendants' wishful imaginations. It is more reasonable, but only a speculation, that this work was one of the group of "Original Water Color and Charcoal Sketches" Homer sent to that city for display and disposal at auction in December 1879.

PROVENANCE
Arthur Pickering, Chicago, nd; Hubert Pickering Harmon, his nephew, nd; Welthau H. Brydon (Mrs. John Brydon), Peoria, IL, his daughter, nd; (Christie's, 26 May 1994, sale 7894, no. 18); private collection, 1994; (Sotheby's, 24 May 2000, sale 7480, no. 56)

LITERATURE
"Art in Chicago. The Studios," *(Chicago) Art Journal* 1 (1 May 1868): 89; "Art in Chicago," *(Chicago) Art Journal* 3 (8 Apr. 1870)

639

Woman in the Autumn Woods

[1877]

Oil, 38 × 24 (96.520 × 60.960)

The Santa Barbara (CA) Museum of Art, gift of
Mr. Sterling Morton to the Preston Morton
Collection, 60.63

LG's first opportunity to examine—and photograph—this painting was when it came to the
Babcock Galleries as one of a group of studies sold
by the Carnegie Institute in 1941. Mrs. Charles S.
Homer, Jr. had given this group to the Carnegie in
1918 with the idea they might serve the art school
division of the Institute as examples of the painting
process. As his photograph and descriptive notes
demonstrate, the canvas had been abandoned well
short of completion: LG recorded the figure as fairly
finished, but the background had not been brought to
an equivalent state of detailing; the woman's features
and hairline were barely touched in. The lack of facial
character was apparently soon "corrected." The painting had surely attained its present appearance by the
time it was photographed for illustration in Forbes
Watson's monograph on Homer published in 1942.

ABG: It is questionable that Homer would have put
this painting on exhibition at the Century in April
1878, paired with *Gathering Autumn Leaves* (No.
637). Showing works-in-process was acceptable in
the informal, protected context of club exhibitions,
however, even the culturally sophisticated members
of the Century might have been expected to have a
negative response to an essentially faceless figure.
On the other hand, *Autumn* (no. 640), the alternate
candidate for the *Autumn Study (Girl)* presented
at the Century had likely already been seen at the
Century just four months earlier, in December 1877,
as *Autumn Leaves*.

See commentary No. 640.

PROVENANCE
Charles S. Homer, Jr., by bequest, 1910; Mrs. Charles
S. Homer, Jr., by bequest, 1917; Carnegie Institute,
Pittsburgh, by gift, 1918; (Downtown Gallery,
1941); (Babcock Galleries, 1941); (Hirschl & Adler
Galleries, 1960)

EXHIBITIONS
Century Association, New York, 6 Apr. 1878, no. 31
(as *Autumn Study (Girl)* [?]; Babcock 1941, no. 11;
Parthenon 2000

LITERATURE
Forbes Watson, *Winslow Homer* (New York: Crown
Publishers, 1942), 112

No. 639. Woman in the Autumn Woods

640

Autumn

1877

Oil, 38¼ × 23³⁄₁₆ (97.155 × 58.898)
Inscribed lr: Homer '77

National Gallery of Art, Washington, DC, collection of Mr. and Mrs. Paul Mellon, 1985.64.22

When LG first examined this painting in May 1936 it was at the Frank K. M. Rehn Galleries, presumably for consideration by a client who did not choose to acquire it. Mr. Hegarty (then its owner), had told Mr. Rehn he had had the painting for about twenty-five years, and had obtained it from a friend who had purchased it at auction some six or seven years earlier. Allowing for the human propensity to tele-scope time, Mr. Hegarty's source may be supposed to have been the buyer of record from the 1902 Runge sale, E. A. Rourke. Either Rourke or Hegarty may have placed the painting at the Macbeth gallery in 1909.

LG immediately recognized the painting as the work described by J. Eastman Chase in his 1910 memoir of Homer: "Some of the pictures produced by Homer at this period [the 1870s] may be unfamiliar to the students of his later and better-known works. Among these I recall a rather large canvas represent-ing an attractive young woman, in somewhat fash-ionable attire, walking through autumn woods. This picture was purchased by the late Charles T. Barney." (Mrs. Charles Tracy Barney responded to LG's inquiry by a letter of 2 April 1936: "Neither my son or I have any remembrance of the picture you ask about: 'an attractive young woman, walking through the autumn woods,' by Winslow Homer.")

Chase had been a salesman at Doll & Richards gallery in Boston in the 1870s, and probably had been aware of—if not directly involved in—the 1878 sale of the painting to Stephen Nickerson. His memory of the work, itself, may have been refreshed by its appearance at the Macbeth gallery in spring 1909; that he was not similarly accurate in recalling the buyer of thirty years past is a forgivable lapse.

The reverse of the canvas was exposed at the time LG examined the painting, and he recorded the fol-lowing makers' stamp: Prepared by / P. DeCHAUX & CO. / Artists Colourmen / New York.

ABG: It is easy to imagine this notably pretty, fashionably costumed young lady as Homer's final realization for a project on the theme of the Seasons after having tested and rejected images of a country-bred adolescent (No. 637) and of a mature figure, clothed and posed to suggest a mythical nature sprite (No. 639). However, there is no evidence, or rational basis for speculation, on which to establish a chronological sequence for the three paintings.

Homer regularly created works in complementary pairs: e.g. *The Mill* (2:No. 388) and *The Country School* (2:No. 389); *A Visit from the Old Mistress* (2:No. 603) and *Sunday Morning in Virginia* (No. 620). The painting now known as *Butterflies* (No. 641), but originally entitled *Summer*, was introduced in company with this *Autumn*. That the paintings match in the physical attractiveness of their models and in the elegance of their costumes, seems indica-tion Homer had opted for the contemporary and urban as his mode for personification of the Seasons. The costume may have been part of Homer's studio equipment. This lady's jacket is also worn by the figure on the left in the 1875 oil known as *Rab and the Girls* (2:No. 570).

The *Autumn Leaves* described as a "single figure" when shown at the Century Association in December 1877 could have been either of the unfinished canvases appropriate to that titling, *Gathering Autumn Leaves* (No. 637) or *Woman in the Autumn woods* (No. 639). However, this finished and dated canvas seems the more likely choice to show at the Century—and to be the work available and welcomed three weeks later for display at the Union League Club on the special occasion of the dinner given to President and Mrs. Rutherford B. Hayes. Identifying the work seen at both clubs in December 1877 is complicated by the appearance just four months later at the Century of *Autumn Study (Girl)* paired with *Autumn Study (Boy)*. It is questionable Homer would have showed the same work at the Century twice in so short a time.

A reporter for the New York *Daily Graphic* taking a New Year's 1878 circuit of the studios noted:

> Winslow Homer, whose original and forcible method is so readily recognizable . . . has two portrait studies, which are excellent. In one, a young lady stands under a canopy of brown autumn foliage and scatters the crisp leaves with one hand; in the other she has just caught a butterfly in her net and is looking up at the mate which hovers above. The pictures do not profess to tell any story, for which true art has no necessity, and the adjuncts are simply used to intensify the attitude and beauty of the figures, which possess a strong vitality and interest.

Within a few days of the *Graphic*'s flattering report *Autumn* and *Summer* were at the Leavitt Art Rooms for an exhibition preliminary to auction. It

No. 640. Autumn

see color illustration, p. 414

was uncharacteristic for Homer to put such major paintings into the market before at least one showing in a conspicuous public exhibition, such as a National Academy *Annual*. But the Leavitt auction was, as the *Evening Post*, termed it "The Annual Sale of American Pictures," the latest in an informal series of sales which appear to have been organized by the community of New York artists with the calculated intent to advance their recognition as well as their fortunes. For these events to accomplish their purpose only "fresh" material should be on offer, and the quality of the lots needed to be above average.

Homer's contributions to this auction were well received in the ample press coverage of the exhibition period, and their successful sale was equally prominent in wide reporting of the hammer prices. The *Evening Post*'s coverage is representative. On 25 January 1878 the paper noted: "Mr. Winslow Homer's two full-length figures entitled 'Summer' and 'Winter' [*sic*] are the most characteristic and noteworthy specimens he has exhibited since the appearance of his 'Cotton Pickers [2:No. 602].' Unlike many of his productions, they introduce two women of some physical beauty." On 31 January the *Post* published a "complete list of all sums said to have been received, except those less than one hundred dollars . . . . Winslow Homer's 'Summer' $285; Winslow Homer's 'Autumn' $265"

The price lists showed that the healthy amounts said to have been brought by the Homers were not exceptional. Yet it seems the artist-sellers were not above the infamous practice of false bidding, doubtless to maintain the standard of valuation they thought appropriate to their work. *Butterflies* (that is, *Summer*) was up for auction again in 1879, this time at Schenck's, and apparently again failed to find a buyer, for it was still in Homer's possession at his death.

And it surely was this *Autumn* which was for sale at Doll & Richards by summer 1878, and it was surely consigned to that Boston gallery by Homer, himself: Doll & Richards noted its sale for $300 to Stephen Westcott Nickerson on 1 July 1878, adding that the $11 cost for putting the frame in order was to be charged to Homer.

(Doll & Richards moved to 2 Park Street in 1878. The change in quarters may have been the catalyst to Homer's initiating association with the firm. Apparently, in these earlier years Doll & Richards' practice was to record—or to retain record—only for completed sales. Thus, the transaction for *Autumn* was in their ledgers, and was the first appearance of Homer's name in them. However, *At the Window* (2:No. 403), *Corn Husking* (2:No. 540), and *Dressing for the Carnival* (No. 619) are known to have been exhibited at Doll & Richards in the autumn of 1878, but from a press report only.)

It is axiomatic to note the sharp division in Homer's career marked by his stay in England in 1881-1882. The change was not only in the character of his work, but also in his audience's experience of it. With the exception of the small group of pre-1881 paintings in Thomas B. Clarke's collection which he showed occasionally at the Union League Club, and put forward for the exhibitions for the Columbian celebrations in 1892 and 1893, Homers of the 1860s and 1870s were rarely and fleetingly seen in public between the mid 1880s and the memorial retrospective exhibitions held in 1911. Throughout the latter twenty years of his career connoisseurs and critics essentially knew nothing of Homer's work of the first twenty.

Theodore Robinson, like the generality of his generation of American artists, greatly admired Homer's contemporary work, and was therefore understandably perplexed when in 1896 he saw *Autumn* at the Fifth Avenue Art Galleries in a pre-auction exhibition. He noted in his diary for 20 January: "A rum Homer at Ortgies. 'Autumn,' a neat study of a model in walking dress and gloves, about 1870 with conventional brown background. A watercolor [in the same sale], fisherman walking along the shore, holding a little girl's hand, is better." The watercolor Robinson preferred was *Home-coming* (4:No. 1178), of 1883 and thus in a style and subject with which he would have been familiar.

Apparently Edward Runge was not deterred by *Autumn* being atypical for Homer in 1896. Indeed, he seems to have had a taste for the artist's early work; in 1894 he had purchased *Country School* (2:No. 421), a work of 1873. Both paintings were in the auction of the Runge collection held 9 January 1902, although Knoedler alerted Homer to *Autumn* only, and apparently offered to bid on it for him. Homer's response, written on 8 January (too late to be relevant) is revealing in his assumption that the intent of acquiring the painting would be to touch up any worn or faded parts and to make such substantive changes as would *then* make it a "fine picture"—the sort of reworking of early canvases still in his possession which engaged Homer's attention at just this time.

> I thank you for the notice of that picture in the collection of Mr. Edward Runge — I sold it for $350 – to some man in Conn[ecticut] – Someone has had that amount of pleasure out of it & it is no matter if it is now given away by the owner, *I care not.* If it looks as if it could be put in good order & a fine picture made out of it – I am the man to do it — if you should get stuck in bidding on it I would make it worth all the money you paid by working on it *a Day*.

(The letter also demonstrates the fallibility of Homer's memory: *Autumn* had sold for $300 to a man from Rhode Island.)

Autumn was again on view at a New York gallery seven years later. This time Guy Pène du Bois, an American artist a generation younger than Theodore Robinson, and two younger than Homer, featured it in his newspaper review.

Winslow Homer's "American Girl" is prominent among other pictures shown at the Macbeth Gallery. It is a delightful note of the past. Its manner—clean, concise, almost tight—will not please those who have come to consider Sargent a master, because of the assurance and freedom of his brush. Homer has become indelibly associated with the sea. He is invariably described as our greatest marine painter, while little or no attention is paid to the way in which he interprets figures.

Often complaint has been lodged against his figures when the sea, the rocks, their surroundings have been greatly admired. There is never anything sweet, never anything 'artistic,' about his methods. This is true in a manner, of this picture, executed in 1869 [*sic*]. In superficial appearance it borders upon photography, and yet it is very distant from the photograph.

Individual interpretation is here, and Whistler's "L'Americaine" is not a greater ode to the beauty of the American women than this canvas. Shown on the brow of a hill, trees of a forest in Autumn surrounding her, this figure lifts her yellow-gray skirt with a gesture that is exquisitely womanly. There is no water in this composition; but it is a very charming Winslow Homer.

PROVENANCE

(Doll & Richards, Boston, by 1878); Stephen Westcott Nickerson, Providence, 1878; Marsden J. Perry, Providence, by 1881; (Ortgies & Co., 22 Jan 1896, no. 35); Edward Runge, New York, probably 1896; (American Art Association, 9 Jan. 1902, Edward Runge sale, no. 71); E. A. Rourke, 1902; M. J. Hegarty, White Plains, NY, nd; (M. Knoedler & Co., 1936); Dr. Philip G. Stevens, New Haven, CT, 1943; H. B. Yotnakparian, nd; Polly M. Leavitt, Bangor, ME, c. 1950; (Robert Carlen Galleries, Philadelphia, 1951); Dr. Irving H. Vogel, Philadelphia, 1951; (Wildenstein & Co., by 1954); Mr. and Mrs. Nathan Shaye, Detroit, 1958; (Marlborough-Gerson Gallery, 1964); Mr. and Mrs. Paul Mellon, Upperville, VA, 1964

EXHIBITIONS

Century Association, New York, 1 Dec. 1877, no. 28 (as *Autumn Leaves*) [?]; Union League Club, New York, [special exhibition in honor of the visit to the Club of Pres. and Mrs. Rutherford B. Hayes], 21 Dec. 1877 (as *October*) [?]; Leavitt Art Rooms, New York, *Fine American Paintings* [auction], [by 25]–30 Jan. 1878, no. 95; Providence (RI) Art Club, [loan collection of paintings], 11 Feb. 1881 (as *Autumn Leaves*); Providence (RI) Art Institute, *Loan Exhibition of Paintings*, 29 Oct.–12 Nov. 1891, no. 115 (as *Autumn Leaves*); Fifth Avenue Art Galleries, New York, *Paintings by American Artists*, 22 Jan. 1896, no. 35; American Art Association, New York, *Mr. Edward Runge's Collection of American Paintings* [auction], c. 4–9 Jan. 1902, no. 71; Macbeth Gallery, New York, May 1909 (as *American Girl*); Whitney 1936, no. 16; Babcock 1941, no. 19; Worcester 1944, no. 13; Whitney 1973, no. 38; NGA 1995, no. 88; NGA 2005

LITERATURE

"The Exhibition of Paintings," *New-York Times*, 22 Dec. 1877; "Gossip of Local Art Circles . . . Paintings Now in Progress on the Easels of Prominent Artists," *(NY) Daily Graphic*, 10 Jan. 1878; "American Picture Sale," *New York Herald*, 23 Jan. 1878; "The Annual Sale of American Pictures. A Brilliant Display in the Leavitt Art Rooms," *(NY) Evening Post*, 25 Jan. 1878; "The Sale of American Pictures," *(NY) Evening Post*, 31 Jan. 1878; "Larger Prices Than Usual Obtained for American Paintings," *(NY) World*, 31 Jan. 1878; "Picture Sale," *New York Herald*, 31 Jan. 1878; "Sale of American Pictures," *New-York Daily Tribune*, 31 Jan. 1878; Theodore Robinson diaries, Frick Art Reference Library, New York; Guy Pène du Bois, "A Winslow Homer of Unusual Charm," *New York American*, 10 May 1909; J. Eastman Chase, "Some Recollections of Winslow Homer," *Harper's Weekly* 54 (22 Oct. 1910): 13; Cikovsky and Kelly 1995, 158–59; Nicolai Cikovsky, Jr., "Autumn," in Franklin Kelly, et al., *American Paintings of the Nineteenth Century, Part I* (Washington, DC: National Gallery of Art, 1996), 318–22

641

Butterflies

1878

The Summer; Butterfly Girl

Oil, 37¾ × 24 (95.885 × 60.960)
Inscribed ll: Winslow Homer / 1878

New Britain (CT) Museum of American Art,
Friends of William F. Brooks Fund, 1950.3

ABG: Homer regularly created works in complementary pairs: e.g. *The Mill* (2:No. 388) and *The
Country School* (2:No. 389); *A Visit from the Old
Mistress* (2:No. 603) and *Sunday Morning in Virginia*
(No. 620). The painting now known as *Butterflies*,
but originally entitled *Summer*, was introduced in
company with *Autumn* (No. 640). That the paintings
match in the physical attractiveness of their models
and in the elegance of their costumes, seems indication Homer had opted for the contemporary and
urban as his mode for personification of the Seasons.
The costume may have been part of Homer's studio
equipment. This lady's bodice is also worn by the
figure on the right in the 1875 oil known as *Rab and
the Girls* (2:No. 570), and the figures in the watercolors *Woman Peeling a Lemon* (2:No. 609) of 1876, and
Backgammon (No. 614) of 1877.

A reporter for the New York *Daily Graphic* taking
a New Year's 1878 circuit of the studios noted:

> Winslow Homer, whose original and forcible
> method is so readily recognizable . . . has two por-
> trait studies, which are excellent. In one, a young
> lady stands under a canopy of brown autumn
> foliage and scatters the crisp leaves with one hand;
> in the other she has just caught a butterfly in her
> net and is looking up at the mate which hovers
> above. The pictures do not profess to tell any
> story, for which true art has no necessity, and the
> adjuncts are simply used to intensify the attitude
> and beauty of the figures, which possess a strong
> vitality and interest.

Within a few days of the *Graphic's* flattering
report *Autumn* and *Summer* were at the Leavitt Art
Rooms for an exhibition preliminary to auction. It
was uncharacteristic for Homer to put such major
paintings into the market before at least one showing in a conspicuous public exhibition, such as a
National Academy *Annual*. But the Leavitt auction
was, as the *Evening Post*, termed it "The Annual
Sale of American Pictures," the latest in an informal
series of sales which appear to have been organized
by the community of New York artists with the
calculated intent to advance their recognition as well
as their fortunes. For these events to accomplish their
purpose only "fresh" material should be on offer, and
the quality of the lots needed to be above average.

Homer's contributions were well received in the
ample press coverage of the pre-auction exhibition,
and their successful sale was equally prominent in
wide reporting of the hammer prices. The *Evening
Post's* coverage is representative. On 25 January 1878
the paper noted: "Mr. Winslow Homer's two full-
length figures entitled 'Summer' and 'Winter' [*sic*]
are the most characteristic and noteworthy specimens
he has exhibited since the appearance of his 'Cotton
Pickers [2:No. 602].' Unlike many of his productions,
they introduce two women of some physical beauty."
On 31 January the *Post* published a "complete list of
all sums said to have been received, except those less
than one hundred dollars . . . . Winslow Homer's
'Summer' $285; Winslow Homer's 'Autumn' $265"

The price lists showed that the healthy amounts
said to have been brought by the Homers were not
exceptional. Yet it seems the artist-sellers were not
above the infamous practice of false bidding, doubtless to maintain the standard of valuation they thought
appropriate to their work. *Butterflies* (that is, *Summer*)
was up for auction again in 1879, this time at
Schenck's, and apparently again failed to find a buyer,
for it was still in Homer's possession at his death.

PROVENANCE
Charles S. Homer, Jr., by bequest, 1910; Mrs. Charles
S. Homer, Jr., by bequest, 1917; (William Macbeth,
Inc., 1935); Stephen C. Clark, New York, 1935;
(William Macbeth, Inc., c. 1950)

EXHIBITIONS
Leavitt Art Rooms, New York, *Fine American
Paintings* [auction], [by 25]–30 Jan. 1878, no. 94
(as *Summer*); Schenck Art Gallery, New York, *High
Class Modern Oil Paintings*, 9–11 Jan. 1879, no. 151 (as
The Butterfly); Pennsylvania 1936, no. 12; Whitney
1936, no. 17; Whitney 1973, no. 42; New Britain 2003

LITERATURE
"Gossip of Local Art Circles . . . Paintings Now in
Progress on the Easels of Prominent Artists," *(NY)
Daily Graphic*, 10 Jan. 1878; "American Picture Sale,"
New York Herald, 23 Jan. 1878; "The Annual Sale of
American Pictures. A Brilliant Display in the Leavitt
Art Rooms," *(NY) Evening Post*, 25 Jan. 1878; "The
Sale of American Pictures," *(NY) Evening Post*,
31 Jan. 1878; "Picture Sale," *New York Herald*, 31 Jan.
1878; "Larger Prices Than Usual Obtained for
American Paintings," *(NY) World*, 31 Jan. 1878;
"Sale of American Pictures," *New-York Daily
Tribune*, 31 Jan. 1878

No. 641. Butterflies

see color illustration, p. 415

No. 642. Charles Prentice Howland

642

Charles Prentice Howland

1878

Oil, 21⅛ × 13¼ (53.658 × 33.655)
Inscribed ll: Homer 1878

Private collection

ABG: Charles P. Howland was the son of Judge Henry E. Howland and nephew of Alfred C. Howland. Mrs. Charles Howland told LG her husband was about nine years of age in this portrait.

Alfred Cornelius Howland and his brother, Henry E. Howland, were already resident at Mrs. Alexander Cushman's boarding house on East 16th Street in New York when Homer took a room there in early autumn 1859. The brothers came from Walpole, New Hampshire, but Homer had known them in Boston, and may have gone to Mrs. Cushman's on their advice, and for their company. As Henry Howland began his rise to prominence in the political and social world of New York, Alfred pursued a successful, if uncelebrated, career as a painter, and naturally had more involvement with Homer in the years he lived and worked in New York. Homer's friendship with Henry Howland clearly extended at least into 1878, when he made a rare departure from his preferred subject matter in executing this cabinet portrait of Howland's elder son.

See commentaries 1:No. 45 and 1:No. 48.

PROVENANCE
Judge Henry E. Howland, New York, 1878; Charles P. Howland, his son, and the subject of the portrait, by 1914; Mrs. Charles P. Howland, Walpole, NH, 1932

643
Peach Blossoms
1878

The Convent Wall

Oil, 13¼ × 19⅝ (33.655 × 49.848)
Inscribed lr: W H / 1878

The Art Institute of Chicago, gift of George B. Harrington, 1946.338

ABG: Although inscribed with a date of 1878, this painting does not seem to have been put on view until early in 1880. Visitors to Homer's studio from both the New York *Daily Tribune* and *Evening Post* reported on it on the same day. The *Tribune*'s description was the more objective and detailed:

> Mr. Winslow Homer has finished a picture of moderate size called "Peach Blossoms." A gray stone fence runs across the front of the canvas, upon which is sitting a maiden of sixteen or so, draped in white, and herself in the bloom of the springtime of womanhood. A field beyond and the gray sky assist to set her off to advantage. Near by her, a peach tree in blossom shows its flower-laden branches above the fence."

But the *Post*'s was the more appreciative: "Mr. Winslow Homer has painted 'Peach Blossoms,' a country lass sitting on a stone wall near a blossoming peach tree. She is a peach-blossom herself."

Homer may have given the painting a conspicuous place, on a day the press was welcomed to his studio because he planned to put it in an auction within the following week; publicity would have been beneficial. And, indeed, the *Post* followed up on its first notice handsomely when the painting was on view preliminary to Daniel A. Mathews's early February sale.

> Mr. Winslow Homer's charming "Peach Blossoms," a farmer's daughter in gray dress and blue bonnet sitting on a stone wall near a blossoming peach tree, is the principal attraction in the Mathews's Art Gallery in Cedar street. The picture was noticed in the Evening Post a few days ago, as on an easel in Mr. Homer's studio. Its answering harmonies of color constitute one element of its artistic and decorative worth

These descriptions of the painting serve to distinguish this work from the closely similar rendering of the subject, also known as *Peach Blossoms* (No. 767),

No. 643. Peach Blossoms

see color illustration, p. 416

that Homer executed at about the same time. The repeated mention of the girl as seated on the stone wall, as well as the reporters' perception of her as quite young, confirms that it is this *Peach Blossoms* they saw in Homer's studio and at Mathews's.

Gordon Hendricks added a superfluous complication to understanding of the two *Peach Blossoms* in arbitrarily reading the obscure fourth digit in the year date inscribed on No. 767 as "o," thus making it—and discussing it—as a work of 1870. There is nothing in the style or subject details of No. 767 which would support such an early dating. Also, the address "51 West 10th St. / City" inscribed by Homer on its stretcher, while not irrefutable evidence of execution after Homer took space in the Tenth Street Studio Building in 1872, is persuasive on that point. However, having pushed No. 767 far behind this *Peach Blossoms*, Hendricks dismissed this work as "surely a spin-off from the earlier picture."

Hendricks further announced that "Both *Peach Blossoms*, incidentally, are related to a *Harper's Weekly* illustration of May 21, 1870." The background of that illustration, "Spring Blossoms," is filled with flowering branches of a quite large tree, however, the "blossoms" of the illustration's title are as much a reference to the five children who occupy its foreground as to the flowering branches over their heads. The upper body of a fashionably dressed young woman is at the far left of the composition; a stone wall supports her elbow, and provides seating for several of the children. Coincidence of features does not constitute relationship.

For all the flattering attention *Peach Blossoms* received preliminary to the Mathews sale of early February 1880, it apparently did not attract a buyer. Just a month later Homer had the Mathews venue all to himself for the exhibition and auction of more than seventy works. The exhibition and sale were consistently described as a collection of watercolors and drawings, but in reporting its highlights the *New-York Times* noted that "a sketch in oil . . . brought $31." In its extensive review of the pre-sale exhibition the New York *World* described "the plump and pretty maiden seated on 'The Convent Wall;' and easily depending a shapely foot far enough below her gray-white dress to disclose a bit of scarlet stocking above a well-turned ankle." The *New York Commercial Advertiser* named "Among the best in the display . . . 'A Convent Wall.'" Neither the *World* or the *Advertiser* made any mention of the medium of *The*—or A—*Convent Wall* as exceptional within the assembly of Homer works on view; the authors might not have noticed a contradiction to their expectation of a consolidated body of works on paper, or may not have cared to complicate their articles by making a digression from generalities. Yet it seems likely *Peach Blossoms* was in this company of watercolors and drawings.

See commentary No. 767.

PROVENANCE
(Daniel A. Mathews Art Gallery, 4 Mar. 1880, Homer sale, no. 25); (Thurber Art Gallery, Chicago, by 1922); George B. Harrington, Chicago, 1922

EXHIBITIONS
Daniel A. Mathews Art Gallery, New York, [auction], c. 2.–c. 6 Feb. 1880; Mathews 1880, no. 25 (as *The Convent Wall*); Nelson-Atkins 2001

LITERATURE
"Brush and Pencil," *New-York Daily Tribune*, 26 Jan. 1880; "Fine Arts," *(NY) Evening Post*, 26 Jan. 1880; "Art Sales," *(NY) Evening Post*, 2 Feb. 1880; "Art Notes. Winslow Homer's Water Colors, &c.," *New York Commercial Advertiser*, 2 Mar. 1880; "Water-Colors by Winslow Homer," *(NY) World*, 4 Mar. 1880; Hendricks 1979, 80; Nelson-Atkins Museum of Art, "Moving On," by Margaret C. Conrads, in *Winslow Homer and the Critics: Forging a National Art in the 1870s* (Kansas City, MO, 2001), 169

644
Day is Done
1878

Watercolor, 14 × 20 (35.560 × 50.800)
Inscribed lr: Homer 1878

Private collection

This watercolor was introduced to LG in 1947 with
a story of its having been bought some eight or ten
years earlier by Mrs. Frank Brunner at the auction of
the contents of an "old mansion" in Far Rockaway
on Long Island. Mrs. Brunner supposedly was
attracted to the work by its pretty colors, and
thought it entirely worth the $6 she paid. The sale
was said to have been occasioned by the deaths of
the two elderly sisters who had lived in the house for
more than fifty years. No one could remember the
sisters' names. Once the attribution of the watercolor

was confirmed and it had become an object of commercial interest, this quaint tale had its moment of
celebrity in several newspapers and popular journals.
As late as 1979 the story was the watercolor's distin-
guishing characteristic. Gordon Hendricks repeated
its high points as the caption to an illustration in his
1979 monograph—adding his musing on how much
the work had appreciated in value by that time.

In fact, the Brunners seem to have been the lead
actors in a small troupe of Rockawayites, including
the sisters, who collaborated in bringing the painting
into the market. It seems that it had come out of a
third-floor closet in the sisters' house after the house
(with its contents) had been sold.

Part of the story was that when the matting and
frame had been removed a faint inscription, in
pencil and in Homer's hand, had been found on
the sheet: "Day is Done. Winslow Homer. Price fifty
dollars. Will entertain offer." The phrase "Day is
Done" is written at the left below the image, although

No. 644. Day is Done

by whom is open to opinion; the rest of the reported inscription is not known to have been seen by a reliable witness.

When this watercolor was brought to him LG, of course, immediately recognized its central figure as virtually identical to that in Homer's 1876 oil *The Song of the Lark* or *In the Field* (2:No. 600). However, his confirmation of attribution was determined as much on the stylistic character of the work as on the familiarity of its subject. He noted the figure of the man is more finished than details of the landscape setting.

ABG: While the attribution of this watercolor is not in doubt, several exceptional aspects of its character are intriguing: the detailed replication of the figure from an oil of two years earlier; the ruling off of a rectangle to confine the image within a larger sheet; the signature in paint within the image, and another in pencil immediately below the bottom edge of the image. The question comes to mind: what special use might Homer have planned for this watercolor? Several lines of speculation suggest themselves.

Homer was experimenting in these years with methods of generating multiples of his works, even to having several reproduced by photolithography (see No. 883 and No. 884). Although *Day is Done* was created in color, not black and white, might it have been intended to be the base for some sort of reproductive process. In connection with such a scenario, the changes from the 1876 oil *Song of the Lark* that Homer introduced into this watercolor tend to give the figure a narrative context and make the form easier to distinguish—changes appropriate to mass production. The distant group of co-workers in the watercolor draws viewers' attention to the facts of farm labor, where the focus in the oil painting on the single figure conveyed the spirituality in the farmer's harmony with nature. Shifting the mass of the tree from its position behind the figure in the oil to a place by itself in the watercolor assured the silhouette of the figure would be clearly defined.

It is also possible Homer created this watercolor in connection with George W. Sheldon's article "American Painters. Winslow Homer and F. A. Bridgman" published in the August 1878 issue of the *Art Journal*, and illustrated by images of *Song of the Lark* and *The Watermelon Boys* (2:No. 595). The reproductions were made from wood engravings, and thus required the engraver to work from the original painting, or some other model. The illustration of *Song of the Lark* seen in Sheldon's article closely approximates the design of Homer's oil painting. It is conceivable, however, that *Day is Done* had been offered as a model—and rejected.

PROVENANCE

Mr. and Mrs. Frank Brunner, Rockaway Beach, NY, c. 1945; (M. Knoedler & Co., 1947); (Hirschl & Adler Galleries, by 1968); Dr. and Mrs. John J. McDonough, Youngstown, OH, 1968; (Sotheby Parke-Bernet, 22 Mar. 1978, sale 4098, no. 25); (Provenance Gallery, Fort Worth, TX, 1978)

LITERATURE

"A Homer for $6," *Art Digest* 21 (1 July 1947): 22; Hendricks 1979, 124

645
A Littoral Tile
1878

Ceramic, 8 × 8 (20.320 × 20.320)
Inscribed lr: Homer 78

The Detroit Institute of Arts, Dexter M. Ferry, Jr.
Fund, Merrill Fund, and partial gift from Barbara
and Martha Fleischman, 2003.153

Homer's design for this tile used an image
probably first composed some four years earlier
for his *Harper's Weekly* illustration "Flirting on the
Seashore," published 19 September 1874. All the
essential elements of the 1874 composition were
repeated in the 1878 version, although the landscape
background to the two figures was considerably
altered to adapt the exaggeratedly horizontal format
of the illustration to the square of the tile. The two
versions are, however, mirror images of each other,
suggesting Homer used a sketch upon which he
based his 1874 drawing made on the wood block as
his source in designing the tile, rather than the
illustration, itself.

See commentary 2:No. 529-R.

ABG: "Littoral" is derived from the Latin for shore
or beach, and therefore means "of the seashore;" it
applies to a coastal region including both land and
sea. The somewhat pompous choice of vocabulary
in titling such an ephemeral work is characteristic
of the Tile Club's sense of humor. *A Littoral Tile* is
loosely brushed in blue and black, and may be
accepted as a work executed in the course of a Tile
Club evening meeting. It may be speculated that
its survival is owed to it having been among the
subjects used to illustrate William Mackay Laffan's
article, "The Tile Club at Work," in the January
1879 issue of *Scribner's Monthly*.

The *Scribner's* illustration is probably based on
a photographic process. That is, an image would
have been transferred to a wood block from a
photograph, rather than having been drawn directly
on the block. The source photograph could have
been made of the tile, itself, but a drawing made
for the purpose of replication would probably have
been preferred, as a more reliable means to guide
the engraver in the desired relationship of values.
The wide differences in style among the images used
to illustrate the article suggest that the Tile Club
members, including Homer, may have provided the
original source drawings.

No. 645. A Littoral Tile

see color illustration, p. 417

Just over a year after Laffan's article appeared
in *Scribner's* the New York *Sun* reported on an
exhibition of such source drawings:

> One of the most successful and interesting
> exhibitions that the Art Students' League has
> given was their last. The Messrs. Scribner & Co.
> were kind enough to contribute for the occasion
> over one hundred and fifty original drawings
> which had been made from time to time for recent
> numbers of *Scribner's Monthly* and *St. Nicholas*
> by various artists. Among these were examples of
> R. Swain Gifford, Arthur Quartley, E. A. Abbey . . .
> Winslow Homer, ... A majority of the drawings
> that appear in our magazines are not drawn upon
> the block, but are transferred to it by the aid of
> photography. This enables the engraver to have in
> front of him for constant reference, the original
> work of the artists, which is a great assistance to
> him; and if by some awkwardness or mischance
> the engraving should fail, the loss of the artist's
> labor is not involved. The publishers, too, gain by
> it, inasmuch as they acquire uncommon collections
> of sketches and finished drawings some of which
> are of little value, while all are interesting.

Excepting a single book illustration done in 1876
for Scribner, Armstrong & Co., up to the time of

No. 645.5. Couple on the Shore

this occasion at the Art Students' League, the only illustrations Homer had surely done for Scribner's were "The Sower" (see No. 661) and "Pumpkins Among the Corn" (No. 662) which accompanied an article in the August 1878 issue of *Scribner's Monthly*. If Homer did supply a graphic replica of *A Littoral Tile* for Laffan's article it also would have been at Scribner's disposal.

PROVENANCE
Private collection, c. 1970; (Kennedy Galleries, 2003)

LITERATURE
W. Mackay Laffan, "The Tile Club at Work," *Scribner's Monthly* 17 (Jan. 1879): 403; "Art Notes," *(NY) Sun*, 16 Feb. 1879

645.5+
Couple on the Shore
[1878]

Ceramic, 8 × 8 (20.320 × 20.320)
Inscribed ll: Homer

Private collection

PROVENANCE
(Unidentified auction, Boston area, 2004)

646

Sailing a Boat

1878

Ceramic, 8 × 8 (20.320 × 20.320)
Inscribed lc, on trough: Homer 1878

Private collection

LG did not have an opportunity to examine this tile but had the loan of a good, professionally made photograph from which he felt confident he recognized the vitality and assurance of Homer's style. The image accompanying this entry is LG's drawing made in 1937 over the base of his line-tracing of the photograph.

The owner described the work as executed in blue against the white ground of the tile. LG noted the work was "painted quite freely and strongly, with vigorous, dashing brushstrokes, and strongly marked draughtsmanship with the brush. It seems very characteristic of [Homer's] style, but even freer and more graphic than usual, as would be natural working in this medium." The color scheme and LG's description of Homer's technique suggest this is another example of a tile done within the time frame and under the conditions of a Tile Club meeting.

The subject is a near replica of the group of four children in the watercolor *Sailing Boats in the*

Watering Trough (1:No. 43-R), who reappeared in the wood engraving, "Spring Blossoms," designed by Homer and published in the 21 May 1870 issue of *Harper's Weekly*. There are significant differences, however. Notably among them is the tree branch and bird which intrude into the picture from above, a device Homer often used in the later 1870s. The use of a motive Homer seems to have had at his fingertips for perhaps as long as twenty years further suggests this tile was done during a Club evening, when the tiles were executed quickly and entirely from the artists' imaginations and memories.

The owner also reported to LG that the tile bore a stamp on its reverse: Salvador Diez-Manises, presumably the name of the tile manufacturer, or exporter. The Tile Club was said to have favored tiles of Spanish make at first, before changing to English-made squares.

ABG: Earl Shinn (1837–1886) was known as "Bone" to his fellow members of the Tile Club, and as "Edward Strahan" to readers of his art criticism. It is likely Shinn acquired this tile as part of the standard reward given the host of a Club meeting: all the tiles executed during the evening.

PROVENANCE
Earl Shinn, New York, c. 1878; Mrs. Thomas K. Brown, West Town, PA, his niece, by bequest, 1886

Drawing by Lloyd Goodrich made over his tracing of the tile *Sailing a Boat*

No. 647. Morning

647
Morning
nd

Cock of the World

Ceramic, 8 × 8 (20.320 × 20.320)
Inscribed ll: H; lc: Morning; within image of the
globe: o Boston

Private collection

In a letter of 12 April 1940 to LG, Charles L. Homer
said that the principal figure of this tile was intended
to represent Charles S. Homer, Jr. as "cock-of-the-
walk." He elaborated on this story the next year when
LG had the opportunity to examine the family's
Homers in warehouse storage in Portland, Maine,
stating that Homer had made the tile to give to his
older brother when Charles S. Homer received a
medal from the Chemical Society, and was a bit
puffed up about it. Some time later the medal of this
story had been transformed into an award made at
the Paris Exposition Universelle of 1900.

It is entirely in character for Homer to have
turned his rooster from its original intent as an
emblem of dawn to a good-natured gibe at his
brother. That he had turned back to working with
ceramics in 1900 is not credible, however.

ABG: The day following the opening of the
National Academy of Design annual exhibition
of 1878 the New York *Daily Graphic*'s critic noted
that "Two tiles by Winslow Homer and Edward
Wimbridge (77 and 79) evince high decorative
sense." Wimbridge was one of the two artists who
initiated the Tile Club, and was its "Grasshopper."
His contribution to the 1878 *Annual* was titled
Night. Both Homer's and Wimbridge's tiles were
priced at $25, and it is easy to imagine them as
a complementary pair. They were hung in close
proximity, but probably on either side of the exhibition catalogue's number 78, a group of "Seven
Tiles—Representing types of the last century" by
Mrs. Alfred Wordsworth Thompson. (All these tiles
were displayed in the Academy's Corridor gallery,
in company with etchings; a group of "Woodcuts"
by *Aldine* staff engravers; and "porcelain plates" on
which C. Dulon had depicted *Landscape on the
Rhine* and *Peach and Flowers*, that is, among the
exhibition's ephemera.)

Well into the run of the exhibition a writer for
the *New York Evening Mail* scolded patrons and
public for their failure to support American artists
by buying from the *Annual*: "The list of picture thus

far sold at the Academy is as follows: . . . 'Night' (tile) E. Wimbridge . . . 'Morning' (tile) Winslow Homer . . . The only Academicians who have sold pictures are J. G. Brown and R. M. Pratt, unless we include Winslow Homer who has disposed of one tile for $25!"

Press reports of the sale of *Morning* might have been inaccurate; the buyer might have reneged and, thus, the tile would have come back to Homer; Homer's older brother might have been the buyer from the *Annual*—with or without Wimbridge's *Night*; or Homer might have made more than one example of the subject. Just how and when the tile came into Charles Homer's possession is not likely ever to be surely known.

In contrast to No. 645, No. 645.5, and No. 646, *Morning* is not a work executed in haste and poor light of an evening party in a friend's studio. It is carefully crafted, and it is made in many colors: the rooster's comb is red; neck and chest, yellow; lower body, dark green; legs, golden; and globe, gray; and an area of massed spots of colors represents the iridescence of the rooster's wing and tail feathers. In this attention to detail Homer has not fully yielded precedence to decorative effect over naturalism.

PROVENANCE
Charles S. Homer, Jr., nd; Charles L. Homer, by 1941

EXHIBITIONS
National Academy of Design, New York, *Fifty-third Annual Exhibition*, 2 Apr.–1 June 1878, no. 77

LITERATURE
"National Academy of Design," *(NY) Daily Graphic*, 3 Apr. 1878; "Art and Artists," *New York Evening Mail*, 15 May 1878; "American Art. The Sale of Pictures Exhibited at the National Academy," *(NY) World*, 2 June 1878

No. 648. The Shepherdess

648
The Shepherdess
1878

Ceramic, 7¾ × 7¾ (19.685 × 19.685)
Inscribed ll: Decorations / Winslow Homer 1878

Lyman Allyn Art Museum, New London, CT, 1945.155

The feminine figure in the drawing *Shepherd and Shepherdess* (No. 632) is the source for this tile.

PROVENANCE
Charles S. Homer, Jr., by bequest, 1910; Mrs. Charles S. Homer, Jr., by bequest, 1917; Charles L. Homer, by bequest, 1937; Robert W. Macbeth, New York, by gift, c. 1938; Robert G. McIntyre, New York and Dorset, VT, his cousin, c. 1940

EXHIBITIONS
Nelson-Atkins 2001; Cooper-Hewitt 2006

No. 649. Shepherdess Resting

649

Shepherdess Resting

[1877–1878]

Charcoal, 14¼ × 22¹⁄₁₆ (36.195 × 56.040)

Cooper-Hewitt, National Design Museum, Smithsonian Institution, gift of Charles Savage Homer, Jr., 1912-12-206

ABG: This drawing may have been done at approximately the same time as the drawings similar in character and subject which are dated 1877, No. 630 through No. 636. It is equally possible Homer executed it specifically in preparation for the tiles *Shepherdess Resting* (No. 651). The shepherdess's fancy crook is at her side, and her sheep have strayed far away to the brow of the hill in the composition of the tiles just as they are placed here. These details are not repeated in the closely related watercolor *Shepherdess Reclining* (No. 650).

PROVENANCE
Charles S. Homer, Jr., by bequest, 1910

EXHIBITIONS
Carnegie 1937, no. 146; University Club 1938, no. 13; Hamilton 1964, no. 22; Cooper-Hewitt 1972, no. 38; Lowe, Syracuse, 1979, no. 5; Cooper-Hewitt 2006

650

Shepherdess Reclining

1878

Watercolor, 7⅞ × 13⅛ (20.003 × 33.338)
Inscribed ll: Homer

Destroyed

ABG: This realization in full color of the indolent shepherdess is likely a later stage in Homer's process of creating the tiles of the same subject, No. 651. Unlike the drawing (No. 649) and the tiles the young woman's attention is here engaged by a pair of butterflies, and she seems not entirely irresponsible in that another figure is supervising some of the herd of sheep in the far distance.

The more significant differences between this painting and the tiles are in their colors: In the painting the shepherdess' skirt and hat are light brown, her hair ribbon, bodice, and stockings are blue, and the ruffles at her elbows and hips are white, with gray detailing; white clouds fill much of blue sky. In the tiles the hat, skirt and bodice are yellow, the hair ribbon is red, the ruffles are pale gray, and stockings are dark gray; the same light and dark grays are repeated in the sky. These changes are probably less the result of free choice than of accommodation to the effects of firing glazes.

The watercolor was a victim of Hurricane Andrew in 1992.

PROVENANCE
Mrs. Margaret Prenty, nd; Arthur G. Wright, Massapequa, NY, by bequest, 1945; unnamed mother of Mrs. Stollburger, after 1965; Mrs. Stollburger, by 1983; (Christie's, 1 June 1984, sale 5580, no. 63); (Montgomery Gallery, San Francisco, 1984); (Gerald Peters Gallery, Santa Fe, NM, 1986); (John H. Surovek Gallery, Palm Beach, FL, 1990); private collection, 1992

651

Resting Shepherdess

1878

Bo-Peep and her Sheep

Ceramic, 8 × 16 (20.320 × 40.640)
Inscribed ll: Winslow Homer '78

Heckscher Museum of Art, Huntington, NY, partial gift of Karen H. Bechtel in memory of Ronald G. Pisano and partial Museum purchase with funds from the Acquisition Fund, the Eva Gatling Fund and the Baker/Pisano Fund, 2005.2

ABG: See commentary No. 650.

No. 650. Shepherdess Reclining

With the precedent of Dutch, and presumably, New Amsterdam's extensive use of tiles, the favored—perhaps, sole—destination for the Tilers' productions was as decorative insets around fireplaces. The insets did not necessarily entirely surround the opening.

Homer clearly took his tile work seriously, and liked to show it off. This composition extended cross two tiles, each being 8 inches square in size. The New York *Daily Graphic* identified the function which would have determined its form, in the course of reporting on the December 1878 Art Students' League exhibition.

> The third of this season's monthly art receptions was held at the rooms of the Art Students' League, on Fifth avenue, last evening. . . . There was not a bad piece of work on the walls . . . . Of the home [American] artists, Winslow Homer contributed a collection of his summer studies in water-color, exquisite little bits of color representing American child life and landscape in this painter's most characteristic manner. A mantelpiece painted on tiles by the same artist attracted much attention.

The *Art Interchange*'s report on this Art Students' League reception confirmed the identification: "Mr. Winslow Homer sent quite a number of his water-color portraits on which the eye could not but linger, a mantel-piece of tiles, subject, 'Bo-Peep and her Sheep' was especially noticeable."

PROVENANCE
Charles S. Homer, Jr., by bequest, 1910; Thomas Allen, by gift, before 1917; (Sotheby Parke-Bernet, 17 Oct. 1980, sale 4435, no. 139); private collection, 1980; (Berry-Hill Galleries, Inc., 1993); Karen H. Bechtel, New York, c. 1996

EXHIBITIONS
Art Students' League, New York, 3 Dec. 1878; Cooper-Hewitt 2006

LITERATURE
"The Art Students' League," *(NY) Daily Graphic*, 4 Dec. 1878; "Fine Arts. Art Students' League Monthly Exhibition," *New York Herald*, 4 Dec. 1878; "Monthly Reception at the Art Students' League," *Art Interchange* 1 (11 Dec. 1878): 51

No. 651. Resting Shepherdess

see color illustration, p. 417

No. 652. Shepherd

No. 653. Shepherdess

652

Shepherd

[1878]

Charcoal, chalk, 24¼ × 14½ (61.595 × 36.830)
Inscribed ll: Homer

Private collection

PROVENANCE
Edward Hill, Yonkers, NY, c. 1880; Gertrude Hill,
New York, his daughter, by bequest, c. 1930;
(Sotheby Parke-Bernet, 18 Nov. 1977, sale 4048,
no. 527); (Hirschl & Adler Galleries, 1977); (Phyllis
Hattis, San Fancisco, c. 1978)

EXHIBITIONS
Knoedler 1986, no. 34

653

Shepherdess

1878

Charcoal, chalk, 24¼ × 14½ (61.595 × 36.830)
Inscribed lr: Winslow Homer / 1878

Private collection

PROVENANCE
Edward Hill, Yonkers, NY, c. 1880; Gertrude Hill,
New York, by bequest, c. 1930; (Sotheby Parke-
Bernet, 18 Nov. 1977, sale 4048, no. 526); (Hirschl &
Adler Galleries, 1977); (John H. Surovek Gallery,
Palm Beach, FL, c. 1984)

EXHIBITIONS
Knoedler 1986, no. 35

654

Fireplace Surround: Shepherd and Shepherdess

1878

Ceramic, 36 × 49¼ (91.440 × 125.095)
Inscribed ll: H / No 1. / Copyright 1878 by Winslow
Homer; lr: H

The Metropolitan Museum of Art, bequest of
Arthur G. Altschul, 2003.140

ABG: This design is the most complex of Homer's
ceramic compositions; conceived as a unit its realization required twelve contiguous 8 inch square tiles.
The potential for distortion in the firing process
would have been formidable. The successful outcome
is probably as much a testament to Homer's tenacity
as to his artistry. The time and effort Homer dedicated
to this work is demonstrated by the fully detailed
drawings of the figures (No. 652 and No. 653) done in
exactly the scale at which they appear in these tiles.

The indolent shepherdess of No. 651 is here on
her feet and attentive to her responsibilities. Homer
also varied the colors of her costume. Here her skirt
is blue and stockings yellow. The sky streaked in
grays of No. 651, is also changed to fluffy white clouds

against clear blue; shepherd, shepherdess and flock
appear permanently safe from rain.

This suite of tiles is generally described as having
been executed for presentation to Homer's older
brother, Charles S. Homer, Jr. It certainly remained
imbedded around a fireplace in Charles's country
home in West Townsend, Massachusetts, as late as
1937, and may have been installed soon after its
completion. However, the "No. 1" inscribed with
the copyright claim on the lowest left tile, suggests
there were hopes it was the first in a "line" to be
commercially manufactured.

PROVENANCE
Mr. and Mrs. Charles S. Homer, Jr., by gift of
Homer, probably c. 1878; Mrs. Charles S. Homer,
Jr., by bequest, 1917; Charles L. Homer, by bequest,
1937; (Giovanni Castano, Boston, c. 1954); (Milch
Galleries, 1958); Arthur G. Altschul, New York, 1958

EXHIBITIONS
Century Association, New York, 1 June 1878, no. 21;
Behn-Moore 1953; NGA 1958, no. 244; Cooper-
Hewitt 2006

No. 654. Fireplace Surround: Shepherd and Shepherdess

see color illustration, p. 418

655

Evening on the Beach

[1878]

Graphite, watercolor, 8½ × 15 (21.590 × 38.100)
Inscribed lr: Homer '71 [?]

Colby College Museum of Art, Waterville, ME,
The Lunder Collection

ABG: This drawing is consistently considered as
a work of 1871 because of the apparently clearly
inscribed numerals at the lower right corner. The
drawing is also the specific source of the undated
oil *Evening on the Beach* (No. 656), and of the central
image in the suite of tiles (No. 657-a), which is dated
1878. LG assigned the oil to 1878 primarily on the
basis of its immediate relationship to the dated tiles.
To have such a closely related drawing and painting
at opposite ends of a decade is not inconceivable,
but is unconventional.

LG examined this drawing enclosed in its frame;
the matting covered the lower portion of the
inscribed dating. Were the inscription fully visible
the numeral "1" might prove to be a carelessly written
"8." Very few drawings by Homer from the years
1870 to 1872 survive, and none is comparable in
intent and degree of finish to this *Evening on the
Beach*. *Lady on the Beach* (2:No. 478), undoubtedly
signed and dated 1873, is comparable in subject,
media, composition, and degree of finish. The style
of this latter drawing is not so radically different
from that of *Evening on the Beach* as to endorse the
wide discrepancy in date. However, Homer's many
drawings of the late 1870s are stylistically much closer
to *Evening on the Beach* than is this one drawing of
1873. Also, Homer's manner of writing his signature,
seen frequently in drawings of 1878 and 1879, is
exactly that seen on *Evening on the Beach* (e. g., No.
682, No. 699, No. 784, and No. 798). And finally,
these two young women are dressed in the fashion of
the later years of the decade. Indeed, the left-hand
figure appears to be wearing the same costume as the
model in *Autumn* (No. 640) of 1877.

PROVENANCE
Mrs. Kathryn Huber, Florida, nd; (Newhouse
Galleries, 1946); (Wildenstein & Co., 1946); Mrs.
Thomas Hitchcock, New York, 1948; (Thomas
Colville Fine Art, LLC, New Haven, 2003)

EXHIBITIONS
Wildenstein 1947, no. 90; Maynard Walker 1953,
no. 18; NGA 1958, no. 198; Knoedler 1986, no. 44

No. 655. Evening on the Beach

No. 656. Evening on the Beach

656

Evening on the Beach

[1878]

Oil, 13¼ × 20¼ (33.655 × 51.435)
Inscribed lr: Homer

Private collection

This oil painting, *Evening on the Beach* is obviously dependent upon the drawing known by the same title, No. 655. Its relationship to the somewhat larger oil painting, dated 1880, commonly known as *Promenade on the Beach* (No. 874) is equally obvious; the differences are essentially only in details of costume. Homer repeated the elegant ladies strolling along a beach at sunset seen in No. 655 and No. 656 as the central image in the group of three tiles, No. 657-a.

Evening on the Beach—the oil—has been published in black and white three times previously: in (Nathaniel Pousette-Dart, *Winslow Homer*, 1923; in Theodore Bolton, "The Art of Winslow Homer," *Fine Arts*, February 1932; and in Hendricks, 1979, so its compositional similarity to No. 657-a, and especially to No. 874 is well known. However, the painting, itself, has not been seen in public since October 1946 when it was briefly displayed at Parke-Bernet preliminary to the Martin estate sale. Thus, for the time being, knowledge of Homer's color choices in this earlier version of the subject may come only from LG's description:

The sky is a peculiar darkish warm green. The sea is a darker green; cold at the horizon, warmer inshore, but practically the same value. A white sail at the horizon at the right, just indicated. The beach is a warm sand-color. Shadows on the beach are greenish. The woman at the left has a very dark, warm brown hat and jacket, and a lighter sienna brown skirt, with ruffles at the bottom; a light red-brown scarf at her neck, and braid trimmings of the same color on her jacket; yellow gloves. The woman at the right wears a grayed bluish-green dress, the same color all over; and a darker, stronger green hat; she has an orange scarf at her throat, and white gloves. Their ruddy, sunlit faces stand out against the dark green sky.

ABG: The subject of this painting makes it eligible to be the *On the Seashore* Homer showed at the Century Asociation in November 1878. However, the painting on exhibition under that title could just as well have been *Woman on the Beach* (No. 658).

PROVENANCE
Charles S. Homer, Jr., by bequest, 1910; (M. Knoedler & Co., 1912); Dr. and Mrs. George Woodward, Chestnut Hill, PA, 1913; (M. Knoedler & Co., 1934); Robert Sterling Clark, New York, 1934; (M. Knoedler & Co., 1938); Mrs. George A. Martin, Cleveland, 1938; (Parke-Bernet Galleries, 18–19 Oct. 1946, sale 795, no. 317); (David B. Findlay Galleries, 1946)

657-A

Fireplace Surround, top: Beach Scene
1878

Ceramic, 8 × 24 (20.320 × 60.960)
Inscribed ll: Winslow Homer 1878

Private collection

Mrs. Harold Farnsworth told LG her father had purchased J. Foxworth Cole's house, and thereby had come into possession of these tiles, which had been integral to the structure. By 1937 the Cole house was no longer in existence. Apparently the tiles survived as nine separate units, for they first came to light when Mrs. Farnsworth carried them to the Museum of Fine Arts, Boston. When LG examined them in Mrs. Farnsworth's home soon after, he saw them arranged in obviously rational sequences, but free-standing; that is, not serving any decorative or architectural function.

LG described the coloring of the women's costumes in the beach scene as entirely in blue; the sea and sky, also blue; the beach, an orange-yellow, with orange-red lines of seaweed, and the distant sails in cream-yellow and orange-yellow. He described the coloring of the accompanying sea horses (No. 657-b and No. 657-c) as an intermingling of yellow, red and blue, against pale blue backgrounds. He noted the rising bubbles and undulating lines around these creatures, which place them in their natural habitat: under water.

The image on the central, horizontal three-tile group is repeated in the drawing, No. 655, and oil No. 656—both of which were probably executed before Homer made this tile group.

ABG: Homer and Joseph Foxcroft Cole (1837–1892) had a long, and apparently close relationship. Born in Maine, Cole's family had moved to Boston when he was seven years old. He became an apprentice at Bufford's lithography establishment at the same time as Homer, and like Homer he aspired to become a painter. Cole went to France in 1860 and spent several years studying in the Paris atelier of Eugene Lambinet. He had returned to Boston by 1863, the first year he contributed to an annual exhibition of the National Academy of Design. He was back in Paris in 1865, this time becoming associated with Charles Jacques. As his training would suggest, Cole was a landscapist in the Barbizon mode. He was in Paris during the period of Homer's stay there, and is said to have taken Homer with him on tours into the nearby countryside. Cole continued to divide his time between France, Belgium (where he found his wife) and Boston, until 1877, when he built a house and studio in Winchester, near Boston, and settled in that spot for the remainder of his life.

Although presented by Maynard Walker in abutting sections—with two squares carrying scallop shell designs added to fill out the corners—to create complete framing for a fireplace, there is no way to know just how they were initially placed in the Cole house. Considering the disparate character of the horizontal member of the set, and the paired, vertical members as well as the comparatively small size of each three-tile grouping and that each carries a signature, it seems they were conceived as complementary parts which could be adapted to architectural forms of various dimensions. Homer may have made this suite of tiles with his friend's new home specifically in mind, or he may have given Cole the prototype for a design he hoped to market.

The *New York Herald*'s brief notice of the Tile Club's exhibition demonstrates that these tiles—presented in three distinct units—were Homer's principal contribution

> The work done during the present year by the members of the Tile Club was on exhibition yesterday at Winslow Homer's studio. There is much of creditable performances among which we note some signed in Greek to us; good heads by C. S. Reinhart; old time scenes by E. A. Abbey; flowers and a good ape study by Walter Paris; several by Julian Weir, F. H. Smith's facile work, and three sets of three tiles each, on which are sea monsters and a pair of young ladies on the beach by Winslow Homer.

The tiles may have been delivered to Winchester that summer, or held until the summer of 1879, when it is known Homer visited Cole, and his young daughter, Adelaide; see No. 845.

PROVENANCE
J. Foxworth Cole, Wincester, MA, by gift of Homer, c. 1878; unnamed father of Mrs. Harold Farnsworth, Winchester, MA, probably c. 1892; Mrs. Harold Farnsworth, Wincester, MA, by bequest, by 1937; (Maynard Walker Galleries, 1963)

EXHIBITIONS
Tile Club, New York, 4–5 May 1878 (exhibited in Winslow Homer studio, Tenth Street Studio Building); Vose 1940; MFA, Boston, 1959 (not in catalogue)

LITERATURE
"The Tile Club Exhibition," *New York Herald*, 6 May 1878; "Unique Homer Show at Vose," *Boston Herald*, 13 Oct. 1940

No. 657-A.

No. 657-B.

No. 657-C.

657-B

Fireplace Surround, left side:
Fantastic Sea Horse

1878

Ceramic, 24 × 8 (60.960 × 20.320)
Inscribed ll: Copyright, 1878, by Winslow Homer

657-C

Fireplace Surround, right side:
Fantastic Sea Horse

1878

Ceramic, 24 × 8 (60.960 × 20.320)
Inscribed ll: Copyright, 1878, by Winslow Homer

No. 658. Woman on the Beach

costumed identically to the right-hand figure in the drawing and in the painting, as well as in the central tile of the fireplace surround, (No. 657-A), which repeats the image. Her dress and hat are a uniform dark greenish blue; her gloves are fawn color, and the bit of linen at her throat and edge of petticoat at her feet are bright white.

For discussion of the question of dating the two *Evening on the Beach*s—which inevitably extends to *Woman on the Beach*—see commentary No. 655.

If *Woman on the Beach* is a work of about 1878, than it might have been the *On the Seashore* Homer showed at the Century Association in November 1878. However, that title is equally appropriate to the painting *Evening on the Beach*, or to what we know of *Sundown* (No. 775) which Homer put in the National Academy of Design annual exhibition a few months later. *Woman on the Beach* and *Evening on the Beach* are the same size, but the former is the more studied and highly finished of the two, making it the better candidate for exhibition. The *Sundown* Homer showed at the Century in November 1879 was very probably his Academy picture, which makes it unlikely he had already shown it there just a year earlier.

658

Woman on the Beach

[1878]

Oil, 20 × 13 (50.800 × 33.020)
Inscribed lr: Winslow Homer N. A.

Unlocated

ABG: This previously unknown work was brought to LG in 1986. No information on its history was provided to him, but he had no hesitation in accepting it into the Homer canon based on its stylistic character and its obvious relationship in subject with the drawing and painting both titled *Evening on the Beach* (No. 655 and No. 656). The young woman who stands alone in this painting appears to be

659

Startled

1878

Watercolor, 12 × 19½ (30.480 × 49.530)
Inscribed lr: Homer 1878

Philadelphia Museum of Art, gift of Dr. and Mrs. George Woodward, 1939.7.5

ABG: In reviewing the Brooklyn Art Association's spring 1881 exhibition of watercolors, the *Art Journal* mentioned that about half its content had been "transferred" from the American Water Color Society's *Fourteenth Annual Exhibition*, which had concluded 23 February, just two weeks before opening day of the Brooklyn exhibition. Homer had twenty paintings in the Society's exhibition, most catalogued with titles inappropriate to *Startled*, although several cannot be identified. However, the *Journal*'s specific notice of the painting placed it: "Among the new work was . . . Winslow Homer's 'Startled,' which represented a young woman on the sea-shore suddenly terrified by a string of sea-weed resembling a snake." The New York *Tribune* made the same distinction between the portion of the Brooklyn show which was "new," and that recently seen in New York: "Winslow Homer, in addition to some pictures seen before, displays 'Startled,' which depicts a young woman whose walk on the beach has been interrupted by coming across some sea weed resembling a snake."

PROVENANCE
George H. Buek, Brooklyn, probably 1881; (American Art Association, 4 Nov. 1927, Buek sale, no. 68); (M. Knoedler & Co., 1927); Dr. and Mrs. George Woodward, Chestnut Hill, PA, c. 1935

EXHIBITIONS
Brooklyn Art Association, exhibition of watercolors, 8–18 Mar. 1881, no. 420; Pennsylvania 1936, no. 32; Carnegie 1937, no. 59; Philadelphia 1953, no. 4; Colorado Springs 1947, no. 15

LITERATURE
"Art Reception in Brooklyn," *New-York Daily Tribune*, 8 Mar. 1881; "Water-Colors in Brooklyn," *(NY) Art Journal* 7 (Apr. 1881): 126

660

Startled

[1878]

Watercolor, 14 × 19½ (35.560 × 49.530) sight
Inscribed ll (probably not in Homer's hand):
Winslow Homer / 79

Private collection

Homer has significantly varied the color scheme of the lady's costume in repeating her image. In No. 659, the version of *Startled* in which beach, sea, and threatening sky occupy more of the sheet than the figure, her dress is red. In this version the coloring—and weather—is more subdued: the lady's bodice and skirt are white and gray, respectively; only her fan is bright red.

ABG: Although not strictly colorless, it is possible this watercolor was the centerpiece of a work catalogued as number 233. *Coney Island*, in the Salmagundi Sketch Club's *First Annual Exhibition of Original Black and White Drawings, Sketches and Etchings & c.*, which opened at the Kurtz Gallery 12 February 1879. The *New York Herald*'s reviewer described it: "In another [frame] are grouped three decidedly impressionistic memoranda of scenes at Coney Island and an incisively drawn, characterful sketch of a pretty, determined girl standing on the beach with set face and threatening fan."

No. 659. Startled

PROVENANCE
Mrs. Kathryn Huber, Florida, nd; (Newhouse Galleries, 1946); Mr. and Mrs. Lawrence A. Fleischman, Detroit, c. 1955); (Kennedy Galleries, c. 1960); Dr. and Mrs. Irving Levitt, Southfield, MI, 1961

LITERATURE
"Fine Arts. The Black and White Exhibition of the Salmagundi Sketch Club," *New York Herald*, 12 Feb. 1879

No. 660. Startled

661

The Sower

[1878]

[Ink]

Unlocated

ABG: Two illustrations by Homer accompanied the article "Glimpses of New England Farm Life" by Rowland E. Robinson published in the August 1878 issue of *Scribner's Monthly*. They represented the most important moments in a farmer's year: spring planting, and autumn harvesting. No drawing for "The Sower" is known to survive, but that for "Pumpkins among the Corn" (No. 662) does.

The detail of the farmer and his plow horses in the background of this scene immediately suggests connection with the watercolor paintings No. 665, No. 666, and No. 668, which focus on this image. The relationship is only in the general facts of the subject, however; nor would Homer have needed a specific model to recreate such a common sight.

See commentary No. 662.

EXHIBITIONS
Art Students' League, New York, [drawings lent by Scribner & Co.], 4 Feb. 1879 [?]

LITERATURE
Rowland E. Robinson, "Glimpses of New England Farm Life," *Scribner's Monthly* 16 (Aug. 1878): 515; "Art Notes," *(NY) Sun*, 16 Feb. 1879

Illustration: "The Sower," Rowland E. Robinson, "Glimpses of New England Farm Life," *Scribner's Monthly* 16 (Aug. 1878): 515

662

Pumpkins among the Corn

[1878]

Ink on cardboard, 7⅜ × 10¾ (18.733 × 27.305)

The Carnegie Museum of Art, Pittsburgh, Andrew Carnegie Fund, 06.3.12

Although Homer had not been a substantial contributor to the illustrated journals since 1874, he returned to the field at isolated intervals well into the 1880s. In the 1860s and earlier 1870s he had executed his graphic designs in the then standard technology: the image was drawn directly on the block and was lost as skilled engravers cut away the wood to make the surface relief fit the printing press. The illustrations captioned "The Sower" and "Pumpkins among the Corn" which accompanied the article "Glimpses of New England Farm Life," published in the *Scribner's Monthly* of August 1878 were created by a different method.

Homer's drawings were reproduced on blocks by photo transfer and served as a basic guide for the engraver, while the original drawing remained at his disposal to serve as his model in creating the illustration. The unusual technique used in this drawing would have been intended to imitate the appearance of the finished engraving as closely as possible. The support is cardboard coated on one side with a white glazing. The masses of the design were washed onto this ground in black ink at full strength and diluted to gray. Homer then drew the details of the scene by scratching lines into the ink layer revealing white lines. Although the original drawing for the "The Sower" is not known to survive, it may be presumed to have been executed by the same method. (See No. 1016, the other surviving example of Homer working in this technique.)

"Pumpkins among the Corn" was engraved on wood, and signed by Henry Wolf. The engraving was used again in a book by Eugene Hall, *Lyrics of Homeland* published by Scribner's in 1881.

ABG: This scene calls to mind the watercolor now known as *The Pumpkin Patch* (No. 748), however, the painting seems likely to be a work of late 1878, and therefore would post-date this *Scribner's* illustration. Homer was hardly a stranger to the appearance of farm fields in autumn, or to rendering them (e.g., see 2:No. 493 and 2:No. 494) and the related *Harper's Weekly* illustration, dating from 1873 and 1874). As with the pendant to this illustration, "The Sower," he would not have needed immediate visual experience of such a scene in order to depict it.

Original source drawings for illustrations became the property of their publishers. They were treated with respect, and were distributed to the firms' owners and senior managers and editors. The New York *Sun* reported on an exhibition of such drawings, which took place in 1879.

One of the most successful and interesting exhibitions that the Art Students' League has given was their last. The Messrs. Scribner & Co. were kind enough to contribute for the occasion over one hundred and fifty original drawings which had been made from time to time for recent numbers of *Scribner's Monthly* and *St. Nicholas* by various artists. Among these were examples of R. Swain Gifford, Arthur Quartley, E. A. Abbey . . . Winslow Homer, ... A majority of the drawings that appear in our magazines are not drawn upon the block, but are transferred to it by the aid of photography. This enables the engraver to have in front of him for constant reference, the original work of the artists, which is a great assistance to him; and if by some awkwardness or mischance the engraving should fail, the loss of the artist's labor is not involved. The publishers, too, gain by it, inasmuch as they acquire uncommon collections of sketches and finished drawings some of which are of little value, while all are interesting.

Excepting a single book illustration done in 1876 for Scribner, Armstrong & Co., up to the time of this occasion at the Art Students' League, the only illustrations Homer had surely done for Scribner's were "The Sower" and "Pumpkins among the Corn".

The Salmagundi Sketch Club's "First Annual Exhibition of Original Black and White Drawings, Sketches and Etchings, &c." opened just a week following the Art Students' League exhibition. Homer's own contribution of sketches were noticed in the press coverage of exhibition, but number 117 in its catalogue, "Pumpkins among the Corn, engraved by H. Wolf, Scribner collection," was not mentioned. It was surely the original art work owned by the Scribner firm which had been on view at the Art Students' League shortly before the Salmagundi event, and given that the Salmagundi defined its exhibition as being of "Original" works, it seems more probable that it was Homer's drawing, rather than Wolf's engraving which was on display. Dr. Josiah Gilbert Holland, a founder, and the first editor of *Scribner's Monthly* purchased Homer's *Husking*—now titled *The Pumpkin Patch*—from the American Water Color Society's 1879 exhibition. It is difficult not to suppose the painting had a special appeal for Dr. Holland because of its similarity to the illustration published in his magazine just six months before the Society's exhibition.

No. 662. Pumpkins among the Corn

PROVENANCE
Scribner & Company, New York, 1878; The Century Company, New York, 1881

EXHIBITIONS
Art Students' League, New York, [drawings lent by Scribner & Co.], 4 Feb. 1879 [?]; Salmagundi Sketch Club, New York, [second annual black and white exhibition, auction], 12–c. 26 Feb. 1879, no. 117; NGA 1958, no. 201; Knoedler 1986, no. 26

LITERATURE
Rowland E. Robinson, "Glimpses of New England Farm Life," *Scribner's Monthly* 16 (Aug. 1878): 520; "Art Notes," *(NY) Sun*, 16 Feb. 1879

No. 663. The School Mistress

663

The School Mistress

nd

Watercolor, 9⅝ × 7¾ (24.448 × 19.685)
Inscribed ll: Homer

The Speed Art Museum, Louisville, KY, gift of
Mr. Henry Strater in memory of Adeline Helene
Strater, 1931.4

ABG: The superficial resemblance between the oil
painting known as *The Red Schoolhouse* (2:No. 424)
and this watercolor presumably supports its titling.
However there is no authority for that topical
identification of either work; the association of the
scene and figure in the oil with the concept of country
school and its teacher has no history earlier than its
passage through the Milch Galleries in 1919.

Dating this painting is problematical. The resemblance to *The Red Schoolhouse* invites assignment
to 1873, the date inscribed on that oil. Stylistically,
however, the watercolor is more comfortable in the
later 1870s. Also, the style of signature Homer used
here is found on other watercolors of this period
(e. g. No. 665, No. 668, and No. 669).

PROVENANCE
Henry Strater, Louisville, KY, nd

EXHIBITIONS
Parthenon 2000

No. 664. The Card Game

664

The Card Game

1878

Graphite, watercolor, 7³⁄₁₆ × 8¹¹⁄₁₆ (18.258 × 22.068)
Inscribed lr: W.H. / July 5th 1878

Museum of Fine Arts, Boston, gift of Maxim
Karolik for the M. and M. Karolik Collection of
American Watercolors, Drawings, and Prints,
1800–1875, 58.906

In October 1940, in response to a New York *Times*
article drawing attention to LG's unending search for
information on, and works by, Winslow Homer,
Dr. Frederick Reynolds brought this drawing to show
to him. Dr. Reynolds told LG it was a momento—
or possibly part of the winnings—of the card game
being played on the porch of John Orr's boarding
house in Mountainville, New York. It was common
at the time for businessmen who could afford it to
send their families out of the summer heat of the

No. 665. Horse and Plowman, Houghton Farm

city to boarding houses or hotels in the country. The men Dr. Reynolds identified (from left): Joe Warren, Charles McNeely, his father, Wakeman F. Reynolds, and George Rice, were likely up from the city visiting their families over the Fourth of July holiday. It is also likely Homer was staying at Orr's, in close proximity to Lawson Valentine's Houghton Farm. Dr. Reynolds told LG he had been six years old at the time, and remembered watching Homer making the drawing.

ABG: Gordon Hendricks decided this drawing was made when Homer was visiting Mr. and Mrs. Charles S. Homer, Jr. at their summer residence in West Townsend, Massachusetts; that the scene is specifically their "veranda;" and the men shown were Homer family friends who were visiting in West Townsend *en masse*. Hendricks says nothing about what may have lead him to these unique conclusions.

PROVENANCE
Wakeman F. Reynolds, New York, 1878; Dr. Frederick G. Reynolds, New York, nd; (Old Print Shop, c. 1957); Maxim Karolik, Newport, RI, 1957

EXHIBITIONS
MFA, Boston, 1977, no. 45

LITERATURE
Hendricks 1979, 133, 138

665

Horse and Plowman, Houghton Farm
[1878]

Watercolor, 6¼ × 11 (15.875 × 27.940)
Inscribed lr: Homer

Berger Collection Educational Trust, Denver Art Museum, PTL-3159

PROVENANCE
Lawson Valentine, New York, c. 1879; Lucy Houghton Valentine (Mrs. Lawson Valentine), 1891; Almira Valentine Pulsifer (Mrs. Nathan Trowbridge Pulsifer), her daughter, 1911; Lawson Valentine Pulsifer, Mountainville, NY, her son, nd; Natalie Pulsifer Byles, his daughter, 1957; Pamela B. Miller, Brooklyn, her daughter, 1976; (Hirschl & Adler Galleries, 1984); (Sotheby's, 25 May 1988, sale 5721, no. 66); private collection, 1988; (Christie's, 5 June 1997, sale 8662, no. 25)

EXHIBITIONS
Storm King 1963, no. 29; Katonah 1963, no. 5; Portland 1998

No. 666. The Plowman

666

The Plowman

[1878]

Watercolor, 12¼ × 19¾ (31.115 × 50.165) sight
Inscribed lr: Homer

Private collection

PROVENANCE
(Wm. A. Butters & Co., Chicago, 10 Dec. 1879,
Homer sale) [?]; Charles D. Hamill, Chicago, probably 1879; Powers Hapgood, Indianapolis, his great-
nephew, before 1911; (William Macbeth, Inc., 1934)

EXHIBITIONS
Butters, Chicago, 1879 [?]; Herron 1911, no. 14

667

Farmhouse on a Hill

1878

Watercolor, 9⅝ × 17½ (24.448 × 44.450)
Inscribed ll: Winslow Homer 1878

Private collection

ABG: This painting is a likely candidate for the work
numbered 356 in the 1879 American Water Color
Society exhibition. The reviewer for the *New York
Herald* "noted Mr. Homer's 'Old House' (356), a
strong landscape, with what seems to us inapposite
reds in cows and foliage." Marianna Van Rensselaer's
description of number 356 as marked by "a deep laven-
der heaven and scarlet cows dabbed in with the same
brush that had been loaded for the autumn sumach
bushes" also seems to apply to *Farmhouse on a Hill*.

PROVENANCE
(Wm. A. Butters & Co., Chicago, 10 Dec. 1879,
Homer sale) [?]; Mrs. Gannon, Chicago, nd; Mrs.
Dallas Phemister, Chicago, her daughter, by bequest,
before 1936; Bruce Phemister, her son, by 1961; (Victor
Spark, 1961); (Hirschl & Adler Galleries, 1966)

EXHIBITIONS
AWS 1879, no. 356 (as *Old House*) [?]; Butters,
Chicago, 1879 [?]; Storm King 1963, no. 19

LITERATURE
"Fine Arts. Water Color Exhibition-Fifth and
Concluding Notice-The Corridor and Black and
White Room," *New York Herald*, 24 Feb. 1879;
M[arianna] G. Van Rensselaer, "Recent Pictures in
New York," *American Architect and Building News* 5
(22 Mar. 1879): 93

No. 667. Farmhouse on a Hill

No. 668. The Last Furrow

668

The Last Furrow

1878

Watercolor, 13½ × 20 (34.290 × 50.800)
Inscribed lr: Homer '78

Karen A. and Kevin W. Kennedy, New York

ABG: In early November 1878, a reporter for the *New York Herald*, making the usual rounds of the studios as the artists returned from their summer absence, paid a visit to Homer. After commenting on "the very admirable water colors and pencil drawings" the artist had made during the summer, the writer went on to notice several pictures Homer was developing from such sketches. His description of "a watercolor drawing . . . . also underway, show[ing] a man and team ploughing in the foreground shade, a house on a hill, and sunset sky" very probably refers to *The Last Furrow. Horse and Plowman, Houghton Farm* (No. 665), *The Plowman* (No. 666), and *Farmhouse on a Hill* (No. 667) would have been among the sketches Homer used to compile the composition of *The Last Furrow*.

The first owner of this watercolor, Alden Finney Brooks (1840–1932) was a successful Chicago painter who worked primarily in portraiture. He was especially impressed by the exhibition Homer mounted at the William A. Butters auction gallery in Chicago in December 1879. In addition to *The Last Furrow*, Brooks acquired *The Chestnut Tree* (No.752) for himself, presumably also from the Butters sale, and urged friends and patrons to purchase from the sale.

Many years later Brooks would accept the opportunity to emulate—literally—Homer's work by taking a commission from the Chicago dealer, J. W. Young, to reproduce the ten watercolors Homer let Young have on consignment in 1907. In a highly imaginative merchandising technique, Young had Brooks paint over black and white, 8 by 10 inch photographs of the Homer paintings, presumably using the originals as models. Brooks's colored reproductions were probably quite accurate duplications, and of a convenient size to be taken or sent to possible purchasers instead of the originals, thus sparing risk of damage or loss of the watercolors.

PROVENANCE
(Wm. A. Butters & Co., Chicago, 10 Dec. 1879, Homer sale) [?]; Alden Finney Brooks, Chicago, 1879; Elizabeth Brooks Maher (Mrs. George W. Maher), Kenilworth, IL, his daughter, 1932; (A. & E. Silbermann Galleries, c. 1947); Dr. John Jay Ireland, Chicago, c. 1948; (Hirschl & Adler Galleries, 1968); Dietrich Foundation, Philadelphia, c. 1972; (Hirschl & Adler Galleries, 1984); private collection, 1984; (Sotheby's, 1 Dec. 1999, sale 7397, no. 136)

EXHIBITIONS
Butters, Chicago, 1879 [?]; AI Chicago 2008

LITERATURE
"Fine Arts. Studio Notes," *New York Herald*, 11 Nov. 1878

No. 669. Cow in Meadow

669

Cow in Meadow

1878

Watercolor, 6 × 10⅞ (15.240 × 27.623)
Inscribed ll: Homer 1878

Private collection

PROVENANCE
Laurence Osterman, Westbury, NY, nd; Cecile
Osterman, Westbury, NY, his daughter, nd; (Hirschl
& Adler Galleries, c. 1980); (Berry-Hill Galleries,
Inc., 1985); (Sotheby's, 4 Dec. 1986, sale 5524, no.
88); private collection, c. 1987; (John H. Surovek
Gallery, Palm Beach, FL, 1989)

No. 670. Cow in Pasture

670

Cow in Pasture

1878

Watercolor, 6½ × 11 (16.510 × 27.940)
Inscribed lr: Homer 1878

Private collection

PROVENANCE
Lawson Valentine, New York, c. 1879; Lucy Houghton
Valentine (Mrs. Lawson Valentine), 1891; Almira
Valentine Pulsifer (Mrs. Nathan Trowbridge Pulsifer),
her daughter, 1911; Lawson Valentine Pulsifer,
Mountainville, NY, her son, nd; Alice Pulsifer Doyle
(Mrs. Joseph Doyle), his daughter, by gift, before
1949; (Sotheby Parke-Bernet, 25 Apr. 1980, sale 4365,
no. 46); (Christie's, 3 June 1983, sale 5372, no. 54-a);
private collection, 1983; (Hammer Galleries, 1987);
(Sotheby's, 1 Dec. 1988, sale 5787, no. 77)

EXHIBITIONS
Storm King 1963, no. 18; Katonah 1963, no. 2

671

A Milkmaid

[1878]

Ink, watercolor, 7¾ × 4⅝ (19.685 × 11.748)
Inscribed lr, on bucket: H

Private collection

This young woman—standing in just this pose,
with her milking stool and pail—is one of the most
frequently repeated images in Homer's oeuvre. She
makes her first appearance in a watercolor of 1874
(2:No. 504), and then in a group of works executed
in 1875: 2:No. 546; 2:No. 547; and 2:No. 548, culminating in the oil *Milking Time* (2:No. 550), in which
she is the principal figure.

This drawing is a page from an album of sketches
apparently contributed to its owner, much as auto-
graphs were contributed to a collector's album.
Frederick Stuart Church and Samuel W. Griggs
made drawings, as did artists whose reputations have
faded from memory; it is likely some of the drawings
in this album were by amateur friends of its owner.
Of those which were dated the earliest were done in
1878. That fact, combined with the reappearance of
the milkmaid figure in a fully realized watercolor of
1878 (No. 672) suggests associating this album page
with 1878, rather than the related works of 1875.

The Clark family who first owned the album were
cousins of the Valentine family.

No. 671. A Milkmaid

PROVENANCE
Alice Clark, nd; Alfred H. Clark, Kansas City, MO,
her brother, by bequest, nd; Mrs. Alfred H. Clark,
by bequest, nd; Mrs. Dorothy Adlow Slonimsky,
Boston, by 1948; (Hirschl & Adler Galleries, 1969);
(Frank Fowler, Lookout Mountain, TN, 1978)

EXHIBITIONS
MFA, Boston, 1959 (not in catalogue)

No. 672. The Milk Maid   see color illustration, p. 420

672

The Milk Maid

1878

Watercolor, 19¾ × 14³⁄₁₆ (50.165 × 36.038)
Inscribed ll: Homer 1878

National Gallery of Art, Washington, DC, gift of
Ruth K. Henschel in memory of her husband,
Charles R. Henschel, 1975.92.11

ABG: This watercolor has been presented as a
Mountainville subject, given its date and bucolic
subject. However, it is clearly a work done in the
studio and combines images from widely different
years and contexts. The milk maid is first seen in
works dated 1874 and 1875 (2:No. 504, 2:No. 546,
2:No. 547, 2:No. 548, and 2:No. 550). The cow
and perhaps other details reflect Homer's 1878
summer travels.

PROVENANCE
Henry C. Valentine, New York, c. 1879; Grace
Barrett Valentine (Mrs. Henry C. Valentine),
Darien, CT, nd; Charles R. Henschel, New York,
c. 1943; Ruth K. Henschel (Mrs. Charles R.
Henschel), New York, 1956

EXHIBITIONS
Century Association, New York, 11 Jan. 1879, no. 53
(as On a Dairy Farm) [?]; Whitney 1944; NGA 1962,
no. 1; Storm King 1963, no. 25; Albright-Knox 1966,
no. 11; NGA 1995, no. 53; NGA 2005

LITERATURE
Marc Simpson, "Revelations for the Eye: Winslow
Homer's Milkmaids," Belvedere 1 (2000): 48–63,
translation 96–104

No. 673. Backyard, Summer

673

Backyard, Summer

[1878]

In the Garden
Watercolor, 6⅝ × 11¼ (16.828 × 28.575)
Inscribed lr: Homer 187

Private collection

This sheet was trimmed at some time, cutting off
the final digit of Homer's inscribed date.

PROVENANCE
Charles W. Bingham, Cleveland, by 1922; Frances
Payne Bolton (Mrs. Chester C. Bolton), Cleveland,
his daughter, 1930

674

Pond and Willows, Houghton Farm

1878

Watercolor, 7 × 8¼ (17.780 × 20.955)
Inscribed ll: Homer 1878

Private collection

ABG: A reporter for the *New York Herald* paid a
visit to Homer's studio in autumn 1878 and noted
he had "made during the summer a number of very
admirable water colors and pencil drawings," and
singled out "a very picturesque [sketch] of willows
by a riverside, a distant mountain and a sunset sky."
This watercolor is a promising match to that
description, and pobably also to the *Willows* Homer
contributed to the American Water Color Society
annual exhibition of 1879. *Willows* was hung in the
Corridor gallery of the National Academy building.
In commenting on that section of the show—and
in the context of denigrating J. Frank Currier's
representation—the *Herald*'s reviewer held Homer
up as the preferable model, especially his *Willows*.

> ... drawings by J. Frank Currier .... are not the
> sort of material he should send to public exhibi-
> tions.... Nothing could point our moral better
> than the landscapes by Winslow Homer, which
> have been admirably hung close to Mr. Currier's
> work. Mr. Homer's "October" (387), "Oak Trees"
> (388), "Corn" (401), "Girl and Boat" (408) and

his very admirable "Willows" (414) are distinctly "impressions" and excellent works, and not "intentions," as somebody has well entitled Mr. Currier's contributions.

Placement in the Corridor gallery is a good—but not infallible—indication of small size; the $50 price Homer set on *Willows* also suggests the moderate scale of the watercolor.

PROVENANCE
Lawson Valentine, New York, c. 1879; Lucy Houghton Valentine (Mrs. Lawson Valentine), 1891; Almira Valentine Pulsifer (Mrs. Nathan Trowbridge Pulsifer), her daughter, 1911; Lawson Valentine Pulsifer, Mountainville, NY, her son, nd; Natalie Pulsifer Byles, his daughter, 1957; Pamela B. Miller, Brooklyn, her daughter, 1976; (Sotheby's, 8 Dec. 1983, sale 5124, no. 75); private collection, 1983

EXHIBITIONS
AWS 1879, no. 414 (as *Willows*) [?]; Brooklyn 1915, no. 22; Storm King 1963, no. 30; Katonah 1963, no. 4

LITERATURE
"Fine Arts. Studio Notes," *New York Herald*, 11 Nov. 1878; "Fine Arts. Water Color Exhibition-Fifth and Concluding Notice-The Corridor and Black and White Room," *New York Herald*, 24 Feb. 1879

No. 674. Pond and Willows, Houghton Farm   see color illustration, p. 421

675

On the Farm

[1878]

Graphite, watercolor, 7³⁄₁₆ × 8½ (18.258 × 21.590)
Inscribed ll: W. H.

Museum of Art, Rhode Island School of Design, Providence, gift of Mrs. Gustav Radeke, 20.471

ABG: On several occasions in the early years of the twentieth century Homer sent William Macbeth portfolios of his drawings from the 1870s and early 1880s. Homer clearly thought of these transactions as outside his usual commercial activity, and made no record of exactly when, how many, or which drawing he let Macbeth show and sell. A Macbeth label on the frame backing of this drawing suggests it came from one of these batches.

PROVENANCE
(William Macbeth, Inc., 1902/1907); Mrs. Gustav Radeke, Providence, c. 1916

EXHIBITIONS
NE Museums 1936

No. 675. On the Farm

676

Two Children in a Field

1878

Graphite, watercolor, 6⅝ × 8⅝ (16.828 × 21.908)
Inscribed ll: Homer 1878

Nasher Museum of Art at Duke University,
Durham, NC, bequest of Nancy Hanks, 1983.10.77

PROVENANCE
(F. W. Bayley & Son, Boston, nd); Hester S.
Cochrane Fearing (Mrs. George R. Fearing, Sr.),
Boston, c. 1922; George R. Fearing, Jr., Westwood,
MA, her son, by gift, by 1936; (Stendahl Galleries,
Los Angeles, c. 1954); Nelson Rockefeller, New York,
c. 1955; Nancy Hanks, Washington, DC, by gift, 1956

No. 676. Two Children in a Field

677

On the Hill

[1878]

Watercolor, 8½ × 11 (21.590 × 27.940) sight
Inscribed lr: Homer

Private collection

ABG: *The Churchman*'s reviewer wrote long and
lavishly on Homer's contribution to the American
Water Color Society exhibition of 1879. He was
particularly taken with Homer's presentation of
young people; *On the Hill* was among the very few
paintings he mentioned with some subject detail.

> Certainly no artist ever marshalled such another
> company of children in any exhibition . . . . They
> are children well suited to the poetical places
> wherein they are pictured and only half belong
> to the ordinary human world; so that among the
> low lights and lengthened shadows they are in
> their own peculiar sphere, and seeming as if the
> mystery of late and early day were finding also
> some expression through them. They sit on hill-
> sides with the air of people who talk of deep and
> wonderful things; and two who are sitting or
> reclining thus, a boy and girl, are so drawn into
> their own shadows lying at their feet, as the light
> slants almost horizontally along the hill that
> shadow and substance are in a manner merged
> so as scarcely to be defined apart (no. 253, West
> Room). . . . These children are the more to be
> wondered at because forming so entire a contrast
> to others in the exhibition.

Both the New York *Daily Graphic* and the *New
York Herald*. reported *On the Hillside* as among the
paintings sold from the Water Color Society *Annual*.

PROVENANCE
unidentified buyer from American Water Color
Society exhibition, 1879; Mrs. Ralph Smillie, nd;
(Wildenstein & Co., c. 1949); (Hirschl & Adler
Galleries, 1955); Alastair Bradley Martin, Glen Head,
NY, 1956; (Martha Parrish & James Reinish, Inc.,
1995); (Guggenheim, Asher Associates, 1995)

EXHIBITIONS
AWS 1879, no. 253; Houston 1952, no. 16; NGA
1958, no. 95; Storm King 1963, no. 27; Whitney 1973,
no. 86; NGA 1986, no. 44

LITERATURE
"The Water-Color Pictures in the New York Academy
II," *The Churchman* 39 (22 Feb. 1879): 208; "Fine
Arts," *(NY) Daily Graphic*, 8 Feb. 1879; "Close of the
Exhibition of the Water Color Society—A Most
Successful Season," *New York Herald*, 2 Mar. 1879

No. 677. On the Hill   see color illustration, p. 422

678

Girl Seated on Hillside Overlooking the Water

1878

Watercolor, 8¾ × 11⁵⁄₁₆ (22.225 × 28.735)
Inscribed ll: 1878 / Winslow Homer

Portland (ME) Museum of Art, gift of Lily W.
Russell, 1998.28

PROVENANCE
Francis Bartlett, Boston, nd; Elizabeth Sears Warren
(Mrs. Bayard Warren), Pride's Crossing, MA, his
granddaughter, by bequest, 1914; Lily Warren
Russell, her daughter, by bequest, 1979

EXHIBITIONS
Storm King 1963, no. 23; Portland 1998

No. 678. Girl Seated on Hillside Overlooking the Water   see color illustration, p. 423

No. 679. On the Fence

679

On the Fence

1878

Watercolor, 6½ × 8½ (16.510 × 21.590)
Inscribed lr: W. H. '78

Private collection

William Howe Downes, author of the biography of Homer, purchased this painting from Frank Bayley on 30 December 1910, approximately three months after Homer's death.

ABG: The New York *Evening Post*, *Sun*, and *Herald* all reported *On the Fence* as having been purchased from the American Water Color Society annual exhibition of 1879, at the price listed in the exhibition catalogue: $75. William Howe Downes was entirely confident that the painting he purchased thirty-one years later was that *On the Fence*; it seems likely his assurance was based on information given him by Frank Bayley; that, in turn, invites speculation that Bayley's source, Horace Hughes, had been the buyer in 1879, or had obtained the painting from that buyer. The specific identification is questionable, however, particularly as the young girl clearly sits on a stone wall rather than a fence. The other 1878 watercolor titled *On the Fence* (No. 721) is the more likely candidate to be the exhibited painting.

PROVENANCE
Horace Hughes, nd; (F. W. Bayley & Son, Boston, nd); William Howe Downes, Boston, 1910; Alfred B. Downes, Boston, his grandson, nd; (Sotheby Parke-Bernet, 19 Oct. 1972, sale 3419, no. 13)

EXHIBITIONS
MFA, Boston, 1911

LITERATURE
"The Water-Color Exhibition. List of Pictures Already Sold," *(NY) Evening Post*, 6 Feb. 1879; "Art Notes," *(NY) Sun*, 10 Feb. 1879; "Close of the Exhibition of the Water Color Society—A Most Successful Season," *New York Herald*, 2 Mar. 1879; Downes 1911, 92, op. 118

680

The Green Hill

1878

On the Hill

Watercolor, 6⅞ × 8¼ (17.463 × 20.955)
Inscribed ll: Homer 1878

National Gallery of Art, Washington, DC, collection
of Mr. and Mrs. Paul Mellon, 1994.59.25

PROVENANCE
Lawson Valentine, New York, c. 1879; Lucy Houghton
Valentine (Mrs. Lawson Valentine), 1891; Almira
Valentine Pulsifer (Mrs. Nathan Trowbridge Pulsifer),
her daughter, 1911; Harold Trowbridge Pulsifer,
New York, her son, nd; Susan Nichols Pulsifer (Mrs.
Harold Trowbridge Pulsifer), in trust, 1948; Alice
Pulsifer Doyle (Mrs. Joseph Doyle), his niece, 1987;
Mr. and Mrs. Paul Mellon, Upperville, VA, 1989

EXHIBITIONS
Metropolitan 1911, no. 27 (as *Hillside*); Brooklyn
1915, no. 24; Bowdoin/Colby 1954; Storm King 1963,
no. 24; Katonah 1963, no. 7; Princeton 1990, no. 11;
NGA 1995, no. 93

No. 680. The Green Hill

No. 681. Shepherdess

681

Shepherdess

1878

Graphite, watercolor, 5⅞ × 8¼ (14.923 × 20.955)
sight
Inscribed ll: W. Homer 1878

Private collection

ABG: This drawing is a source for the unfinished
oil sketch *Shepherd Girl Resting*, (No. 749), and for
the 1880 watercolor painting known as *Daydreaming*
(No. 871).

PROVENANCE
John S. Clark, Brighton, MA, by 1915; (Doll &
Richards, Boston, 1915); Frank C. Smith, Worcester,
MA, 1916

EXHIBITIONS
Worcester 1944, no. 88

682

Girl Resting in a Field

1878

Graphite, watercolor, 7 × 8¼ (17.780 × 20.955)
Inscribed lr: Homer 1878

Private collection

Mr. and Mrs. Charles T. Barney mounted this drawing in a single frame with two other Homer drawings of 1878, No. 684 and No. 718.

ABG: This drawing is a source for the central figure in the watercolors No. 683, and No. 760 of 1879.

PROVENANCE
Charles T. Barney, New York, nd; Mrs. Charles T. Barney, New York, by 1936; James W. Barney, New York, her son, by 1944; (William Macbeth, Inc., 1944); (Wildenstein & Co., 1946); Charles W. Engelhard, Far Hills, NJ, 1956; (Parke-Bernet Galleries, 11 Nov. 1959, sale 1927, no. 11); (Milch Galleries, 1959); Stanley Ross, Maplewood, NJ, nd; (Sotheby's, 3 Dec. 1987, sale 5644, no. 112)

EXHIBITIONS
Wildenstein 1948, no. 1; Wildenstein 1949, no. 16

No. 682. Girl Resting in a Field

683

Shepherdess of Houghton Farm

1878

Watercolor, 11 × 19 (27.940 × 48.260)
Inscribed lr: Winslow Homer 1878

The Sterling and Francine Clark Art Institute, Williamstown, MA, 1955.1483

ABG: In early November 1878, a reporter for the *New York Herald*, making the usual rounds of the studios as the artists returned from their summer absence, paid a visit to Homer. After commenting on "the very admirable water colors and pencil drawings" the artist had made during the summer, the writer went on to notice several pictures Homer was developing from such sketches. One of these was surely this *Shepherdess of Houghton Farm*: "Mr. Homer has started and has well underway a water-color drawing taken from the studies, which is admirably composed. In shadow on the crest of a ridge in gently rolling country lies stretched on the grass, a young girl, surrounded by her sheep. The adjoining rise, on which are a few trees is in full sunlight, up against which the foreground figures are sharply defined."

The figure of the shepherdess is essentially the same figure as that in the drawing *Girl Resting in a Field* (No. 682); the studies of sheep, made in October 1878, No. 740-R, and No. 741 are the sources for the shepherdess' charges. Homer repeated the foreground portion of this composition in his 1879 drawing *Girl and Sheep* (No. 760).

PROVENANCE
(Wm. A. Butters & Co., Chicago, 10 Dec. 1879, Homer sale) [?]; Samuel Raymond, Chicago, probably 1879; Abby M. Raymond, Chicago, his daughter, c. 1918; (William Macbeth, Inc., 1919); (F. W. Bayley & Son, Boston, 1919); unidentified collection/s, c. 1920–c. 1940; (M. A. McDonald, nd); Robert Sterling Clark, New York, 1942

EXHIBITIONS
Century Association, New York, 11 Jan. 1879, no. 55 (as *The Shepherdess*) [?, see also No. 687, No. 702, No. 703]; Butters, Chicago, 1879 [?]; Macbeth 1936, no. 52; Clark AI 1961, no. 19; Clark AI 1986, no. 26; Clark AI 2005

LITERATURE
"Fine Arts. Studio Notes," *New York Herald*, 11 Nov. 1878

No. 683. Shepherdess of Houghton Farm

684

Shepherdess and Flock

[1878]

Graphite, watercolor, 6¾ × 8 (17.145 × 20.320)
Inscribed lr: W. H.

Private collection

Mr. and Mrs. Charles T. Barney mounted this drawing in a single frame with two other Homer drawings of 1878, No. 682 and No. 718.

ABG: This drawing closely resembles the hillside background in the watercolor *Shepherdess of Houghton Farm* (No. 683), but is not necessarily an immediate source.

PROVENANCE
Charles T. Barney, New York, nd; Mrs. Charles T. Barney, New York, by 1936; James W. Barney, New York, her son, by 1944; (William Macbeth, Inc., 1944); (Wildenstein & Co., 1945); David O. Selznick, Beverly Hills, CA, 1946; Jennifer Jones Selznick Simon (Mrs. Norton Simon), Los Angeles, nd; (Parke-Bernet Galleries, 27 Oct. 1971, sale no. 3255, no. 86); (Vose Galleries of Boston, 1971)

No. 684. Shepherdess and Flock

No. 685. Warm Afternoon

685

Warm Afternoon

1878

Shepherdess

Watercolor, 6^{15}/₁₆ × 8⅜ (17.623 × 21.273)
Inscribed ll: Homer 1878

National Gallery of Art, Washington, DC, collection
of Mr. and Mrs. Paul Mellon, 1994.59.24

William Howe Downs described at length this
watercolor and *Green Hill* (No. 680) which had been
lent to the Homer memorial exhibition mounted by
the Metropolitan Museum in 1911 by Mrs. Lawson
Valentine, as examples of Homer's work done at
Houghton Farm in the summer of 1878. He then
stated that the two had been included in the American
Water Color Society annual exhibition of 1879
under the titles *Watching Sheep* and *On the Hill*; the
numbers of those two works in the 1879 exhibition
were 227 and 170, respectively. However, Susan N.
Carter's description of no. 227 in her *Art Journal*
review of the Water Color Society exhibition does
not as neatly correspond to the subject of *Warm
Afternoon* as it does to either *Bo-Peep* (No. 732) or
The Shepherd Girl, Houghton Farm (No. 733).

PROVENANCE
Lawson Valentine, New York, c. 1879; Lucy Houghton
Valentine (Mrs. Lawson Valentine), 1891; Almira
Valentine Pulsifer (Mrs. Nathan Trowbridge Pulsifer),
her daughter, 1911; Harold Trowbridge Pulsifer,
New York, her son, nd; Susan Nichols Pulsifer (Mrs.
Harold Trowbridge Pulsifer), in trust, 1948; Alice
Pulsifer Doyle (Mrs. Joseph Doyle), his niece, 1987;
Mr. and Mrs. Paul Mellon, Upperville, VA, 1989

EXHIBITIONS
Metropolitan 1911, no. 26 (as *Shepherdess*); Brooklyn
1915, no. 18 (as *The Shepherdess, Houghton Farm*);
Bowdoin/Colby 1954; Storm King 1963, no. 36;
Princeton 1990, no. 10; NGA 1995, no. 94; NGA 2005

LITERATURE
Downes 1911, 91–92

686

Sheep and Cattle, Houghton Farm

1878

Watercolor, 6⅞ × 8⅛ (17.463 × 20.638) sight
Inscribed ll: Homer 1878

Fayez Sarofim

This watercolor was not named until Mrs. Pulsifer
lent it to the Brooklyn Institute museum exhibition
of Homer watercolors in 1915. The title under which
it was listed in the exhibition, *Sheep and Cattle,
Houghton Farm* has remained attached to it ever
since. However, the livestock wandering over this
hill is exclusively sheep.

PROVENANCE
Lawson Valentine, New York, c. 1879; Lucy Houghton
Valentine (Mrs. Lawson Valentine), 1891; Almira
Valentine Pulsifer (Mrs. Nathan Trowbridge Pulsifer),
her daughter, 1911; Lawson Valentine Pulsifer,
Mountainville, NY, her son, nd; Alice Pulsifer Doyle
(Mrs. Joseph Doyle), his daughter, 1957; (Coe Kerr
Gallery, 1982); Mr. and Mrs. Charles Ireland,
Birmingham, AL, nd; (Adelson Gallery, c. 1990)

EXHIBITIONS
Brooklyn 1915, no. 25; Storm King 1963, no. 33;
Katonah 1963, no. 1

No. 686. Sheep and Cattle, Houghton Farm

No. 687. Sheep on a Hillside

687

Sheep on a Hillside
[1878]

Watercolor, 13¾ × 19⅞ (34.925 × 50.483)
Inscribed ll: Winslow Homer N. A.

Destroyed

In 1941 Charles L. Homer told LG that his brother and co-heir, Arthur P. Homer had accidentally thrown away this watercolor when he was going through the Homer paintings in Mrs. Charles S. Homer, Jr.'s estate.

   LG had examined and recorded the painting when he met with Mrs. Homer in her New York and West Townsend, Massachusetts, homes; he noted it again when he reviewed her estate collection in storage. Robert W. Macbeth made a formal inventory of the estate in September 1937, taking snapshots of the works as part of his documentation. Macbeth's small photograph is the source of the illustration accompanying this entry. The painting may also be seen in one of the two photographs of the interior of the Benedict building apartment Homer shared

with Samuel T. Preston for part of 1880 and 1881, and again following his return in late 1882 from his extended stay in England.

   Sheep on a Hillside closely resembled *Sheep and Cattle, Houghton Farm* (No. 686). It was substantially larger than No. 686, which suggests it may have been among the several larger paintings developed in his studio by Homer from his small sketches, and was intended for exhibition.

PROVENANCE
Charles S. Homer, Jr., by bequest, 1910; Mrs. Charles S. Homer, Jr., by bequest, 1917; Arthur P. and Charles L. Homer, by bequest, 1937

EXHIBITIONS
Century Association, New York, 11 Jan. 1879, no. 55 (as *The Shepherdess*) [?, see also No. 683, No. 702, No. 703]

688

Sheep in the Meadow

[1878]

Graphite, watercolor, 5½ × 8¾ (13.970 × 22.225)
Inscribed lr: Homer

Private collection

PROVENANCE
(Sotheby's, 26 Oct. 1984, sale 5227, no. 62); private
collection, 1984

No. 688. Sheep in the Meadow

689

Sheep Grazing

1878

Graphite, watercolor, 3 × 7½ (7.620 × 19.050)
Inscribed ll: Homer 78

Private collection

PROVENANCE
(Wm. A. Butters & Co., Chicago, 10 Dec. 1879,
Homer sale) [?]; Eda Hurd Lord (Mrs. George S.
Lord), Evanston, IL, nd; Benjamin K. Smith,
Chicago, by gift, 1914

EXHIBITIONS
Butters, Chicago, 1879 [?]

No. 689. Sheep Grazing

690

Sheep

1878

Graphite, watercolor, 3 × 8½ (7.620 × 21.590)
Inscribed lr: W. H. '78

Private collection

PROVENANCE
Charles S. Homer, Jr., by bequest, 1910; Mrs. Charles
S. Homer, Jr., by bequest, 1917; Mrs. Harold Fowler,
Palm Beach, FL, her cousin, by gift, nd

EXHIBITIONS
Knoedler 1986, no. 30

No. 690. Sheep

No. 691. Sheep Grazing in a Field

691

Sheep Grazing in a Field
[1878]

Graphite, watercolor, 7⅛ × 8½ (18.098 × 21.590)
Inscribed lr: W. H.

Cooper-Hewitt, National Design Museum,
Smithsonian Institution, gift of Charles Savage
Homer, Jr., 1912-12-53

This drawing is a source for the watercolor
Shepherdess Tending Sheep (No. 703).

PROVENANCE
Charles S. Homer, Jr., by bequest, 1910

EXHIBITIONS
Evansville (Indiana) Public Museum [Evansville
Museum of Arts and Science], *Winslow Homer and
Thomas Moran*, 7 Jan.–7 Feb. 1948; Cooper-Hewitt
1972, no. 53

692-R

Sheep Grazing
[1878]

Graphite, 6⅞ × 8⅜ (17.463 × 21.273)
Inscribed cr: W H

Cooper-Hewitt, National Design Museum,
Smithsonian Institution, gift of Charles Savage
Homer, Jr., 1912-12-54

PROVENANCE
Charles S. Homer, Jr., by bequest, 1910

692-V

Hard-a-Port
nd

Charcoal
Inscribed c: Hard - a - Port / [partially erased] A
Quick Passage From Europe

ABG: This rough sketch is conspicuously out of
place among Homer's bucolic themes of the late
1870s. There would be no hesitation in assigning it
a dating in the mid-1880s or later, except that it is
on one side of a sheet on which the more substantial
sketches are of what appear to be the Houghton
Farm sheep fold. There is no convincing explanation
for this incongruity, However, an exchange between
Homer and the Chicago picture dealer, William
O'Brien, Jr., just at the turn of the century seems
to have bearing on the existence of this sketch, and
the more fully realized study also called *Hard-a-Port*
(5:No. 1705) assigned a dating of 1900.

In the autumn of 1898 O'Brien initiated contact
with Homer with a proposition concerning an
exhibition. Homer's letter in reply, dated 23 October
1898, is one of the most characteristic documents
of his artist-as-businessman posture.

> I am in receipt of your letter of Oct the 8th inviting
> me to have an exhibition at your Galleries. In
> reply I would say that I am extremely obliged to
> you for your offer & if I have anything in the
> picture line again, I will remember you. At
> present & for some time past, I see no reason
> why I should paint any pictures.
> P. S. I will paint for money at any time – any
> subject any size.

Two years later O'Brien seems to have taken
Homer up on that post script. Homer wrote
O'Brien on 23 July 1900, "I shall be very happy to
attend to your order & I will submit a sketch to

No. 692-R. Sheep Grazing

you soon – As to the price, that to be fixed when
the picture is completed. The price & Picture to
be perfectly satisfactory to you – or no sale & no
obligation on your part or mine"

On 22 September 1900, Homer followed through
on his promise to submit a sketch.

I send you one subject – (On the Banks) – Hard-
a-Port! – Fog. I do not care to put out any ideas
for pictures — they are too valuable, and can be
appropriated by any art student, defrauding me
out of a possible picture – I will risk this one, & I
assure you that I have some fine subjects to paint.
If that "Oven" cannot keep hot you will have to
do without them; but I will say that when I paint
anything that I think your customer would like,
I will submit it to you. Please return the enclosed
sketch at your convenience.*

It seems more likely Homer sent O'Brien No.
1705, rather than this nearly indecipherable version
of the subject. But then the genesis of this sketch is
difficult to imagine. That Homer used the back of
an old sketch to rough out an idea, preliminary to
making the neater version, No. 1705, is a possibility.

* William O'Brien lent his letters from Homer to
William Howe Downes in November 1910. Downes's
copy is the source of this transcription; the original
letter is unlocated.

No. 692-V. Hard-a-Port

693

Flock of Sheep

[1878]

Graphite, watercolor, 6 × 8⅝ (15.240 × 21.908)
Inscribed ll: Homer

Heide Herz, New York

ABG: Some of these sheep's tails may be recognized
in the watercolor *The Shepherd Girl, Houghton Farm*
(No. 733).

PROVENANCE
George W. H. Ritchie, New York, by gift of Homer,
c. 1890 [?]; Mrs. [George W. H.] Ritchie, nd; Dr.
and Mrs. Herman C. Pitts, Providence, RI, by gift,
1932; Jane Pitts, Boston, their daughter, by 1963;
(Charles D. Childs Gallery, Boston, c. 1977); (Hope
Davis Fine Arts, 1990)

No. 693. Flock of Sheep

694

Girl Seated on a Hillside

[1878]

Graphite, watercolor, 4⅞ × 6¾ (12.383 × 17.145)
Inscribed ll: Homer

Cooper-Hewitt, National Design Museum,
Smithsonian Institution, gift of Charles Savage
Homer, Jr., 1912-12-67

ABG: This study is a source for the highly finished
drawing done in 1879, *Shepherdess* (No. 762).

PROVENANCE
Charles S. Homer, Jr., by bequest, 1910

EXHIBITIONS
Academy of Arts & Letters 1953, no. 163; Ogunquit
1954, no. 19; Lowe, Syracuse, 1979, no. 11

No. 695. Seated Girl in Bonnet

695+

Seated Girl in Bonnet

1878

Graphite, watercolor, 8½ × 6 (21.590 × 15.240)
Inscribed ll: Homer / 1878

Private collection

PROVENANCE
(Wm. A. Butters & Co., Chicago, 10 Dec. 1879,
Homer sale) [?]; Albert Day, Lake Forest, IL, 1879
[?]; James Gamble Rogers, his grandson, nd; Francis
Day Rogers, New York, his son, nd; Pauline Rogers
(Mrs. Francis Day Rogers), New York, by bequest,
1983; children of Pauline Rogers, by bequest, c. 1998;
(Sotheby's, 1 Dec. 1999, sale 7397, no. 122)

EXHIBITIONS
Butters, Chicago, 1879 [?]

696

The Little Shepherdess

1878

Watercolor, 11¾ × 8¾ (29.845 × 22.225)
Inscribed ll: W H. 1878

Cheryl Chase and Stuart Bear

PROVENANCE
Charles T. Barney, New York, nd; Mrs. Charles T.
Barney, New York, by 1936; James W. Barney, New
York, her son, by 1944; (William Macbeth, Inc.,
1944); Bartlett Arkell, New York, 1944; Mrs. Bartlett
Arkell, New York, by bequest, 1946; Elizabeth
Campbell Wilson (Mrs. Stephen A. Wilson), New
York, her daughter, by bequest, 1970; (Spanierman
Gallery, LLC, 1999); private collection, c. 2000

EXHIBITIONS
Vermont Art Center 1957, no. 26; Vermont Art
Center 1964, no. 10

No. 696. The Little Shepherdess

697

Shepherdess with Staff

1878

Graphite, watercolor, 7⅝ × 6½ (19.368 × 16.510)
Inscribed ll: Homer 78

Private collection

In 1939 William Kaula identified a photograph of
this drawing, which LG had sent to him for the
purpose, as a work he acquired at an auction in
New Ipswich, New Hampshire, "sometime during
the World War." If that memory is accurate, then
it may be relevant that New Ipswich was the home
of the Preston family who were close relatives of
Mrs. Charles S. Homer, Jr.

PROVENANCE
(unidentified auction, New Ipswich, NH, c. 1917);
(William J. Kaula, Greenville, NH, c. 1917); (J. W.
McBrine, Boston, nd); Sargent F. Collier, Boston,
by 1939; (Ivan Podgoursky, c. 1946)

No. 697. Shepherdess with Staff

No. 698. The Shepherdess

698

The Shepherdess

[1878]

Graphite, watercolor, 8¾ × 13¾ (22.225 × 34.925) sight
Inscribed ll: Winslow Homer

Private collection

PROVENANCE
Mrs. Kathryn Huber, Florida, nd; (Newhouse Galleries, 1946); (Wildenstein & Co., 1946); Thelma Chrysler Foy (Mrs. Byron C. Foy), 1947; (Parke-Bernet Galleries, 13 May 1959, sale 1905, no. 5); (M. Knoedler & Co., 1959); Steven Juvelis, Lynn, MA, nd; (Anthony Olivo, Providence, RI, 1972); (Hirschl & Adler Galleries, 1972); Mr. and Mrs. Llewellyn Boyd, by 1987

EXHIBITIONS
Wildenstein 1947, no. 94

699

Standing Shepherdess with Her Flock

[1878]

Graphite, watercolor, 9 × 12½ (22.860 × 31.750)
Inscribed ll: Winslow Homer

Private collection

PROVENANCE
Mrs. Irving T. Snyder, Coronado, CA, nd; Henry Bonnell, her son, by bequest, c. 1980; (John E. Parkerson & Company, Houston, 1986)

No. 699. Standing Shepherdess with Her Flock

700

The Shepherdess

[1878]

Graphite, watercolor, 8½ × 12½ (21.590 × 31.750)
Inscribed ll: Homer

Private collection

ABG: This and the closely related drawing and watercolors also of 1878, No. 701, No. 702, and No. 703, are fundamental to the fully developed oil *Shepherdess* (No. 770) of 1879.

PROVENANCE
(Wm. A. Butters & Co., Chicago, 10 Dec. 1879, Homer sale) [?]; Eda Hurd Lord (Mrs. George S. Lord), Evanston, IL, nd; (J. W. Young Galleries, Chicago, 1918); C. W. Dilworth, Chicago, nd; Paul Schulze, Chicago, by 1939; Helen Bennitt (Mrs. Benjamin A. Bennitt, Sr.), his granddaughter, nd; private collection, by bequest, c. 2003; (Gerald Peters Gallery, nd)

EXHIBITIONS
Butters, Chicago, 1879 [?]

No. 700. The Shepherdess

No. 701. The Shepherdess

701

The Shepherdess

1878

Graphite, watercolor, 9½ × 13½ (24.130 × 34.290)
Inscribed ll: Homer 1878

Private collection

ABG: This and the closely related drawing and
watercolors also of 1878, No. 700, No. 702, No. 703,
and No. 704, are fundamental to the fully developed
oil *Shepherdess* (No. 770) of 1879.

PROVENANCE
(M. Knoedler & Co., by 1932); Horace D. Chapin,
Boston, 1932; (M. Knoedler & Co., 1934); Sargent
F. Collier, Boston, 1939; (M. Knoedler & Co., nd);
(Valentine Gallery, 1944); (Parke-Bernet Galleries,
9–10 Apr. 1947, sale 859, no. 6); (Wildenstein & Co.,
1947); Harry Golding, after 1952; (Christie's,
London, 30 Nov. 1976, sale Estella, no. 14); (Hirschl
& Adler Galleries, 1976); Paul Magriel, New York,
1977; private collection, 1978; (Christie's, 23 May
2001, sale 9654, no. 6); (Hollis Taggart Galleries, 2001)

EXHIBITIONS
IMA, Boston, 1941, no. d-10/11; Wildenstein 1948,
no. 4; Wildenstein 1949, no. 17; Houston 1952, no. 30

No. 702. The Young Shepherdess

702

The Young Shepherdess

1878

Watercolor, 11½ × 19 (29.210 × 48.260)
Inscribed ll: Winslow Homer N. A. '78

Private collection

In 1939 Montgomery Schuyler, Jr. told LG that his father had been an editor of the *New-York Times*, and an architecture critic, "and knew a lot of artists, including Homer Martin (very well), and Winslow Homer (not so well). He says his father undoubtedly got this picture directly from Homer." The younger Mr. Schuyler's assumption of a personal acquisition has a better chance of being accurate than is usual with such histories. The Schuyler family was prominent in the social and cultural life of New York. The purchase of this watercolor could have been made from the artist directly or from some some formal exhibition.

ABG: This watercolor and the closely similar *Shepherdess Tending Sheep* (No. 703) are of such a substantial size and high degree of finish to make either a candidate to be *The Shepherdess* Homer contributed to the exhibition mounted for the Century Association monthly reception and meeting of November 1879.

Both watercolors, with the closely related drawings No. 700 and No. 701, are fundamental to the fully developed oil *Shepherdess* (No. 770) of 1879.

PROVENANCE
Montgomery Schuyler, Sr., New York, nd;
Montgomery Schuyler, Jr., New York, 1914;
(Wildenstein & Co., by 1946); Mr. and Mrs.
Lawrence A. Fleischman, Detroit, 1954; (Hirschl & Adler Galleries, 1964); Mr. and Mrs. Stephen Currier, New York, c. 1965; Estate of Mr. and Mrs. Stephen Currier, c. 1970; (Christie's, 1 June 1984, sale 5580, no. 65a)

EXHIBITIONS
Century Association, New York, 11 Jan. 1879, no. 55
(as *The Shepherdess*) [?, see also No. 683, No. 687, No. 703]; Whitney 1944; Wildenstein 1947, no. 49; Wildenstein 1948, no. 3; Houston 1952, no. 15 (as *Shepherdess of Houghton Farm*); Storm King 1963, no. 34; University of Arizona 1963, no. 51 (as *Shepherdess of Houghton Farm*)

No. 703. Shepherdess Tending Sheep

703

Shepherdess Tending Sheep

1878

Watercolor, 11⁹⁄₁₆ × 19¾ (29.370 × 50.165)
Inscribed ll: Winslow Homer 1878

Brooklyn Museum of Art, Dick S. Ramsay Fund,
41.1088

The sheep at lower right, who gazes out at the
viewer, is the principal subject of the drawing *Sheep
Grazing in a Field* (No. 691).

ABG: A reporter for the *New York Herald* paid a
visit to Homer's studio in autumn 1878 and noted
he had "made during the summer a number of very
admirable water colors and pencil drawings of sheep,
with shepherds and shepherdesses. . . . Among the
best we note . . . a girl standing under a stormy sky
with her sheep by her," which is a description
appropriate to this painting.

   This watercolor and the closely similar *The
Shepherdess* (No. 702) are of such a substantial size
and high degree of finish to make either a candidate
to be *The Shepherdess* Homer contributed to the
exhibition mounted for the Century Association
monthly reception and meeting of November 1879.

Both watercolors, with the closely related drawings
No. 700 and No. 701, are fundamental to the fully
developed oil *Shepherdess* (No. 770) of 1879.

   In May 1888 Henry Valentine lent a watercolor
under the title *Shepherdess* to a Union League Club
exhibition. He owned two Homer watercolors to
which that titling was appropriate: this painting and
Fresh Air (No. 735). Either could have been the work
in that exhibition. However, *Fresh Air* is the more
likely choice as it is the more imposing composition
of the two.

PROVENANCE
Henry C. Valentine, New York, nd; Grace Barrett
Valentine (Mrs. Henry C. Valentine), Darien, CT,
nd; (Victor Spark, c. 1940)

EXHIBITIONS
Century Association, New York, 11 Jan. 1879,
no. 55 (as *The Shepherdess*) [?, see also No. 683,
No. 687, No. 702]; Union League Club, New York,
Exhibition of Water Colors, 10–12 May 1888, no. 46
(as *Shepherdess*) [?]; Storm King 1963, no. 35;
Metropolitan/Brooklyn 1972, no. 49; Nelson-Atkins
2001 (Los Angeles County and High, only)

LITERATURE
"Fine Arts. Studio Notes," *New York Herald*,
11 Nov. 1878

No. 704. Four Leaf Clover, Houghton Farm

704

Four Leaf Clover, Houghton Farm

[1878]

Watercolor, $6^{11}/_{16} \times 11^{11}/_{16}$ (16.988 × 29.688)
Inscribed lr: Winslow Homer

Private collection

ABG: The four-leaf clover, and, presumably, the magic qualities associated with it, attracted Homer's attention throughout the 1870s. See 2:No. 380, 2:No. 427, 2:No. 569, 2:No. 570, as well as the near replica of *Four Leaf Clover, Houghton Farm*, No. 705.

Homer placed over seventy drawings and watercolors at auction under the auspices of Daniel Mathews in March 1880. From the ample press coverage of this event it is clear that the majority of the works dated from 1878 and 1879. The *New-York Times* implied that all were sold "at fair prices," and in listing what were presumably examples of the higher amounts paid, named "'The Four-leaved Clover' $20.50." The buyer may have been Samuel V. Wright.

In December the same year the New York *World* reported,

> Mr. Samuel V. Wright of this city, having deter-
> mined to spend several years abroad, caused his
> collection of ceramic wares and of pictures to
> be sold at auction at the Leavitt Gallery, No. 817
> Broadway, yesterday . . . . In the evening the pic-
> tures, ninety-nine in number were sold . . . . There

were two pictures by Winslow Homer, one of a tall girl in white, in a grove "Waiting," [possibly *The Trysting Place* (2:No. 568)] which brought $30 and the other "The Four-leaved Clover," which sold for $35.

The heading for this article refers to Mr. Wright's "Bric A Brac and Paintings," which at the time carried the implication the art works were oils. However, the prices realized were more appropriate to watercolors. If Mr. Wright's *Four-leaved Clover* was a watercolor then it could have been either this painting or No. 705. However, given No. 705's history of ownership rooted in Chicago, this *Four Leaf Clover, Houghton Farm* is the more likely of the two versions of the subject to have been Mr. Wright's—and to have been purchased from the Leavitt auction by Lawson Valentine.

PROVENANCE
(Daniel A. Mathews Art Gallery, 4 Mar. 1880, Homer sale) [?]; Samuel V. Wright, New York, 1880 [?]; (Geo. A. Leavitt & Co., 16 Dec. 1880, Samuel V. Wright sale) [?]; Lawson Valentine, New York, nd; Lucy Houghton Valentine (Mrs. Lawson Valentine), 1891; Almira Valentine Pulsifer (Mrs. Nathan Trowbridge Pulsifer), her daughter, 1911; Lawson Valentine Pulsifer, Mountainville, NY, her son, nd; Alice Pulsifer Doyle (Mrs. Joseph Doyle), his daugh-ter, 1957; (Hirschl & Adler Galleries, c. 1972); Mrs.

Parker Cushman, Houston, 1973; private collection, nd; (Gerald Peters Gallery, Santa Fe, NM, nd); private collection, by 1990; (Christie's, 19 May 2005, sale 1520, no. 94)

EXHIBITIONS
Mathews 1880; Geo. A. Leavitt & Co., New York, [Samuel V. Wright collection, auction], 13–16 Dec. 1880; Brooklyn 1915, no. 27; Storm King 1963, no. 22; University of Arizona 1963, no. 46

LITERATURE
"Winslow Homer's Water-colors," *New-York Times*, 5 Mar. 1880; "Mr. Wright's Bric A Brac and Paintings," *(NY) World*, 17 Dec. 1880

705

Girl Picking Clover

[1878]

Watercolor, 7 × 12¼ (17.780 × 31.115)
Inscribed lr: Homer

Canton (OH) Museum of Art, James C. and Barbara J. Koppe Collection, 992.4

ABG: See commentary No. 704.

Mrs. Grace Earle Harrison, the earliest identified owner of this painting, was described to LG by her great-granddaughter as a painter, whose life span was 1882 to 1945, and who had lived in Chicago. Grace Harrison is briefly noted in artist lexicons, but without more information than that she was born in New York.

PROVENANCE
(Wm. A. Butters & Co., Chicago, 10 Dec. 1879, Homer sale) [?]; Mrs. Grace Earle Harrison, Chicago, nd; Mrs. Mary Harrison Leach, her daughter, nd; Mrs. Helen Leach Elston, her daughter, nd; Elizabeth Elston Ross, Oakland, CA, her daughter by gift, c. 1973; (Hirschl & Adler Galleries, 1983); private collection, 1983; (Taggart, Jorgenson & Putnam, Washington, DC, 1986); United States Fidelity and Casualty Co., Baltimore, MD, 1986; (Keny Galleries, Columbus, OH, nd)

EXHIBITIONS
Butters, Chicago, 1879 [?]

LITERATURE
"Winslow Homer's Water-colors," *New-York Times*, 5 Mar. 1880; "Mr. Wright's Bric A Brac and Paintings," *(NY) World*, 17 Dec. 1880

No. 705. Girl Picking Clover

see color illustration, p. 424

No. 706. Girl and Daisies

706

Girl and Daisies

1878

Watercolor, 6 × 6⅞ (15.240 × 17.463)
Inscribed lr: Homer / 1878

Museum of Art, Rhode Island School of Design, Providence, bequest of Isaac C. Bates, 13.811

ABG: A painting titled *The Daisies* was among the more than seventy watercolors and drawings Homer put up for auction by Daniel Mathews in March 1880. *Daisies* by Homer was lot number 24 in the Leonard & Co., Boston, sale of "The Private Collection of S. H. Linn, M. D. with additions from private collections and estates," held 6–8 February 1896. On neither occasion was the named work described, so there is nothing but appropriate titling to suggest connection with *Girl and Daisies*.

PROVENANCE
(Daniel A. Mathews Art Gallery, 4 Mar. 1880, Homer sale) [?]; (Leonard & Company, Boston, 8 Feb. 1896, S. H. Linn, et. al sale, no. 24) [?]; Isaac Comstock Bates, Providence, RI, nd

EXHIBITIONS
Mathews 1880 (as *The Daisies*) [?]; Leonard & Co., Boston, . . . *Collection of S. H. Linn, M.D. with additions from private collections and estates* [auction], 6–8 Feb. 1896, no. 24 (as *The Daisies*) [?]; RISD 1931, no. 23; Fogg 1932, no. 39; NE Museums 1936

No. 707. Girl in Garden

707

Girl in Garden

1878

Watercolor, 6¾ × 8½ (17.145 × 21.590)
Inscribed ll: Homer / 1878

Scripps College, Claremont, CA, gift of General and Mrs. Edward Clinton Young, YO25

PROVENANCE
(F. W. Bayley & Son, Boston, c. 1910); Henry Sayles, Boston, 1910; (American Art Association, 14–15 Jan. 1920, various owners sale, no. 96); (Milch Galleries, 1920); Gen. and Mrs. Edward Clinton Young, Scarsdale, NY, c. 1928

EXHIBITIONS
MFA, Boston, 1911 (as *Sketch*); NGA 1995, no. 101

708
Apple Picking
1878

In the Orchard

Watercolor, 7 × 8⅜ (17.780 × 21.273)
Inscribed lr: Homer / 1878

Terra Foundation for American Art, Daniel J. Terra
Collection, Chicago, 1992.7

ABG: A representative of the *New York Herald*
probably was referring to this watercolor when on
his early November 1878 visit to Homer's studio
he reported that the artist had "made during the
summer, a number of very admirable water colors
and pencil drawings . . . . Among the best are . . .
two girls standing in the sunlight with their faces
in the shadow of their hats."

   Of Homer's surviving watercolors of this period
Apple Picking most closely approximates the
description of *In the Orchard* given by the New
York *Evening Post*'s reviewer of the American Water
Color Society annual exhibition of 1879.

> It would perhaps be impossible to make Mr.
> Currier or Mr. Homer, or many of their friends
> feel [they "lack unity of pictorial effect"] but the
> statement is true nevertheless and will be seen to
> be true by the unprejudiced spectator who will
> take the most nearly perfect of Mr. Homer's
> twenty nine, the "In the Orchard," in the west
> room . . . . The moment you get near enough to
> see well Mr. Homer's two charming girls "In the
> Orchard," your attention is diverted to his fantastic
> treatment of the dresses they wear and the trees
> in the background. You ask yourself: Is a tree in
> nature ever of the same tint all over? Is even its
> trunk of the same tint? Are its leaves ever only
> green? The sunshine that plays about these rural
> maids, and wraps their brown faces in shadow—
> has it no relations with the tints of these trees?"

The *Post* and the New York *Daily Graphic* reported
In the Orchard as among the earliest sales made from
the Society's *Annual* even before this review had
appeared in print.

No. 708. Apple Picking   see color illustration, p. 425

PROVENANCE
George S. Robbins, Connecticut, nd; Edward C.
Robbins, Haverford, PA, his son, nd; (Hirschl &
Adler Galleries, 1975); private collection, nd;
(Kennedy Galleries, 1981); private collection, 1981;
(Thomas Colville Fine Art, LLC, New Haven, by 1991)

EXHIBITIONS
AWS 1879, no. 234 (as *In the Orchard*) [?]; NGA
1986, no. 38; NGA 1995, no. 95; Nelson-Atkins 2001
(Nelson-Atkins, only); AI Chicago 2008

LITERATURE
"Fine Arts. Studio Notes," *New York Herald*, 11 Nov.
1878; "The Water-Color Exhibition. List of Pictures
Already Sold," *(NY) Evening Post*, 6 Feb. 1879; "Fine
Arts," *(NY) Daily Graphic*, 8 Feb. 1879; "American
Art in Water-Colors. The Twelfth Annual Exhibition
of the Water-Color Society . . . I," *(NY) Evening Post*,
11 Feb. 1879

No. 709. Girl Standing by a Tree

709

Girl Standing by a Tree

[1878]

Graphite, 6 × 8½ (15.240 × 21.590)
Inscribed ll: Homer

Private collection

See No. 710, No. 711 and No. 753 for closely
related images.

PROVENANCE
(Sotheby's, 20 June 1985, sale 5353, no. 110A);
(Thomas Colville Fine Art, LLC, New Haven, 1985);
(Adams-Davidson Galleries, Washington, DC,
1986); private collection, c. 1986; (Hollis Taggart
Galleries, 1996); (Thomas Colville Fine Art, LLC,
New Haven, 1996)

No. 710. A Shady Spot, Houghton Farm

710

A Shady Spot, Houghton Farm

1878

Watercolor, 7 × 8½ (17.780 × 21.590)
Inscribed lr: H 1878

Private collection

PROVENANCE
Lawson Valentine, New York, c. 1879; Lucy
Houghton Valentine (Mrs. Lawson Valentine), 1891;
Almira Valentine Pulsifer (Mrs. Nathan Trowbridge
Pulsifer), her daughter, 1911; Lawson Valentine
Pulsifer, Mountainville, NY, her son, nd; Natalie
Pulsifer Byles, his daughter, 1957; Pamela B. Miller,
Brooklyn, her daughter, 1976; (Christie's, 5 Dec.
2002, sale 1124, no. 23)

EXHIBITIONS
Brooklyn 1915, no. 19; Whitney 1936, no. 44;
Carnegie 1937, no. 97; Storm King 1963, no. 32;
Katonah 1963, no. 6; AI Chicago 2008

711

Weary

[1878]

Watercolor, 9½ × 12¼ (24.130 × 31.115)
Inscribed lr: Homer

Terra Foundation for American Art, Daniel J. Terra
Collection, Chicago, 1992.41

See No. 709, No. 710 and No. 753 for closely
related images.

PROVENANCE
Lawson Valentine, New York, c. 1878; Lucy
Houghton Valentine (Mrs. Lawson Valentine), 1891;
Almira Valentine Pulsifer (Mrs. Nathan Trowbridge
Pulsifer), her daughter, 1911; Lawson Valentine
Pulsifer, Mountainville, NY, her son, nd; Alice
Pulsifer Doyle (Mrs. Joseph Doyle), his daughter,
1957; (Davis & Long Co., 1978); Daniel Terra,
Chicago, 1978

EXHIBITIONS
Brooklyn 1915, no. 29; Carnegie 1917, no. 3; NGA
1958/MFA, Boston, 1959, no. 94/87; Storm King
1963, no. 41; Katonah 1963, no. 3; Terra 1981; NGA
1986, no. 46; NGA 1995, no. 92; Nelson-Atkins 2001
(High, only); AI Chicago 2008

No. 711. Weary

No. 712. Out on a Limb

No. 713. Boy and Girl on a Hillside

712

Out on a Limb

[1878]

Watercolor, 6 × 8 (15.240 × 20.320)
Inscribed lr: Homer

Private collection

PROVENANCE

Mrs. Margaret Prenty, nd; Arthur G. Wright, Massapequa, NY, by bequest, 1945; unnamed mother of Mrs. Stollburger, after 1965; Mrs. Stollburger, by 1983; (Christie's, 9 Dec. 1983, sale 5472, no. 87); (Hirschl & Adler Galleries, 1984)

713

Boy and Girl on a Hillside

1878

Watercolor, 8¹⁵⁄₁₆ × 11¹⁵⁄₁₆ (22.703 × 30.323)
Inscribed lr: Homer 1878

Museum of Fine Arts, Boston, bequest of Katherine Dexter McCormick, 68.568

LG examined Mrs. Katherine Dexter McCormick's five watercolor paintings and three drawings by Homer in her Boston home, in September 1938. (The other seven works are 2:No. 464, No. 713, No. 801, No. 803, No. 814, No. 825, and No. 861.) Mrs. McCormick said they all had been acquired by her mother, Mrs. Wirt Dexter, at an auction in Chicago "in 1876." Mrs. McCormick or Mrs. Dexter's memory was evidently slightly imperfect: all their Homers date from 1878 or 1879, excepting 2:No. 463, an 1873 drawing.

ABG: Marianna Van Rensselaer exactly described the exceptional feature of this painting in her *American Architect and Building News* review of the American Water Color Society 1879 exhibition: "In No. 323 [*Girl and Boy*] we had a sky of untouched white paper, with figures and grass in heavy dark tints."

PROVENANCE

(Wm. A. Butters & Co., Chicago, 10 Dec. 1879, Homer sale) [?]; Mrs. Wirt Dexter, Chicago, probably 1879; Katherine Dexter McCormick (Mrs. Stanley McCormick), Boston, her daughter, probably 1937

AWS 1879, no. 323 (as *Girl and Boy*); Butters, Chicago, 1879 [?]; MFA, Boston, 1959 (not in catalogue); University of Arizona 1963, no. 74; MFA, Boston, 1977, no. 44; MFA, Boston, 1993/ 1996, no. 48/9; Nelson-Atkins 2001 (Los Angeles County and High, only)

LITERATURE

M[arianna] G. Van Rensselaer, "Recent Pictures in New York," *American Architect and Building News* 5 (22 Mar. 1879): 93

714

Shy Sweethearts

1878

Watercolor, 11¼ × 8¾ (28.575 × 22.225)
Inscribed ll: Homer 78; lr: Homer 1878

Private collection

Homer executed this watercolor on a conventionally proportioned rectangular sheet, (ratio of 3 to 4), and then apparently thought better of the composition. Light, ruler-straight lines indicate the area of the painting which was allowed to be visible within the mat aperture. Three-quarters of an inch along the lower edge, and 2½ inches at the right side were to be covered, thus reshaping the image to 10½ by 6¼ inches, focussed on the figures. (The obscured portion of the image is a featureless continuation of the hill and meadow where the children stand.) It may be accepted that Homer made this adjustment, because he signed the work twice: in paint at the lower right corner of the full sheet, and in pencil at lower left, just above the line marking the change in proportion.

PROVENANCE

Lawson Valentine, New York, c. 1879; Lucy Houghton Valentine (Mrs. Lawson Valentine), 1891; Almira Valentine Pulsifer (Mrs. Nathan Trowbridge Pulsifer), her daughter, 1911; Lawson Valentine Pulsifer, Mountainville, NY, her son, nd; Natalie Pulsifer Byles, his daughter, 1957; Pamela B. Miller, Brooklyn, her daughter, 1976; (Sotheby's, 29 May 1986, sale 5463, no. 86)

EXHIBITIONS

Brooklyn 1915, no. 20 (as *Shy Sweethearts, Houghton Farm. 1*); Storm King 1963, no. 38; University of Arizona 1963, no. 18

No. 714. Shy Sweethearts

No. 715. Fishing

715

Fishing

[1878]

Charcoal, watercolor, 8¹³⁄₁₆ × 10⁹⁄₁₆ (22.385 × 26.830)
Inscribed lr: W. H.

Private collection

This drawing is a source for the 1878 watercolor (No. 716), and 1879 oil (No. 763), both also titled *Fishing*.

LG examined this drawing in January 1968. He noted the following observations at that time: "The initials at lower right, W. H. are in pencil ([the inscription] shines, and is lead-colored, not black). The blacks in the drawing itself are really black. In my opinion this is a genuine Homer drawing [however] the signature is a later addition. It is not written as Homer would have done: it is not *alla prima*, but is *gone over*. The writing is weak [and] also in pencil, unlike the rest of the drawing."

PROVENANCE

John G. Pierce, Milton, MA, nd; Mrs. John G. Pierce, Milton, MA, by bequest, nd; Fessenden School, Newton, MA, by gift, c. 1960; (John Nicholson Gallery, 1967); private collection, nd; (ACA Galleries, nd); Herbert A. Goldstone, New York, nd; (ACA Galleries, 1998); (William Vareika Fine Arts, Ltd., Newport, RI, 1999); private collection, 2002; (Sotheby's, 23 May 2007, sale 8322, no. 5)

716

Fishing

1878

Watercolor, 7 × 8½ (17.780 × 21.590)
Inscribed lr: Homer / 1878

Colby College Museum of Art, Waterville, ME,
The Lunder Collection

This watercolor may be presumed to have been
based on the drawing of the same name, No. 715.
Homer executed a nearly identical rendering of the
subject in oil in 1879; see No. 763.

PROVENANCE
(Weyhe Gallery, 1946); private collection, by 1959;
(Sotheby's, 21 May 2003, sale 7904, no. 170); Peter
Lunder, 2003

EXHIBITIONS
Storm King 1963, no. 20; AI Chicago 2008

No. 716. Fishing   see color illustration, p. 426

717+

Boy and Girl in a Landscape

1878

Graphite, watercolor, 8½ × 7 (21.590 × 17.780)
Inscribed lr: Winslow Homer 1878

Private collection

PROVENANCE
(Wm. A. Butters & Co., Chicago, 10 Dec. 1879,
Homer sale) [?]; Albert Day, Lake Forest, IL, 1879
[?]; James Gamble Rogers, his grandson, nd; Francis
Day Rogers, New York, his son, nd; Pauline Rogers
(Mrs. Francis Day Rogers), New York, by bequest,
1983; children of Pauline Rogers, by bequest, c. 1998;
(Sotheby's, 1 Dec. 1999, sale 7397, no. 121); (Babcock
Galleries, nd)

EXHIBITIONS
Butters, Chicago, 1879 [?]

No. 717. Boy and Girl in a Landscape

No. 718. Girl Picking Apples

718
Girl Picking Apples
[1878]

Graphite, watercolor, 7 × 8¼ (17.780 × 20.955)
Inscribed lr: W H

Private collection

Mr. and Mrs. Charles T. Barney mounted this drawing in a single frame with two other Homer drawings of 1878, No. 682 and No. 684.

PROVENANCE
Charles T. Barney, New York, nd; Mrs. Charles T. Barney, New York, by 1936; James W. Barney, New York, her son, by 1944; (William Macbeth, Inc., 1944); (Wildenstein & Co., 1946); Mrs. Dunbar Bostwick, New York, 1956; (Wildenstein & Co., c. 1962); (Country Store Gallery, Inc., Austin, TX, 1967)

EXHIBITIONS
Wildenstein 1947, no. 95; Wildenstein 1948, no. 6; Wildenstein 1949, no. 18

No. 719. Two Figures by a Fence

719
Two Figures by a Fence
[1878]

Graphite, watercolor, 4⅝ × 6¾ (11.748 × 17.145)
Inscribed lr: W H 187[8]

Private collection

PROVENANCE
(Wm. A. Butters & Co., Chicago, 10 Dec. 1879, Homer sale) [?]; Mrs. Converse, 1879 [?]; unidentified daughter of Mrs. Converse, nd; William G. Caskey, Oberlin, OH, by gift, 1874; Mrs. William G. Caskey, nd; Ellen C. Zinn, Evanston, IL, her niece, by gift, 1965; (R. H. Love Galleries, Inc., Chicago, 1983); (Hirschl & Adler Galleries, 1994)

EXHIBITIONS
Butters, Chicago, 1879 [?]

No. 720. Feeding Time

720

Feeding Time

[1878]

Watercolor, 8¾ × 11¼ (22.225 × 28.575)
Inscribed lr: Homer

The Sterling and Francine Clark Art Institute,
Williamstown, MA, 1955.1493

ABG: See commentary No. 721.

PROVENANCE
William C. Oberwalder, New York, nd; (M.
Knoedler & Co., 1926); Robert Sterling Clark,
New York, 1926

EXHIBITIONS
AWS 1879, no. 170 (as *On the Fence*) [?, see also
No. 721]; Clark AI 1961, no. 17; Clark AI 1986,
no. 27; NGA 1995, no. 90; Clark AI 2005

No. 721. On the Fence

see color illustration, p. 428

Either this painting or the watercolor known as *Feeding Time* (No. 720) is more accurately described by the title, *On the Fence* and either is a more likely candidate to be the work shown in the Water Color Society exhibition. It should be noted that the boy and girl in No. 720 are literally on a fence, where the boy in No. 721 is shown balanced on a tree branch, above the fence on which the girl stands. If No. 721 were the *On the Fence* seen in the Society's exhibition, then the title was a suggestion that the boy was trying to decide whether to give up his perch in favor of joining the young lady.

PROVENANCE
Lawson Valentine, New York, c. 1879; Lucy Houghton Valentine (Mrs. Lawson Valentine), 1891; Almira Valentine Pulsifer (Mrs. Nathan Trowbridge Pulsifer), her daughter, 1911; Harold Trowbridge Pulsifer, New York, her son, nd; Susan Nichols Pulsifer (Mrs. Harold Trowbridge Pulsifer), in trust, 1948; Alice Pulsifer Doyle (Mrs. Joseph Doyle), his niece, 1987

EXHIBITIONS
AWS 1879, no. 170 (as *On the Fence*) [?, see also No. 720]; Brooklyn 1915, no. 26; Storm King 1963, no. 26; Princeton 1990, no. 8; NGA 1995, no. 98; NGA 2005

LITERATURE
"The Water-Color Exhibition. List of Pictures," *(NY) Evening Post*, 6 Feb. 1879; "Art Notes," *(NY) Sun*, 10 Feb. 1879; "Close of the Exhibition of the Water Color Society—A Most Successful Season," *New York Herald*, 2 Mar. 1879; Downes 1911, 92

721

On the Fence

1878

Watercolor, 11¼ × 8¹¹⁄₁₆ (28.575 × 22.068)
Inscribed ll: Homer 1878

National Gallery of Art, Washington, DC, collection of Mr. and Mrs. Paul Mellon, 1994.59.22

ABG: The New York *Evening Post, Sun*, and *Herald* all reported *On the Fence* as having been purchased from the American Water Color Society annual exhibition of 1879, at the price listed in the exhibition catalogue: $75. William Howe Downes was entirely confident that No. 679, the painting he purchased thirty-one years later was that *On the Fence*. Downes did not tell LG what evidence he had for his belief; he probably accepted the assurance of the dealer from whom he purchased the painting. However, the young girl in No. 679 clearly sits on a stone wall rather than a fence.

722

Girl with Hay Rake

1878

Girl with Half a Rake

Watercolor, 6¹⁵⁄₁₆ × 8⁷⁄₁₆ (17.623 × 21.433)
Inscribed lr: Homer 1878

National Gallery of Art, Washington, DC, gift of Ruth K. Henschel in memory of her husband, Charles R. Henschel, 1975.92.17

This is probably the *Girl with Half a Rake* Homer contributed to the American Water Color Society exhibition of 1879. It is possible, however, the work shown under that title was No. 723, in which the same rake appears; that the girl stands alone in No. 722, favors it over No. 723 as having been shown in the Society's *Annual*. The *New York Herald* reported *Girl with Half a Rake* as among the works sold from the exhibition; its price was $50.

ABG: Charles R. Henschel was both a collector of Homer watercolors and, from 1927 to his death in 1956, president of the M. Knoedler gallery, which represented Homer in the last decade of his life, and was long thereafter especially closely associated with his work. It may be assumed *Girl with Hay Rake* came to his attention through his position with Knoedler, but he acquired it directly for his private collection, and consequently had no reason to be attentive to recording details of its ownership history.

PROVENANCE
Charles R. Henschel, New York, nd; Ruth K. Henschel (Mrs. Charles R. Henschel), New York, 1956

EXHIBITIONS
AWS 1879, no. 415 (as *Girl with Half a Rake*) [?, see also No. 723]; Albright-Knox 1966, no. 9; NGA 1995, no. 96; Nelson-Atkins 2001 (Nelson-Atkins and Los Angeles County, only); NGA 2005

LITERATURE
"Close of the Exhibition of the Water Color Society—A Most Successful Season," *New York Herald,* 2 Mar. 1879

No. 722. Girl with Hay Rake   see color illustration, p. 427

723

Spring

1878

Watercolor, 11¼ × 9¾ (28.575 × 24.765)
Inscribed lr: Homer / 1878

Private collection

PROVENANCE
Charles T. Barney, New York, nd; Mrs. H. F. Dimock, Washington, DC, his sister, by gift, nd; Ashbel H. Barney, her nephew, by gift, nd; (M. Knoedler & Co., 1936); Barbara Whitney Henry (Mrs. Barklie McKee Henry, later, 1, Mrs. Samuel Peck, 2, Mrs. G. W. Headley), New York, by 1940; (Hirschl & Adler Galleries, 1966); Rita and Daniel Fraad, Scarsdale, NY, 1966; (Sotheby's, 1 Dec. 2004, sale 8032, no. 17)

EXHIBITIONS
AWS 1879, no. 415 (as *Girl with Half a Rake*) [?, see also No. 722]; Walker Art Center 1945; Maynard Walker 1953, no. 14; NGA 1958, no. 93; Whitney 1973, no. 88; NGA 1986, no. 45; NGA 1995, no. 97

No. 723. Spring   see color illustration, p. 429

No. 724. On the Stile

see color illustration, p. 430

No. 725. Towing the Boat

724

On the Stile

[1878]

Watercolor, $8^{11}/_{16} \times 11^{1}/_{8}$ (22.068 × 28.258)
Inscribed lr: Homer

National Gallery of Art, Washington, DC, collection of Mr. and Mrs. Paul Mellon, 1994.59.23

PROVENANCE
Lawson Valentine, New York, c. 1879; Lucy Houghton Valentine (Mrs. Lawson Valentine), 1891; Almira Valentine Pulsifer (Mrs. Nathan Trowbridge Pulsifer), her daughter, 1911; Harold Trowbridge Pulsifer, New York, her son, nd; Susan Nichols Pulsifer (Mrs. Harold Trowbridge Pulsifer), in trust, 1948; Alice Pulsifer Doyle (Mrs. Joseph Doyle), his niece, 1987

EXHIBITIONS
Brooklyn 1915, no. 31 (as *On the Stile, Houghton Farm*); Whitney 1936, no. 46; Worcester 1944, no. 27; Wildenstein 1947, no. 50; Bowdoin/Colby 1954; Storm King 1963, no. 28; Bowdoin 1983, no. 6; Princeton 1990, no. 9; NGA 1995, no. 99; NGA 2005

725

Towing the Boat

[1878]

Watercolor, $6^{1}/_{2} \times 11^{1}/_{4}$ (16.510 × 28.575)

Private collection

ABG: *The Churchman*'s reviewer wrote long and lavishly on Homer's contribution to the American Water Color Society exhibition of 1879. He was particularly taken with Homer's presentation of young people.

> They are children well suited to the poetical places wherein they are pictured and only half belong to the ordinary human world; so that among the low lights and lengthened shadows they are in their own peculiar sphere, and seeming as if the mystery of late and early day were finding also some expression through them. They sit on hillsides with the air of people who talk of deep and wonderful things; and . . . . There are children musing alone in boats as if laying out the plan of a serious poem.

This last sentence applies to the subject of this watercolor, as it does to the title *Girl, Boat and Boy* by Homer which was number 431 in the Society's exhibition.

PROVENANCE
Charles Morrill, Chicago, probably before 1900;
Mrs. Anson J. Cole, Exeter, NH, his daughter, nd;
(Babcock Galleries, c. 1949); (John Nicholson Gallery,
nd); Glenn Saxton, Boston, 1951; (Gustav D.
Klimann, Boston, nd); Nicholas H. Wietzner,
Scarsdale, NY, nd; (Charles Locke Galleries, nd); Mr.
and Mrs. R. Frederick Woolworth, New York, 1956;
Elizabeth, Dowager Duchess of Manchester, Pebble
Beach, CA, Mrs. Woolworth's mother, by gift, nd

EXHIBITIONS
AWS 1879, no. 431 [?]

LITERATURE
"The Water-Color Pictures in the New York
Academy II," *The Churchman* 39 (22 Feb. 1879): 208

726

The Siesta

[1878]

Watercolor, 6¾ × 8 (17.145 × 20.320) sight

Private collection

The following declaration by Samuel Colman
remained pasted to the frame backing of this
watercolor when his estate was auctioned by the
Anderson Galleries: "This picture is unsigned, but
it was bought directly from the Water Color Society
Exhibition to which he contributed and as I was
chairman of that year I can vouch for its authenticity.
[signed] Samuel Colman" (A separate label written
in a different hand, carried the inscription "Winslow
Homer" and the erroneous date 1885.)

Samuel Colman (1832–1920) was a successful,
prominent New York artist who worked in a range
of media. Early in his career he had been particularly
active as a watercolorist. In 1866 he was among the
founders of the American Society of Painters in Water
Colors, as the organization was initially named, and
served as its first president. The Society's exhibitions
were the responsibility of its officers and "Board of
Control," of which Colman was a member in 1879,
and a "Hanging Committee." No "chairman" of
the Committee was publicly identified, but it is
reasonable to believe that Colman had a leading
role in managing the exhibition.

ABG: *The Churchman*'s reviewer wrote long and
lavishly on Homer's contribution to the American
Water Color Society exhibition of 1879. He was
particularly taken with Homer's presentation of
young people; among the very few paintings he

No. 726. The Siesta

noted with some subject detail was "the little one
lying on a garden seat with his head supported by
the girl sitting there." The watercolor known as
Siesta is uniquely appropriate to this description.
Of the otherwise unidentified titles of Homer watercolors listed in the exhibition catalogue no. 367 *A
Rainy Day* is the likely match to this watercolor. This
seems born out by the *New York Herald*'s reviewer's
characterization of *A Rainy Day* as "tender."

PROVENANCE
Samuel Colman, New York, 1879; (American Art
Association/Anderson Galleries, 19–20 Apr. 1927,
S. Colman estate sale, no. 61); John F. Harris, New
York, 1927; (Plaza Galleries, 16 Feb. 1950, Shields,
et al. sale, no. 119-A); (Milch Galleries, 1950); private
collection, c. 1954

EXHIBITIONS
AWS 1879, no. 367 [?]; Storm King 1963, no. 39;
Katonah 1963, no. 8

LITERATURE
"The Water-Color Pictures in the New York
Academy II," *The Churchman* 39 (22 Feb. 1879):
208; "Fine Arts. Water Color Exhibition-Fifth and
Concluding Notice-The Corridor and Black and
White Room," *New York Herald*, 24 Feb. 1879

No. 727. Woman Seated on Bench

see color illustration, p. 431

727

Woman Seated on Bench

[1878]

Girl on a Garden Seat

Watercolor, 6⅜ × 8¼ (16.192 × 20.955)
Inscribed ll: Homer

McNay Art Museum, San Antonio, Mary and
Sylvan Lang Collection, 1975.34

ABG: Susan Carter, writing on the American Water
Color Society annual exhibition of 1879 for the *Art
Journal* was the only reviewer to make a substantive
mention of what presumably is this painting: "'The
Girl on a Garden Seat' is another brilliant bit of
light and shade. But here again Mr. Homer charms
us by the naturalness of his model and her dress, the
action of her figure, and the vigorous colour of the
sketch." That the girl here wears the alternative costume Homer sometimes imposed on his farm-
worker girls, the fanciful ruffled skirt, laced bodice
and useless little straw hat, seems to raise a question
about whether Ms. Carter was discussing this or
another, now unknown painting. It is more likely,
however, that by the time she wrote her article, Ms.

Carter's memory of costume detail had—appropri-
ately—receded in favor of "naturalness . . . [and] the
action of her figure."

Although reported by the New York *Evening Post*
and *Sun* as sold from the American Water Color
Society exhibition early in February 1879, this work,
or, rather its appropriate title, appeared in an exhibition in Boston a few months later, and then apparently moved on to be included in an auction Homer
mounted at the Mathews gallery in March 1880.

According to the *New-York Times* it finally found
a buyer at the Mathews sale: "Seventy-one of Winslow
Homer's water-colors were sold at auction yesterday
by Daniel A. Mathews, at No. 55 Cedar-street. The
attendance of art-lovers was large and the pictures
were sold at fair prices. . . . 'The Rustic Seat,' one of
the most attractive pictures of the collection, was
sold for $36."

PROVENANCE
(Daniel A. Mathews Art Gallery, 4 Mar. 1880,
Homer sale) [?]; John S. Clark, Brighton, MA, nd;
(Doll & Richards, Boston, 1915); Dr. Hugh Williams,
Boston, 1916; (Doll & Richards, Boston, 1923, and
1928); Hester S. Cochrane Fearing (Mrs. George R.
Fearing, Sr.), Boston, 1928; George R. Fearing, Jr.,
Westwood, MA, her son, by gift, by 1936; (Stendahl
Galleries, Los Angeles, c. 1954); Mary and Sylvan
Lang, San Antonio, 1955

EXHIBITIONS
AWS 1879, no. 235 (as IGirl on a Garden Seat) [?];
Boston Art Club, Boston Society of Architects,
Schools at the Museum of Fine Arts, *Exhibition of
Contemporary Art*, 22 Apr.–24 May 1879, no. 683
(as *Girl on a Garden Seat*) [?]; Mathews 1880 (as
The Rustic Seat) [?]; Doll & Richards 1923, no. 17;
Nelson-Atkins 2001 (Nelson-Atkins and Los Angeles
County, only)

LITERATURE
"The Water-Color Exhibition. List of Pictures
Already Sold," *(NY) Evening Post*, 6 Feb. 1879; "Art
Notes," *(NY) Sun*, 10 Feb. 1879; S[usan] N. Carter,
"The Water-Colour Exhibition," *(NY) Art Journal* 5
(Mar. 1879): 93–94; "Winslow Homer's Water-colors,"
New-York Times, 5 Mar. 1880

728

The Flock of Sheep, Houghton Farm
1878

Watercolor, 8¾ × 11⅜ (22.225 × 28.893)
Inscribed lr: Homer 1878

H. Rodes Hart Collection

ABG: This painting was noticed twice in the columns of the *New York Herald*. The first time was in a report of a visit to Homer's studio just as the 1878–1879 season was beginning: the *Herald*'s representative reported that Homer had "made during the summer, a number of very admirable water colors and pencil drawings . . . . Among the best we note . . . a girl and boy seated in the shade with their dog by them and the sheep near." The second time was in the *Herald*'s review of the American Water Color Society exhibition of 1879 when the writer's opinion was that there "is a rather exposed air about the figures of the boy, girl and dog in Winslow Homer's sterling sketch (129)." The painting was lent by Mrs. Lawson Valentine, indicating it had been sold within the brief period between Homer's return to New York late in 1878 and the opening of the Society's *Annual* early in 1879. It was common for feminine collectors to be shielded from publicity by lending in the names of their husbands or fathers. However, there could be no reason for a lady's name to be substituted for an actual gentleman lender. Evidently Lucy Valentine was herself the possessor of this watercolor, and proud to have that fact known.

PROVENANCE
Lucy Houghton Valentine (Mrs. Lawson Valentine), 1878; Almira Valentine Pulsifer (Mrs. Nathan Trowbridge Pulsifer), her daughter, 1911; Lawson Valentine Pulsifer, Mountainville, NY, her son, nd; Natalie Pulsifer Byles, his daughter, 1957; (Davis & Langdale, 1975); (Meredith Long Gallery, Houston, c. 1977); private collection, 1977; (Christie's, 4 Dec. 1987, sale 6512, no. 63); (Berry-Hill Galleries, Inc., 1987)

EXHIBITIONS
AWS 1879, no. 129 (as *Sketch*); Brooklyn 1915, no. 23; Carnegie 1917, no. 4; Whitney 1936, no. 43; Carnegie 1937, no. 117; Storm King 1963, no. 21; University of Arizona 1963, no. 16; NGA 1986, no. 40; NGA 1995, no. 89

LITERATURE
"Fine Arts. Studio Notes," *New York Herald*, 11 Nov. 1878; "Fine Arts. The Water Color Exhibition—Fourth Notice—East and West Rooms," *New York Herald*, 17 Feb. 1879

No. 728. The Flock of Sheep, Houghton Farm   see color illustration, p. 432

No. 729. Scene at Houghton Farm

729
Scene at Houghton Farm
[1878]

Watercolor, 7¼ × 11¼ (18.415 × 28.575)
Inscribed lr: Homer

Hirshhorn Museum and Sculpture Garden,
Smithsonian Institution, Washington, DC, gift of
the Joseph H. Hirshhorn Foundation, 66.2489

PROVENANCE
Elizabeth Montezinos (Mrs. Joseph Montezinos),
New York, by 1959; Jon N. Streep, New York, 1959;
Joseph H. Hirshhorn, Greenwich, CT, 1959

EXHIBITIONS
Storm King 1963, no. 31; University of Arizona 1963,
no. 61; Lowe, Syracuse, 1979, no. 20; NGA 1995,
no. 91; Nelson-Atkins 2001 (Nelson-Atkins and
High, only)

730

Bo-Peep

[1878]

Graphite, watercolor, 5¼ × 7¹¹⁄₁₆ (13.335 × 19.528)
Inscribed lr: W H

Unlocated

PROVENANCE
Horace D. Chapin, Boston, nd; Margaret Chapin
Osgood (Mrs. Robert B. Osgood), Boston, his sister,
c. 1936; private collection, 1957

EXHIBITIONS
MFA, Boston, 1959, no. 156

731

Shepherdess Resting

[1878]

Watercolor, 5⅜ × 8¼ (13.653 × 20.955)

Private collection

PROVENANCE
(Wm. A. Butters & Co., Chicago, 10 Dec. 1879,
Homer sale) [?]; Charles D. Hamill, Chicago,
probably 1879; Mrs. Dudley, Chicago, by gift, 1882;
Katherine Dudley, Paris, her daughter, by bequest,
c. 1935; (Weyhe Gallery, c. 1935); Charles M. Ayer,
New York, c. 1935; (Parke-Bernet Galleries, 14 Mar
1940, sale 181, no. 74); (Babcock Galleries, 1940);
(Valentine Gallery, nd); Arthur Bradley Campbell,
Palm Beach, FL, nd; (Parke-Bernet Galleries,
27 Oct. 1954, sale 1542, no. 22); William Woodward,
1954; (Meredith Long Gallery, Houston, by 1978)

EXHIBITIONS
Butters, Chicago, 1879 [?]

No. 730. Bo-Peep

No. 731. Shepherdess Resting

No. 732. Bo-Peep
see color illustration, p. 433

732
Bo-Peep
1878

Girl with Shepherd's Crook Seated by a Tree

Watercolor, 7 × 8¼ (17.780 × 20.955)
Inscribed lr: Homer / '78

Museum of Fine Arts, Boston, bequest of John T.
Spaulding, 48.724

ABG: Susan Carter singled out several of Homer's
contributions to the American Water Color Society
annual exhibition of 1879 in her review of the show
for the *Art Journal*; among them was number 227 in
the exhibition catalogue:

> With a number of little studies which hang close
> together, "Watching Sheep" (227), "Girl on a
> Garden-Seat" (235), "In an Orchard" (234), the
> visitors to the Academy are much delighted. We
> have rarely seen anything more pure and gentle
> than the little American girl in the first of these
> sketches, half hidden away under the dark shade
> of the trees, with her sheep at her side... the
> picture, too, is delightful in *chiaro-oscuro*. But it
> takes an artist as well informed as Mr. Homer to
> dare to contrast such a dark, clear shadow with
> the brilliant dash of sunshine which isolates the
> little shepherdess from the spectator, and throws
> her woody retreat into a poetical remoteness.

Carter's description of the *Watching Sheep* on view
in the Water Color Society's exhibition is equally
appropriate to this *Bo-Peep* and to the watercolor
now known as *The Shepherd Girl, Houghton Farm*
(No. 733).

See commentary No. 685.

PROVENANCE
unidentified woman, Boston, nd; John T. Spaulding,
Boston, before 1930

EXHIBITIONS
AWS 1879, no. 227 (as *Watching Sheep*) [?, see also
No. 733]; MOMA 1930, no. 23; MFA, Boston, 1936;
Whitney 1936, no. 48; Carnegie 1937, no. 132; MFA,
Boston, 1959, no. 86; Storm King 1963, no. 17;
MFA, Boston, 1977, no. 43; MFA, Boston, 1996,
no. 8 (Edinburgh and Amsterdam)

LITERATURE
S[usan] N. Carter, "The Water-Colour Exhibition,"
(NY) Art Journal 5 (Mar. 1879): 93-94

733

The Shepherd Girl, Houghton Farm

1878

Watercolor, 6¾ × 8¼ (17.145 × 20.955)
Inscribed lr: Homer 1878

Private collection

ABG: See commentary No. 685 and No. 732.
     The drawing *Flock of Sheep* (No. 693) is a source
for the background details of this watercolor.

PROVENANCE
Lawson Valentine, New York, c. 1879; Lucy
Houghton Valentine (Mrs. Lawson Valentine),
1891; Almira Valentine Pulsifer (Mrs. Nathan
Trowbridge Pulsifer), her daughter, 1911; Lawson
Valentine Pulsifer, Mountainville, NY, her son, nd;
Alice Pulsifer Doyle (Mrs. Joseph Doyle), his daughter,
1957; (unidentified dealer, nd); Paul Seifer, nd;
private collection, c. 1975; private collection, 1988

EXHIBITIONS
AWS 1879, no. 227 (as *Watching Sheep*) [?, see also
No. 732]; Brooklyn 1915, no. 21; Whitney 1936, no. 45;
Carnegie 1937, no. 95; Storm King 1963, no. 37;
University of Arizona 1963, no. 47

LITERATURE
S[usan] N. Carter, "The Water-Colour Exhibition,"
(NY) Art Journal 5 (Mar. 1879): 93–94

No. 733. The Shepherd Girl, Houghton Farm

734

Tending Sheep, Houghton Farm
[1878]

Watercolor, 8½ × 11⅛ (21.590 × 28.258)
Inscribed lr: Homer

Weil Brothers Cotton, Inc., Montgomery, AL

ABG: This watercolor is the likely model for the
unfinished oil sketch *Shepherdess* (No. 756), and for
Shepherdess of Houghton Farm (No. 772), one of the
three major canvases Homer introduced at the
National Academy of Design annual exhibition in
the spring of 1879.

See commentary No. 772.

PROVENANCE
Lawson Valentine, New York, c. 1879; Lucy
Houghton Valentine (Mrs. Lawson Valentine), 1891;
Almira Valentine Pulsifer (Mrs. Nathan Trowbridge
Pulsifer), her daughter, 1911; Lawson Valentine
Pulsifer, Mountainville, NY, her son, nd; Alice
Pulsifer Doyle (Mrs. Joseph Doyle), his daughter,
1957; private collection, after 1963; (Kennedy
Galleries, 1974); (Christie's, 22 May 1980, sale
Irene, no. 41)

EXHIBITIONS
Brooklyn 1915, no. 28; Storm King 1963, no. 40;
University of Arizona 1963, no. 48

No. 734. Tending Sheep, Houghton Farm

see color illustration, p. 434

No. 735. Fresh Air   see color illustration, p. 436

735

Fresh Air

1878

Watercolor, 20 1/16 × 14 (50.960 × 35.560)
Inscribed lr: Winslow Homer / 1878

Brooklyn Museum, Dick S. Ramsay Fund, 41.1087

ABG: The critical press perceived *Fresh Air* as
Homer's principal representation in the annual
exhibition of the American Water Color Society
of 1879, and consequently gave it greater scrutiny
and held it to a somewhat higher standard than
the many small sketches which characterized his
contribution to the exhibition.

The *New York Herald* reviewer was wholly admiring:

Winslow Homer is well represented in the collection by a number of fine little pastorals which we
shall speak of later; his largest picture, "Fresh Air"
(5)—a young shepherdess standing in the breeze
on a hilltop—is a bold and effective work, excellent in its strong light and shade and full of the
feeling of a blustering day.

The New York *Daily Graphic*, on the other hand,
thought "Winslow Homer is not so happy in his
large work 'Fresh Air,' as in the delightful little pastoral sketches of which he has made a fine display."
   One of New York's most perceptive critics,
Susan Carter, in her review of the watercolor Society's
Annual for the *Art Journal* singled out Homer

for attention. She expanded on his consistent artistic growth as demonstrated in the major annual exhibitions, before declaring of his representation in the Society's 1879 show:"Never before has a collection of his works been so beautiful in sentiment and evinced such a feeling of truth as this year. The girl in the picture called "Fresh Air" (5), standing up against the light with her sheep around her, on the breezy hillside, is blown by the fragrant country wind, and the clinging folds of her gown and the bent leaves of the tree behind her are animated with life."

Boston's major newspaper's point of view on Homer's participation in the Water Color Society's *Annual* was quite different. Maurice Mauris, reviewed the exhibition for the *Evening Transcript*.

> Winslow Homer's numerically great display of sketches will be more extensively treated in a paper devoted to landscape. Mr. Homer is certainly a shrewd business man and well does he take advantage of the popularity he has gained by his Parisian triumph. His sketches, in fact, have a ready sale. He will, however, lose soon his prestige if he does not exhibit better work. "Fresh Air" (5), the only sketch of his which has a serious claim to be classified with figure paintings, besides having all the faults common to the artificial style in which he paints and which is not true art, but a clever and cheap substitute for it, is ruined by the most unnatural treatment of light and shade. It is my earnest desire to be corrected if I mistake, but I must candidly confess that though I have seen and studied many faces half in light and half in shade, I had never seen before, either in painting or in nature, a face half flesh and half chocolate. I had never seen a straw hat, bound up in front, cast a perpendicular shadow all over one-half the face, except in the case of an almost perpendicular light of which no sign is to be seen in "Fresh Air;" nor can I conceive why a consistent intensity of shade is not to be found on the left side of the girl's garment.

In 1879 Homer repeated the windswept figure standing on the crest of a hillside in a horizontal format in a highly finished drawing, known as *Shepherdess and Sheep* (No. 758).

Henry Valentine had two watercolors in his collection which could have been identified as "Shepherdess," this painting and the work known by the assigned title *Shepherdess Tending Sheep* (No. 703). Thus the watercolor Valentine lent under that title to a Union League Club exhibition in 1888 cannot be positively identified. However, as the figure in *Fresh Air* is more imposing than that in No. 703, and had been much noticed when it was shown at the 1879 Water Color Society exhibition, it is the more probable choice.

PROVENANCE
Henry C. Valentine, New York, 1878; Grace Barrett Valentine (Mrs. Henry C. Valentine), Darien, CT, nd; (Victor Spark, c. 1940)

EXHIBITIONS
AWS 1879, no. 5; Union League Club, New York, *Exhibition of Water Colors*, 10–12 May 1888, no. 46 (as *Shepherdess*) [?]; Worcester 1944, no. 26; Munson-Williams-Proctor 1946, no. 2; Colorado Springs 1947, no. 9; Slater 1952; Metropolitan/Brooklyn 1972, no. 50; Whitney 1973, no. 85; Baltimore 1978, no. 4; Terra 1981; Bowdoin 1983, no. 5; NGA 1986, no. 43; Brooklyn 1998, no. 72; Nelson-Atkins 2001 (Nelson-Atkins, only)

LITERATURE
"Twelfth Annual Exhibition of the Water Color Society—Private View Last Evening," *New York Herald*, 1 Feb. 1879; "The Water Color Exhibition," *(NY) Daily Graphic*, 1 Feb. 1879; Maurice Mauris, "Twelfth Exhibition of the New York Water Color Society. I. Figure Painting," *(Boston) Daily Evening Transcript*, 28 Feb. 1879; S[usan] N. Carter, "The Water-Colour Exhibition," *(NY) Art Journal* 5 (Mar. 1879): 93–94

736
The Reaper
1878

Watercolor, 20 × 14 (50.800 × 35.560)
Inscribed lr: Homer / 1878

Private collection

ABG: Before 1878 Homer rarely ventured beyond a
very small scale for his watercolor paintings. Nine-
teen, or about a third, of his surviving watercolors
of this year attain 19 to 20 inches at their largest
dimension. Most of these are landscape subjects;
some are enlivened with a subordinate figure. There
are just three in which a figure is dominant. All
three were acquired by Henry C. Valentine, probably
soon after Homer completed them. The three are
The Milk Maid (No. 672) which Homer exhibited
at the Century Association early in January 1879;
Fresh Air (No. 735) lent by Valentine for the American
Water Color Society's *Twelfth Annual Exhibition*
which opened on 3 February 1879; and this *Reaper*
(No. 736), which cannot be identified as being
publicly exhibited in Homer's lifetime.

These three paintings are highly finished,
detailed productions of the studio—surely meant
for major exhibition, and perhaps to appeal to a
particular patron. It is puzzling that such an occasion
of exhibition cannot be connected with *The Reaper*,
especially as it is a comfortable pendant to either *The
Milk Maid* or the shepherdess enjoying *Fresh Air*.

(Henry Valentine also owned another of Homer's
larger 1878 watercolors, *Shepherdess Tending Sheep*
(No. 703).)

PROVENANCE
Henry C. Valentine, New York, probably 1878;
Grace Barrett Valentine (Mrs. Henry C. Valentine),
Darien, CT, nd; (Victor Spark, c. 1940); I. M.
Cohen, New York, 1941; (Sotheby Parke-Bernet,
25 Apr. 1980, sale 4365, no. 44)

No. 736. The Reaper   see color illustration, p. 437

737

Shepherdess Resting under a Tree

1878

Graphite, watercolor, 5¼ × 8⁹⁄₁₆ (13.335 × 21.750)
Inscribed lr: W H 1878

Cooper-Hewitt, National Design Museum,
Smithsonian Institution, gift of Charles Savage
Homer, Jr., 1912-12-88

PROVENANCE
Charles S. Homer, Jr., by bequest, 1910

EXHIBITIONS
Cooper-Hewitt 2006

No. 737. Shepherdess Resting under a Tree

No. 738. Waverley Oaks

738

Waverley Oaks

[1878]

Graphite, watercolor, 5¹³⁄₁₆ × 8¹⁄₁₆ (14.765 × 20.480)
Inscribed lr: Homer; rev: Waverley Oaks /
$10; rev: No. 14

Cooper-Hewitt, National Design Museum,
Smithsonian Institution, gift of Charles Savage
Homer, Jr., 1912-12-87

PROVENANCE
Charles S. Homer, Jr., by bequest, 1910

EXHIBITIONS
Carnegie 1937, no. 202; Cooper-Hewitt 1972, no. 35;
Columbia/Telfair 1974, no. 12; Greenville County
1986; Knoedler 1986, no. 25

739
Waverley Oaks
1878

Watercolor, 13 × 20¼ (33.020 × 51.435) sight
Inscribed lr: Winslow Homer 1878

Private collection

In July 1941 Mrs. Charles Lowell Homer recounted for LG the oft-told tale of the visit of the Belmont policemen to Prout's Neck in reaction to having seen an illustration of this painting in a Boston newspaper. The illustration had accompanied a story on the *Century Loan Exhibition as a Memorial to Winslow Homer* mounted by the Prout's Neck Association in the summer of 1936. The story relayed to LG was that as a boy living in Belmont, Massachusetts, the policeman had occasionally posed for Homer and been paid 25 cents for his participation. He said he remembered posing for *Waverley Oaks* because he had commanded double the usual fee before he would put on the shepherdess dress.

ABG: The Belmont policemen was thoroughly investigated by Henry Adams, as he was the pivotal figure in Adams's third article devoted to *Shall I Tell Your Fortune?* (2:No. 611), published in 1990. Adams identified him as one Sergeant Keenan. The Sergeant enjoyed some local celebrity when he recognized the Boston *Globe*'s illustration of *Waverley Oak*s as a subject for which he had posed when a boy. Adams also brought to light an interview the Sergeant gave to his hometown newspaper, the *Belmont Citizen*, published 25 September 1936. In that article, Keenan stated he had posed for Homer for a period of about five days in 1876. In addition to *Waverley Oaks*, he said he was a model in *The Blue Boy* (2:No. 442) and a third work which cannot be identified.

The Sergeant was seventy-two years old when he recounted his memories to the Homer family and to the *Belmont Citizen*. While it is entirely believable he posed for Homer at some time, his recollection of the specifics is belied by facts. *The Blue Boy* carries the inscribed date 1873, the first year Homer used watercolor as a painting medium; *Waverley Oaks* is inscribed 1878, a date compatible with its style and subject features. Illustrations of these two watercolors (both mistakenly captioned as dating to 1872) shared a page in the catalogue of the Prout's Neck

No. 739. Waverley Oaks

exhibition, which, as the Sergeant did not get to see the exhibition, itself, was probably his only visual cue. The juxtaposition of the two images could well have prompted the Sergeant's faulty identification.

Adams, having discovered the old tale of Keenan's relationship to this watercolor, also, apparently, accepted the *Globe* reporter's description of the shepherdess as holding a hand of playing cards, and the 1872 dating of the painting. On this questionable foundation he constructed his final interpretation of *Shall I Tell Your Fortune?*, which included the unequivocal statement that this watercolor "served as a prototype for . . . Shall I Tell Your Fortune?." However, *Waverley Oaks* is surely a work of 1878, and thus, cannot have been a "prototype" for a painting completed in 1876. Further, the detail A. J. Philpot (and, thus, Adams) took to be a fan of playing cards awkwardly held over the hip is, in fact, the stiffened elbow ruffle of the fancy-dress costume.

This watercolor was probably one of the larger, more finished paintings among the twenty-four works in color Homer submitted to the 1879 American Water Color Society exhibition; several of Homer's submission of this character were hung in the North Room of the suite of galleries in the National Academy of Design building occupied by the exhibition. The *New York Herald* reviewer's column on the works in that gallery thought: "'Husking,' the first of [Homer's] landscapes which we come to, is strongly handled, but, like the majority of his work of this class in the exhibition does not come up to his little figures in landscape settings. His 'Oak Trees with Girl' (7) is one of the exceptions. The wide-spreading trees are admirably given."

The $75 price Homer set on "Oak Trees with Girl" in the Society's *Annual* is indication it was fairly imposing in size and complexity, in comparison with the majority of the works he had in other rooms.

"Oak Trees with Girl" did not find a buyer at the Water Color Society exhibition, and therefore was likely among the over seventy works Homer put up for auction by Daniel Mathews in March 1880. Reports of the outcome of such sales were unreliable as much from the carelessness of the newspaper coverage as from the practice of false bidding to keep up the appearance of a favorable market.

This *Waverley Oaks* may—or may not—be the work cited by the *New-York Times* as sold for what hardly approaches an appropriate price for the time: "Seventy-one of Winslow Homer's water-colors were sold at auction yesterday by Daniel A. Mathews, at No. 55 Cedar-street. The attendance of art-lovers was large and the pictures were sold at fair prices. . . . Others were knocked down as follows:. . . 'The Waverley Oaks,' $19." Even if the *Times* report does refer to this painting, it remained in Homer's possession throughout his life.

PROVENANCE
Charles S. Homer, Jr., by bequest, 1910; Mrs. Charles S. Homer, Jr., by bequest, 1917; Charles L. Homer, by bequest, 1937; (William Macbeth, Inc., 1938); Mr. and Mrs. Thomas N. Metcalf, Boston, 1939

EXHIBITIONS
AWS 1879, no. 7 (as *Oak Trees with Girl*) [?]; Boston Art Club, Boston Society of Architects, Schools at the Museum of Fine Arts, *Exhibition of Contemporary Art*, 22 Apr.–24 May 1879, no. 690; Mathews 1880; Prout's Neck 1936, no. 29; Whitney 1936, no. 42; Mount Holyoke 1940, no. 18

LITERATURE
"The Water Color Exhibition—Third Notice—The North Room," *New York Herald*, 11 Feb. 1879; "Water-Colors by Winslow Homer," *(NY) World*, 4 Mar. 1880; "Winslow Homer's Water-colors," *New-York Times*, 5 Mar. 1880; A. J. Philpot, "Winslow Homer Exhibit at Prout's Neck. Maine Sea Paintings on View All Summer," *(Boston) Globe*, 24 July 1936; Henry Adams, "The Identity of Winslow Homer's 'Mystery Woman'," *Burlington Magazine* 132 (Apr. 1990): 249–52

740-R

Sheep Resting

1878

Watercolor, 8⅞ × 11³⁄₁₆ (22.543 × 28.418)
Inscribed ll: Homer Oct 15th 1878; uc: Bt. Sienna

Cooper-Hewitt, National Design Museum,
Smithsonian Institution, gift of Charles Savage
Homer, Jr., 1912-12-55

ABG: Homer used the sheep in this sketch and in
No. 741 to supply *The Shepherdess* (No. 869), a
watercolor of 1880, with her flock.

PROVENANCE
Charles S. Homer, Jr., by bequest, 1910

EXHIBITIONS
Cooper-Hewitt 1972, no. 34; Cooper-Hewitt 2006

No. 740-R. Sheep Resting

740-V

Figures in a Landscape

1878

Graphite
Inscribed lr: Leeds Oct. 10th 1878

741

Sheep Resting

[1878]

Watercolor, 7¼ × 8¾ (18.415 × 22.225)

Cooper-Hewitt, National Design Museum,
Smithsonian Institution, gift of Charles Savage
Homer, Jr., 1912-12-56

ABG: See commentary, No. 740-R.

PROVENANCE
Charles S. Homer, Jr., by bequest, 1910

No. 740-V. Figures in a Landscape

No. 742. The Chestnut Tree

742

The Chestnut Tree

1878

Watercolor, 14 × 20 (35.560 × 50.800) sight
Inscribed ll: Winslow Homer 1878

Private collection

PROVENANCE
(Wm. A. Butters & Co., Chicago, 10 Dec. 1879,
Homer sale); Alden Finney Brooks, Chicago, 1879;
Carol Louise Brooks MacNeil (Mrs. Hermon A.
MacNeil), New York, his daughter, 1932; Hermon A.
MacNeil, New York, c. 1944; (Milch Galleries, 1946);
private collection, c. 1950; (R. H. Love Galleries,
Inc., Chicago, nd)

EXHIBITIONS
Century Association, New York, 11 Jan. 1879, no. 52
(as *Chestnutting*) [?]; AWS 1879, no. 54 [?]; Butters,
Chicago, 1879

743

Autumn, Mountainville, New York

1878

Watercolor, 13¼ × 20¼ (33.655 × 51.435)
Inscribed lr: Homer '78

Private collection

ABG: *Autumn, Mountainville, New York* acquired
that geographically meticulous titling in 1912 when
it was among a small selection of watercolors in
Homer's estate that Charles S. Homer, Jr. put with
the Doll & Richards gallery in Boston for exhibition
and sale. The association with Mountainville, and
therefore, Lawson Valentine's Houghton Farm, was
assumed by Charles Homer or by Doll & Richards,
and has no factual basis. The landscape represented
in this and the others in this group of autumnal
scenes (No. 742 through No. 748) was likely found
in the neighborhood of Hurley and Leeds, New
York, where Homer surely was in October 1878.

This watercolor is very probably the *October*
Homer showed in the 1879 American Water Color
Society exhibition—with an exceptionally high
monetary valuation. Homer had twenty-two works
in color for sale in the Society's 1879 *Annual*. Nine

were priced at $30 to $50; ten were priced at $75; the three remaining watercolors carried conspicuously higher prices: *Old House*, $100 (see *Farmhouse on a Hill*, No. 667); *Oak Trees*, $300 (see *Autumn Trees*, No. 745); and *October*, $350.

The *New York Herald* singled out *October* for attention: ".... landscapes by Winslow Homer, which have been admirably hung close to Mr. Currier's work. Mr. Homer's 'October' (387), 'Oak Trees' (388), 'Corn' (401), 'Girl and Boat' (408) and his very admirable 'Willows' (414) are distinctly 'impressions' and excellent works, and not intentions,' as somebody has well entitled Mr. Currier's contributions." The *Post* mentioned the painting with a descriptive adjective—which only reinforces the title: "Mr. Winslow Homer's russet 'October' in the corridor."

The reviewer for *The Nation* provided the curiously admiring description of the painting, which identifies it with *Autumn, Mountainville, New York*: "[Homer] gave a ghastly effect of stormy light in an ugly and true sketch called 'October'."

Homer used elements of this landscape as the setting for the 1880 watercolor known as *Daydreaming* (No. 871).

PROVENANCE
Charles S. Homer, Jr., by bequest, 1910; Mrs. Charles S. Homer, Jr., by bequest, 1917; Arthur P. and Charles L. Homer, by bequest, 1937; (Giovanni Castano, Boston, c. 1950); International Business Machines Corporation, New York, 1950; (Hirschl & Adler Galleries, c. 1970); private collection, 1970; (Kennedy Galleries, by 1979); Arthur and Holly Magill, Lucca, Italy, 1979; (Sotheby's, 30 Nov. 2000, sale 7565, no. 135)

EXHIBITIONS
AWS 1879, no. 387 (as *October*) [?]; Boston Art Club, Boston Society of Architects, Schools at the Museum of Fine Arts, *Exhibition of Contemporary Art*, 22 Apr.– 24 May 1879, no. 686 (as *October*) [?]; Mathews 1880 (as *October*) [?]; Doll & Richards, Boston, [watercolors], Oct. 1912; Prout's Neck 1936, no. 12; Ogunquit 1954, no. p-14; Bowdoin/Colby 1954; Storm King 1963, no. 16; University of Arizona 1963, no. 63

LITERATURE
"Fine Arts. Water Color Exhibition-Fifth and Concluding Notice-The Corridor and Black and White Room," *New York Herald*, 24 Feb. 1879; "American Art in Water Colors. The Twelfth Annual Exhibition of the Water Color Society. II," *(NY) Evening Post*, 1 Mar. 1879; "Fine Arts. The Growing School of American Water-Color Art," *The Nation* 28 (6 Mar. 1879): 171

No. 743. Autumn, Mountainville, New York

see color illustration, p. 435

No. 744. Autumn Foliage with Two Youths Fishing

744

Autumn Foliage with Two Youths Fishing

[1878]

Watercolor, 11¼ × 8½ (28.575 × 21.590)
Inscribed lr: W. H.

Museum of Fine Arts, Boston, bequest of Katherine Dexter McCormick, 68.571

LG examined Mrs. Katherine Dexter McCormick's five watercolor paintings and three drawings by Homer in her Boston home, in September 1938. (The other seven works are 2:No. 464, No. 713, No. 801, No. 803, No. 814, No. 825, and No. 861.) Mrs. McCormick said they all had been acquired by her mother, Mrs. Wirt Dexter, at an auction in Chicago "in 1876." Mrs. McCormick or Mrs. Dexter's memory was evidently slightly imperfect: all their Homers date from 1878 or 1879, excepting 2:No. 463, an 1873 drawing.

ABG: See commentary No. 743, in reference to the probable location for this and the other autumnal landscapes of 1878.

PROVENANCE
(Wm. A. Butters & Co., Chicago, 10 Dec. 1879, Homer sale) [?]; Mrs. Wirt Dexter, Chicago, probably 1879; Katherine Dexter McCormick (Mrs. Stanley McCormick), Boston, her daughter, probably 1937

EXHIBITIONS
Butters, Chicago, 1879 [?]; MFA, Boston, 1959 (not in catalogue); University of Arizona 1963, no. 77; MFA, Boston, 1977, no. 46

745

Autumn Trees

1878

Watercolor, 13½ × 20¼ (34.290 × 51.435)
Inscribed ll: Winslow Homer 1878

Private collection

ABG: This watercolor is very probably the *Oak Trees* Homer showed in the 1879 American Water Color Society exhibition—with an exceptionally high monetary valuation. Homer had twenty-two works in color for sale in the Society's 1879 *Annual*. Nine were priced at $30 to $50; ten were priced at $75; the three remaining watercolors carried conspicuously higher prices: *Old House*, $100 (see *Farmhouse on a Hill*, No. 667); *Oak Trees*, $300; and *October* (see *Autumn, Mountainville, New York*, No. 743), $350.

The *New York Herald* singled out *Oak Trees* for attention: ".... landscapes by Winslow Homer, which have been admirably hung close to Mr. Currier's work. Mr. Homer's 'October' (387), 'Oak Trees' (388), 'Corn' (401), 'Girl and Boat' (408) and his very admirable 'Willows' (414) are distinctly 'impressions' and excellent works, and not intentions,' as somebody has well entitled Mr. Currier's contributions."

See commentary No. 743, in reference to the probable location for this and the other autumnal landscapes of 1878.

PROVENANCE
(Wm. A. Butters & Co., Chicago, 10 Dec. 1879, Homer sale) [?]; Cornelia Lunt, Evanston, IL, probably 1879; Anne Evans, by bequest, nd; Denver Art Museum, by bequest, 1941; (M. Knoedler & Co., 1947); (unidentified auction, Meredith Galleries, 1947); (Milch Galleries, 1947); private collection, 1956; private collection, after 1963

EXHIBITIONS
Century Association, New York, 11 Jan. 1879, no. 51 (as *Old Oaks*) [?]; AWS 1879, no. 388 (as *Oak Trees*) [?]; Boston Art Club, Boston Society of Architects, Schools at the Museum of Fine Arts, *Exhibition of Contemporary Art*, 22 Apr.–24 May 1879, no. 688 (as *Oak-Trees*) [?]; Butters, Chicago, 1879 [?]; Katonah 1963, no. 9

LITERATURE
"Fine Arts. Water Color Exhibition-Fifth and Concluding Notice-The Corridor and Black and White Room," *New York Herald*, 24 Feb. 1879

No. 745. Autumn Trees

see color illustration, p. 438

No. 746. The Buckwheat Field

746

The Buckwheat Field

[1878]

Watercolor, 14 × 20 (35.560 × 50.800)
Inscribed ll: Homer

Private collection

ABG: In early November 1878, a reporter for the *New York Herald*, making the usual rounds of the studios as the artists returned from their summer absence, paid a visit to Homer. He commented on "the very admirable water colors and pencil drawings" the artist had made during the summer, and on several watercolor paintings Homer was developing from those sketches. The writer also noted a "study of turkeys in a buckwheat field is interesting," which is probably this watercolor, despite its stock of fowl being limited to one exemplar.

See commentary No. 743, in reference to the probable location for this and the other autumnal landscapes of 1878.

PROVENANCE
(Wm. A. Butters & Co., Chicago, 10 Dec. 1879, Homer sale); William Lathrop Moss, Chicago, 1879; private collection, nd

EXHIBITIONS
Butters, Chicago, 1879

LITERATURE
"Fine Arts. Studio Notes," *New York Herald*, 11 Nov. 1878

747

Pumpkin Patch

1878

Watercolor, 11½ × 19¾ (29.210 × 50.165)
Inscribed lr: Homer '78

Mead Art Museum, Amherst (MA) College, 1948.30

ABG: See commentary No. 743, in reference to the
probable location for this and the other autumnal
landscapes of 1878.

PROVENANCE
Anna Reese, New York, nd; (Milch Galleries, nd);
(American Art Association, 28 Apr. 1928, Kennedy,
et al. sale, no. 110); (Ferargil Galleries, 1928); (John
Nicholson Gallery, by 1946); (William Macbeth,
Inc., by 1948)

EXHIBITIONS
Carnegie 1937, no. 77; NGA 1958, no. 91; University
of Arizona 1963, no. 7; Albright-Knox 1966, no. 10;
Whitney 1973, no. 87

No. 747. Pumpkin Patch

No. 748. The Pumpkin Patch

see color illustration, p. 439

748

The Pumpkin Patch

1878

Husking

Watercolor, 13¾ × 20 (34.925 × 50.800)
Inscribed lr: Homer 1878

The Arkell Museum at Canajoharie (NY), 317107

ABG: The Century Association exhibition for the evening of 11 January 1879 included six watercolors by Homer, which were treated as substantial paintings, worthy to be catalogued individually. One of these was titled *In a Cornfield*, and another as *A Cornfield*; either of these could have been the work now known as *The Pumpkin Patch*.

The annual exhibition of the American Water Color Society opened just three weeks later, on 3 February 1879. Number 2 in that exhibition, *Husking* by Homer, was surely this watercolor. *Husking* was reported in several newspapers as having been sold from the Society's *Annual*; the *New York Evening Mail* went beyond that bare fact to note it had been "bought by Dr. Holland." Mrs. Theodora Ward told LG in 1939 that her grandfather, Dr. Josiah Gilbert Holland, a founder and, until his death in 1881, editor of *Scribner's Monthly*, had acquired this watercolor by purchase. The watercolor may have had special appeal for Dr. Holland, as Homer's closely related illustration "Pumpkins among the Corn" (see No. 662) had been published in the August 1878 *Scribner's Monthly*.

The title *Husking* is presumably a reference to the activity of the boys seated amidst the corn stalks at the right. See commentary No. 743, in reference to the probable location for this and the other autumnal landscapes of 1878.

PROVENANCE
Dr. Josiah Gilbert Holland, New York, 1879; Mrs. Bleecker Van Wagener, Alstead Center, NH, his daughter, 1881; Garrat B. Van Wagener, Denver, her son, nd; Mrs. Garrat Van Wagener, Denver, 1937; (William Macbeth, Inc., 1938); Bartlett Arkell, New York, 1939

EXHIBITIONS
AWS 1879, no. 2 (as *Husking*); NGA 1958/MFA,
Boston, 1959, no. 92/85; University of Arizona 1963,
no. 24; Hamilton 1964, no. 8; Lowe, Syracuse, 1979,
no. 19; AI Chicago 2008

LITERATURE
"Art Notes," *(NY) Sun*, 10 Feb. 1879; "Fine Arts. The
Water Color Exhibition—Third Notice—The North
Room," *New York Herald*, 11 Feb. 1879; "Close of the
Exhibition of the Water Color Society—A Most
Successful Season," *New York Herald*, 2 Mar. 1879;
"Art Notes," *New York Evening Mail*, 5 Mar. 1879

749
Shepherd Girl Resting
[1878]

Oil, 8 × 13 (20.320 × 33.020)
Inscribed ll: Homer

Private collection

ABG: See the drawing, *Shepherdess* (No. 681), which
was a source for this unfinished painting.

PROVENANCE
Charles S. Homer, Jr., by bequest, 1910; Mrs.
Charles S. Homer, Jr., by bequest, 1917; Carnegie
Institute, Pittsburgh, by gift, 1918; (Downtown
Gallery, 1941); (E. C. Babcock Art Galleries, 1941);
Alexander L. Hillman, New York, 1941

EXHIBITIONS
Babcock 1941, no. 10

No. 749. Shepherd Girl Resting

No. 750. Boy and Girl in a Field with Sheep

750

Boy and Girl in a Field with Sheep
[1878]

Oil, 15½ × 22½ (39.370 × 57.150)

Cooper-Hewitt, National Design Museum,
Smithsonian Institution, gift of Mrs. Charles Savage
Homer, Jr., 1918-20-6

PROVENANCE
Charles S. Homer, Jr., by bequest, 1910; Mrs.
Charles S. Homer, Jr., by bequest, 1917

EXHIBITIONS
Spanierman 1966, no. 17; Cooper-Hewitt 1972,
no. 99; Cooper-Hewitt 2006

751

Two Girls with Sunbonnets in a Field

[1878]

Oil, 15¾ × 22½ (40.005 × 57.150)

Cooper-Hewitt, National Design Museum,
Smithsonian Institution, gift of Mrs. Charles Savage
Homer, Jr., 1918-20-5

PROVENANCE
Charles S. Homer, Jr., by bequest, 1910; Mrs. Charles
S. Homer, Jr., by bequest, 1917

EXHIBITIONS
Storm King 1963, no. 8; Spanierman 1966, no. 18;
Cooper-Hewitt 1972, no. 100; Cooper-Hewitt 2006

No. 751. Two Girls with Sunbonnets in a Field

No. 752. Girl Seated in a Garden

752

Girl Seated in a Garden

[1878]

Oil, 21½ × 13¾ (54.610 × 34.925)

Virginia Museum of Fine Arts, Richmond, gift of
Mrs. William Evans Massey, Sr., 77.23

When LG first examined this painting in the
mid-1930s it bore this label:

> From / P. Ulrich, / 116 Fourth Avenue, near 12th
> Street, / Depot of all kinds of / ARTISTS' MATERIALS

Peter J. Ulrich had his shop at that address from
1870 into 1877. The same label was on the reverse
of the stretcher of the oil sketch known as *A Shady
Spot* (No. 753).

PROVENANCE
Charles S. Homer, Jr., by bequest, 1910; Mrs.
Charles S. Homer, Jr., by bequest, 1917; Carnegie
Institute, Pittsburgh, by gift, 1918; (Downtown
Gallery, 1941); (E. C. Babcock Art Galleries, 1941);
(Milch Galleries, 1941); Mrs. Jacob H. Rand,
Brooklyn, 1942; (Milch Galleries, by 1945); (Guy
Mayer, nd); Mrs. Irving D. Karpas, New York, nd;
(Sotheby Parke-Bernet, 29 Apr. 1976, sale 3865,
no. 35); (Coe Kerr Gallery, 1976)

EXHIBITIONS
Babcock 1941, no. 3; New Britain 1942

753
A Shady Spot
[1878]

Oil, 20 × 13 (50.800 × 33.020)

Private collection

In 1901 Homer had a cottage—which came to be called "Kettle Cove"—constructed on one of his properties at Prout's Neck. Despite Arthur Benson Homer's claim that his brother said he had built it to die in, it is questionable Homer ever intended to occupy the cottage himself. He surely put it to use to generate rental income, and as a sort of open storage for a number of his early works. On Homer's death "Kettle Cove," along with all Homer's other property passed to his older brother, Charles S. Homer, Jr. Charles immediately made a gift of "Kettle Cove" and all its contents to Arthur. William Howe Downes described some of the works which had thus come into Arthur's possession. Among them was this canvas: "[Homer] hung in the ground-floor rooms a few of his early oil paintings, which I saw when I was at Prout's Neck in the fall of 1910. There were among other canvases, all unframed . . . a study of a girl in a rose-pink shirt-waist leaning against the massive trunk of a great beech tree."

When LG first examined this painting in 1936 at the Macbeth gallery, it bore this label:

> From / P. Ulrich, / 116 Fourth Avenue, near 12th Street, / Depot of all kinds of / ARTISTS' MATERIALS

Peter J. Ulrich had his shop at that address from 1870 into 1877. The same label was on the reverse of the stretcher of the oil sketch known as *Girl Seated in a Garden* (No. 752).

See No. 709 and No. 711 for closely related images.

PROVENANCE
Charles S. Homer, Jr., by bequest, 1910; Arthur B. Homer, by gift, 1910; Charles L. Homer, by bequest, 1916; (William Macbeth, Inc., 1936); (Maynard Walker Galleries, 1937); unidentified private collection, c. 1940; private collection, by gift, 1941; (Sotheby's, 1 Dec. 2004, sale 8032, no. 115)

EXHIBITIONS
Maynard Walker 1953, no. 5 (as *A Shady Spot, Houghton Farm*); Storm King 1963, no. 7; University of Arizona 1963, no. 69

LITERATURE
Downes 1911, 116

No. 753. A Shady Spot

754

Shepherdess and Sheep

[1878]

Oil, 15½ × 22½ (39.370 × 57.150)
Inscribed rev: [cut edge of canvas] . . . re Picture of
Value

The Arkell Museum at Canajoharie (NY), 317110

See commentary No. 755.

ABG: This work may be a variant of the conception
which became the major oil *Shepherdess of Houghton
Farm* (No. 772).

PROVENANCE
Charles S. Homer, Jr., by bequest, 1910; Mrs.
Charles S. Homer, Jr., by bequest, 1917; Carnegie
Institute, Pittsburgh, by gift, 1918; (Downtown
Gallery, 1941); (E. C. Babcock Art Galleries, 1941);
Bartlett Arkell, New York, 1942

EXHIBITIONS
Babcock 1941, no. 4; Vermont Art Center 1957, no.
10; Vermont Art Center 1964, no. 11 (as *Shepherdess
and Sheep*); Farnsworth 2006

No. 754. Shepherdess and Sheep

755
Girl at the Fence
nd

Oil, 15⅜ × 22½ (39.053 × 57.150)

The Arkell Museum at Canajoharie (NY), 317274

In July 1969 the distinguished conservators, Sheldon and Caroline Keck, notified LG of the discovery of a second canvas beneath, and tacked to the same stretcher as, *Shepherdess and Sheep* (No. 754), which they were treating for the Canajoharie Library and Art Museum. LG gave his positive opinion on the authorship of the rough sketch which was given the title *Girl at the Fence*. Homer went beyond simply setting aside a first sketch in his use of this work to reinforce another canvas. It would seem that in obscuring the image he expressed his opinion of its merits, and his intention that it not be exposed to view.

As a fellow-traveler of *Shepherdess and Sheep*, this work shares its history of ownership.

EXHIBITIONS
Farnsworth 2006

No. 755. Girl at the Fence

No. 756. Shepherdess

756
Shepherdess
[1878]

Oil, 15 × 12¼ (38.100 × 31.115)

Private collection

This rough sketch repeats the subject features of the left side of the horizontally formatted watercolor known as *Tending Sheep, Houghton Farm* (No. 734). The composition was probably brushed in, and then abandoned, not long after Homer's return to his New York studio from his summer absence, that is, in later autumn 1878 or early winter 1879. It is possible, however, that the sketch was produced to serve as a model for the engraver of the illustration to

George Sheldon's article in the November 1880 issue of the *Art Journal*, "Sketches and Studies. VII. From the Portfolios of R. Swain Gifford, Winslow Homer, Arthur Quartley, and A. T. Britcher." The illustration, captioned "Shepherdess. From a Sketch by Winslow Homer," clearly relied more specifically on the image in this oil sketch than the watercolor, but eliminated even more of the landscape and grazing sheep at the right of the figure.

See commentary No. 899.

ABG: It is difficult not see this sketch as a preliminary, and rejected, conception for the work which would be a culminating expression of the pastoral imagery which preoccupied Homer from 1877 through 1878: the large oil painting he introduced at the annual exhibition of the National Academy of Design in the spring of 1879, entitled *The Shepherdesss of Houghton Farm*. That painting was a development of the essential composition seen here. In the final version the figure of the shepherdess had assumed classical proportions, her sheep had become much more substantial and had been given more prominent places in the scene.

None of the three large paintings Homer placed in the Academy *Annual* of 1879 attracted full critical approbation, or a buyer. Consequently *The Shepherdesss of Houghton Farm* remained in Homer's possession, and in about 1906 he returned to it, making major revisions—most significantly by cutting off the lower portion of the canvas and thus reformatting the work to horizontal—and put it in the market as *Spring: The Shepherdess of Houghton Farm* (No. 772).

PROVENANCE
Charles S. Homer, Jr., by bequest, 1910; Mrs. Charles S. Homer, Jr., by bequest, 1917; Arthur P. and Charles L. Homer, by bequest, 1937; (William Macbeth, Inc., c. 1937); (Wildenstein & Co., 1943); private collection, 1950

EXHIBITIONS
Babcock 1941, no. 14; New Britain 1942

LITERATURE
[George William Sheldon], "Sketches and Studies VII. From the Portfolios of R. Swain Gifford, Winslow Homer, Arthur Quartley, A. T. Britcher," *(NY) Art Journal* 6 (Nov. 1880): 326. Reprinted in, G. W. Sheldon, *Hours with Art and Artists* (New York: D. Appleton and Company, 1882), 138

Illustration: "Fresh Air," catalogue of the
American Water Color Society, New York,
Twelfth Annual Exhibition, 1879

757
Fresh Air
[1879]

[Ink]

Unlocated

ABG: Of the twenty-nine watercolors and drawings
Homer had on view in the Water Color Society
annual exhibition of 1879, only *Fresh Air* (No. 735)
was illustrated in the exhibition catalogue. Although
the process used to create the illustrations was photo-
engraving, the original works being exhibited were
not the images transposed to the catalogue pages.
Drawings which conveyed their salient features were
created in a linear style similar to wood engraving to
represent original works; these were photographed,
and then greatly reduced in scale, so several might fit
onto single pages. Initially, the authors of these line
drawings were not identified. Probably the absence
of credit citations is an indication the artists of the
originals generally executed the "reproductions" of
their own work. Unlike the drawing meant to illustrate *Backgammon* (No. 614) in the catalogue of the
Water Color Society exhibition of 1877, the drawing
representing *Fresh Air* shows characteristics of Homer's
style and skill in graphic expression.

The images published in Water Color Society's
catalogues were not shared with some more commercial form of publication, as were those in the
National Academy of Design catalogues, and thus
were likely carelessly treated, once they had served
their purpose.

758
Shepherdess and Sheep
1879

Girl on a Windy Hill

Graphite, watercolor, 9½ × 14⅞ (24.130 × 37.783)
Inscribed lr: Winslow Homer N. A. / 1879

Hunter Museum of American Art, Chattanooga,
TN, bequest of Margaret Caldwell Morrison
(1895–1984), 1984.5

ABG: The central subject of the watercolor *Fresh
Air* (No. 735) is here repeated in a smaller scale and
horizontal format.

PROVENANCE
(Wm. A. Butters & Co., Chicago, 10 Dec. 1879,
Homer sale) [?]; Cornelia Lunt, Evanston, IL,
probably 1879; Anne Evans, by bequest, nd; Denver
Art Museum, by bequest, 1941; (M. Knoedler &
Co., 1951); Mrs. Dunbar Bostwick, New York,
c. 1954; (Hirschl & Adler Galleries, 1973); private
collection, 1973

EXHIBITIONS
Butters, Chicago, 1879 [?]; Knoedler 1986, no. 32

No. 758. Shepherdess and Sheep

759

Shepherdesses Resting

1879

Watercolor, 8½ × 12½ (21.590 × 31.750)
Inscribed lr: Winslow Homer 1879

Gerald Peters Gallery, New York

ABG: Homer made the figure seen here at the right
the central subject in a watercolor of 1880, called
The Shepherdess (No. 870).

PROVENANCE
(Wm. A. Butters & Co., Chicago, 10 Dec. 1879,
Homer sale) [?]; Eda Hurd Lord (Mrs. George S.
Lord), Evanston, IL, nd; (J. W. Young Galleries,
Chicago, 1918); Paul Schulze, Chicago, by 1939; Helen
Bennitt (Mrs. Benjamin A. Bennitt, Sr.), his grand-
daughter, nd; private collection, by bequest, c. 2003

EXHIBITIONS
Butters, Chicago, 1879 [?]

No. 759. Shepherdesses Resting

760

Girl and Sheep

[1879]

Graphite, watercolor, 7⅝ × 16⅛ (19.368 × 40.958)
Inscribed ll: Winslow Homer N. A. [/ 1879]

Albright-Knox Art Gallery, Buffalo, bequest of
Norman E. Boasberg, 1962:5.3

The Denver Art Museum provided LG with cataloguing information on this drawing in 1941. At that
time it bore the inscription at lower left: Winslow
Homer, N. A. / 1879, and was 7¾ inches in height.
By the time the Albright-Knox Art Gallery acquired
the work ⅛ of an inch had been trimmed from its
bottom edge, and the line of inscription giving its
date, lost.

ABG: This drawing is a composite of elements in
drawings and a watercolor of 1878: the figure alone
is the subject of No. 682; the sheep are seen in No.
740-R and 740-V; and is a repetition of the foreground
group in the watercolor, No. 683.

PROVENANCE
(Wm. A. Butters & Co., Chicago, 10 Dec. 1879,
Homer sale) [?]; Cornelia Lunt, Evanston, IL, prob-
ably 1879; Anne Evans, by bequest, nd; Denver Art
Museum, by bequest, 1941; (M. Knoedler & Co.,
1951); (Hammer Galleries, 1951); Norman E.
Boasberg, Buffalo, 1951

EXHIBITIONS
Butters, Chicago, 1879 [?]; University of Arizona
1963, no. 5; Albright-Knox 1966, no. 12; South Texas
1978, no. 8; Lowe, Syracuse, 1979, no. 8; Nelson-
Atkins 2001

see color illustration, p. 440

No. 760. Girl and Sheep

761

Sheep in a Meadow

1879

Graphite, 4¹⁵⁄₁₆ × 7⅞ (12.543 × 20.003)
Inscribed lr: Winslow Homer / April '79

Private collection

Homer repeated the sheep occupying the left half of this sheet in his watercolor *Shepherdess* (No. 762). The entire flock was the subject of the lead illustration in the June 1880 issue of *Scribner's Monthly* (see No. 872).

ABG: The inscription on this drawing is one of the infrequent instances where Homer left record of the month as well as the year of execution. The drawing happens also to be unusual in the reliablity of the history of its early ownership. It surely was acquired by the Chicago artist, Alden Finney Brooks, from Homer's December 1879 sale in that city. Yet approximately six months following the sale—and nearly a year after this drawing was made—almost its exact image appeared on the cover of the New York publication *Scribner's Monthly*. Homer might have retained a near duplicate of this drawing, which, with landscape details added, served as the model for photographic transfer to the engraving block. It is also remotely possible the illustration for a article focused on the coming of spring was prepared in the previous autumn. However, the repetition is

more likely demonstration of an accomplished artist's capacity to reconstruct almost any image with which he is much practiced without reference to a physical model.

PROVENANCE
(Wm. A. Butters & Co., Chicago, 10 Dec. 1879, Homer sale); Alden Finney Brooks, Chicago, 1879; Elizabeth Brooks Maher (Mrs. George W. Maher), Kenilworth, IL, his daughter, 1932; Violet Wyld, Kenilworth, IL, nd; (Conner-Rosenkranz, 1985)

EXHIBITIONS
Butters, Chicago, 1879

No. 761. Sheep in a Meadow

762

Shepherdess

1879

Graphite, watercolor, 8¹⁄₁₆ × 14¼ (20.480 × 36.195)
Inscribed ll: Winslow Homer 1879

Private collection

ABG: The sketch *Girl Seated on a Hillside* (No. 694) is the source for the figure in this highly finised drawing; the group of sheep sketched in No. 761 provided this *Shepherdess'* companions.

PROVENANCE
(Milch Galleries, by 1919); Gilbert E. Rubens, New York, 1919; (Milch Galleries, 1935); (Victor Spark, 1942); Isadore M. Cohen, New York, nd; Whitney Museum of American Art, by gift, 1972; (Christie's, 31 May 1985, sale 5906, no. 62)

EXHIBITIONS
Macbeth 1936 (not in catalogue); Whitney 1973, no. 169; Knoedler 1986, no. 31

No. 762. Shepherdess

No. 763. Fishin'

763
Fishin'
1879

Oil, 7¼ × 9³⁄₁₆ (18.415 × 23.338)
Inscribed ll: Homer / 1879

Museum of Art, Rhode Island School of Design,
Providence, bequest of Isaac C. Bates, 13.935

The 1878 drawing and watercolor painting, No. 715
and No. 716, respectively—both titled *Fishing*—are
exact sources for this oil.

ABG: The artist should not be held responsible for
the painting's vernacular titling, which seems only to
have been attached to it sometime after 2002.

PROVENANCE
Isaac Comstock Bates, Providence, RI, nd

EXHIBITIONS
MOMA 1930, no. 21 (as *Fishing*); Carnegie 1937,
no. 19 (as *Fishing*); Storm King 1963, no. 5 (as *Fishing*);
FAMSF/Amon Carter 2002, no. 5 (as *Fishing*)

No. 764. Girl Picking Apple Blossoms

764

Girl Picking Apple Blossoms

1879

Oil, 15¾ × 22¾ (40.005 × 57.785)
Inscribed lr: Homer 1879

Cooper-Hewitt, National Design Museum,
Smithsonian Institution, gift of Mrs. Charles Savage
Homer, Jr., 1918-20-7

Homer may have been testing his market when in
1890 he sent four early oils to Doll & Richards, his
Boston dealer. Three of the paintings were approximately twenty years old at the time: *Lobster Cove*
(2:No. 347), *An Open Window* (2:No. 401), and
Sunlight and Shadow (2:No. 411). The fourth was this
somewhat later work, titled *Blossom Time*. None
sold; all four were returned to Homer in May 1892.
   LG recorded a penciled inscription on the
stretcher: Private Stock Homer / 51 West 10th Street,
He noted that the "k" in "Stock" overwrote the "H"

in "Homer," and that the phrase "Private Stock" had
been written more recently than the artist's name
and address, suggesting it was a later addition, possibly made at the Doll & Richards gallery in 1890.

PROVENANCE
Charles S. Homer, Jr., by bequest, 1910; Mrs.
Charles S. Homer, Jr., by bequest, 1917

EXHIBITIONS
Spanierman 1966, no. 22; Cooper-Hewitt 1972,
no. 104; Cooper-Hewitt 2006

765

The Yellow Jacket

1879

Oil, 22¹³⁄₁₆ × 15⅝ (57.945 × 39.688)
Inscribed ll: Homer / 1879

Cooper-Hewitt, National Design Museum,
Smithsonian Institution, gift of Charles Savage
Homer, Jr., 1917-14-4

PROVENANCE
Charles S. Homer, Jr., by bequest, 1910

EXHIBITIONS
Doll & Richards 1912, no. 11; Spanierman 1966,
no. 20; Cooper-Hewitt 1972, no. 102; Whitney 1973,
no. 43; Cooper-Hewitt 2006

No. 765. The Yellow Jacket

see color illustration, p. 441

766

Woman Reading under Oaks

1879

Oil, 15½ × 22½ (39.370 × 57.150)
Inscribed lr: Homer 1879

James and Frances McGlothlin, Bristol, VA

ABG: In February 1880 a writer for the New York *Evening Post* reported, "Two pictures by Mr. Winslow Homer are the most durable attractions of a collection of American and foreign oil paintings soon to be sold in the Mathews's art rooms on Cedar street. The largest [*sic*] of the two is a landscape, brightened by an American farmer's daughter, who reads a letter while seated on the grass and leaning against a tree, . . . In the former especially is a great feeling for sunshine." The fashionable costume of the young *Woman Reading Under Oaks* hardly seems to suggest she is "an American farmer's daughter," however, the *Post* reporter's description otherwise conforms to this painting. If this is the work offered by Daniel Mathews in that sale, it was then titled *Deeply Interested*.

PROVENANCE
C. E. Wood, Brooklyn, NY, nd; Helen C. Wood, Brooklyn, NY, his daughter, by 1936; (William Macbeth, Inc., 1938); Willis A. Trafton, Auburn, ME, 1938; Helen Trafton Gutmann, Auburn, ME, his daughter, by gift, nd; (Vose Galleries of Boston, c. 1996); private collection, 1996; (Christie's, 25 May 2000, sale 9368, no. 19)

EXHIBITIONS
Daniel A. Mathews Art Gallery, New York, *American and Foreign Paintings* [auction], 22–27 Feb. 1880, no. 35 (as *Deeply Interested*) [?]; Macbeth 1938, no. 19

LITERATURE
"Art Sales," *(NY) Evening Post*, 25 Feb. 1880

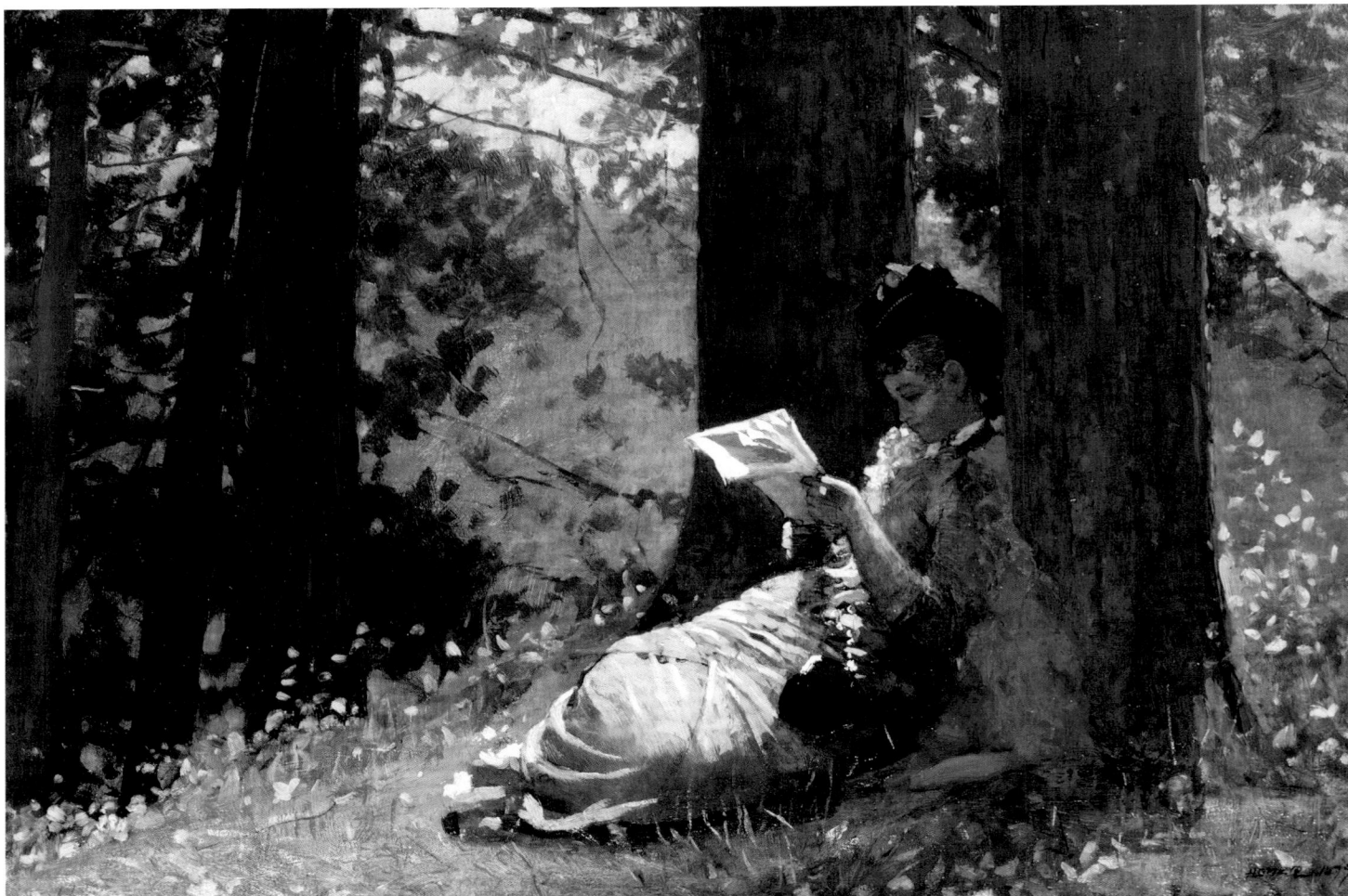

No. 766. Woman Reading under Oaks

see color illustration, p. 442

No. 767. Peach Blossoms

see color illustration, p. 443

767

Peach Blossoms

1879

Oil, 15¾ × 22½ (40.005 × 57.150)
Inscribed ll: W H / 1879

Philip and Charlotte Hanes, Winston-Salem, NC

LG's history of this painting was initiated with his transcription from the Knoedler gallery's 1924 record on it: "Initials and date lower left: W. H. 1879. In pencil on upper part of stretcher: Homer / 51 West 10th St. / City. On lower part of stretcher: At Milford Penn. On right side of road to Dingman Bridge, Delaware River, showing the peculiar gray green of new wheat in Early Spring. This peach tree stands upon this spot."

Knoedler's records also are the source of the early provenance which became firmly attached to the painting. Knoedler's relied on Mrs. Anna Thompson's statement that Gill's shop in Springfield, Massachusetts, had purchased this *Peach Blossoms* from Homer, outright, and that she had acquired the work from Gill's.

LG confirmed the accuracy of Knoedler's copy of the penciled lines on the stretcher bars when he examined the painting in 1940 at the Warrenton home of Col. Albert Peirce. From his observation, he added that he believed the address was written in Homer's own script. The lines written on the lower stretcher bar were printed in block letters, however, and while LG thought they had probably been inscribed by the artist, given the block lettering, he could not be sure. As for the inscribed initials and date on the face of the painting, by 1940, he found the last digit was unclear, but LG read it as either an "8" or a "9;" he opted for a date of 1879, on the basis of Homer's style in executing the painting.

A shield-shaped label for Gill's "Art & Stationery Store" was still in place at the stretcher bar intersection when LG examined the work. In his detailed description of the subject and style of the painting LG especially noted that it was: "Not highly finished. [It] has all the appearance of a sketch made on the spot—painted entirely *alla prima*."

ABG: That obscure fourth digit in the inscribed date of this painting gave Gordon Hendricks the opportunity to introduce a superfluous complication to understanding Homer's two paintings called *Peach Blossoms*, this and No. 643, a work of 1878. Hendricks decided the fourth digit is "o," thus making it—and discussing it as—a work of 1870. There is nothing in the style or subject details of this painting which would support such an early dating. Also, the address inscribed by Homer on its stretcher, while not irrefutable evidence of execution after Homer took space in the Tenth Street Studio Building in 1872, is persuasive on that point.

Hendricks further announced that "Both *Peach Blossoms*, incidentally, are related to a *Harper's Weekly* illustration of May 21, 1870." The background of that illustration, "Spring Blossoms," is filled with flowering branches of a quite large tree; however, the "blossoms" of the illustration's title are as much a reference to the five children who occupy its foreground as to the generic flowering branches over their heads. The upper body of a fashionably dressed young woman is at the far left of the composition; a stone wall supports her elbow, and provides seating for several of the children. Coincidence of subject details does not constitute relationship.

As he had with the earlier dated *Peach Blossoms*, Homer let some time elapse before putting this painting forward for exhibition and possible sale. The "appearance of a sketch made on the spot" noted by LG, probably worked against Homer choosing to show this *Peach Blossoms* in any major New York venue. In 1881, almost exactly a year after he had put the 1878 *Peach Blossoms* up for auction at the Mathews gallery, Homer sent this version to the Springfield, Massachusetts, Art Association's *Fourth Annual Artists' Exhibition*.

The description of the work on view at the exhibition preview given by a reporter for the Springfield *Daily Republican* precludes any question of which of the two *Peach Blossoms* was on view:

> There is a smaller piece near [*Spring: The Shepherdess of Houghton Farm* (No. 772), also] by Homer, exceedingly simple in treatment. It is called "Peach-blossoms," and represents a woman leaning against a rough stone wall and looking at a way-side peach shrub in bloom. The young woods on the hillside over the dell are in the tender green of the season, but nothing is painted, it is only suggested; the woman's face is concealed, except the lower part, by a sun-bonnet, and her mouth looks as if she was on the verge of a good cry. This is a subtle touch in Homer,—a story might be made out of it.

The Springfield Art Association's exhibitions were mounted in, and essentially, by, Gill's Art Galleries, a pillar of Springfield's commercial community. (Apparently the shop assumed the entitlement of "Art Galleries" for the duration of its formal exhibitions.) Homer had been a regular participant from the first of these events in 1879. Of the two paintings he sent for the 1881 exhibition, only *Peach Blossoms* did not come back to him. As the *Art Journal* reported: "At Springfield, Mass., the fourth annual exhibition of paintings by New York artists was held in March, and the sale which followed was as successful as that of any previous year, excepting only that of 1880 . . . The list of sales this year included . . . Winslow Homer's 'Peach Blossoms,' $200." The buyer was neither Mr. Gill nor Mrs. Anna Thompson. It was George Walter Vincent Smith, Springfield's leading patron of the fine arts.

The official preview reception for the Springfield Association exhibition was held 3 February 1881, the day before the public opening. However, Smith, as a very important patron, would have gotten to view the paintings coming into Gill's almost as soon as they arrived. A letter from Homer to Smith written from New York on the same day as the exhibition preview makes clear that he and Smith were negotiating the sale of a painting even before the show opened.

> My dear Mr. Smith
> You certainly have a very graceful style and a way of putting things - I should have returned a plain offer. As it is, you may have the Picture & frame for the amount you offer but I understand that it is with Mr. Gill's consent & that you are to arrange with him about his commission. Thanks to you for your pleasant remembrances & / Believe me / Sincerely yours / Winslow Homer

That it was *Peach Blossoms* Smith was pursuing is demonstrated by the entry of that title with the purchase price "200" in an 1882 inventory ledger on his collection. The entry is annotated "S," Smith's code for having sold a work, with the name "Thompson." Although he only held the painting for some part of one year, Smith seems to have acquired it for himself, not as agent for James M. Thompson, another prominent citizen of Springfield.*

Nicolai Cikovsky, Jr. and Franklin Kelly do not seem to have been aware of the smaller *Peach Blossoms* in the collection of the Art Institute of Chicago when the entry on this version was composed for the catalogue of their 1995 exhibition. That entry consists entirely of quotation of the seemingly appropriate passages from the New York *Daily Tribune* of 26 January 1880, and the New York *Evening Post* of 2 February 1880. However, No. 643 is better described by those newspapers reports than is this work, and it was more likely the other *Peach Blossoms* the reporters saw, and that was offered at auction by Daniel A. Mathews early in February 1880. The provenance which accompanies the Cikovsky and Kelly catalogue entry introduces the Mathews sale at the head of the generally used, but incomplete history of this *Peach Blossoms.*

Milford, Pennsylvania, where the Sawkill River runs, was a summer resort community on the Delaware River, near Port Jervis on the Pennsylvania-New Jersey border, much favored by writers and painters. John Ferguson Weir (among a number of Homer's New York colleagues) was a particularly constant visitor. As late as 1882 a tourist guide book noted Homer as having been "a steady visitor" in the area. The other work in Homer's oeuvre that links him to Milford is the oil sketch, *Sawkill River, Pa.* (2:No. 333) presumed to date from 1869, and to be the work shown under that title in the National Academy of Design *Annual* of 1870. The subject of that work features a defile of ducklings, a motive which inspires association with spring time. The inscription on this *Peach Blossoms* finished nearly a decade later than *Sawkill River, Pa.* seems to demonstrate the accuracy of the 1882 guide book's claim, and with the representation of "new wheat" and flowering fruit tree in this painting, suggests the season Homer favored for visiting along the Delaware.

See commentary No. 643.

*I am indebted to Martha J. Hoppin for sharing the substantial information on Homer and Springfield resulting from her extensive research in support of cataloguing the collections of Springfield's George Walter Vincent Smith, and Fine Arts museums. The discovery of Smith's ownership of *Peach Blossoms* is but one of the contributions she made to this record of Homer's works.

Homer's letter to George Walter Vincent Smith and Smith's collection inventories are held in the George Walter Vincent Smith Museum archive, Springfield.

PROVENANCE

(Gill's Art Galleries, Springfield, MA, 1881); George Walter Vincent Smith, Springfield, MA, 1881; James M. Thompson, Springfield, MA, by 1882; Anna Beadle Thompson (Mrs. James M. Thompson), Springfield, MA, and later, Baltimore, by bequest, 1884; (M. Knoedler & Co., 1924); James A. Dunbar, New York, 1924; (M. Knoedler & Co., 1928); Col. Albert E. Peirce, Chicago, and Warrenton, VA, 1929; (Kennedy Galleries, by 1961); Mr. and Mrs. David T. Workman, New York, nd; (Kennedy Galleries, by 1968)

EXHIBITIONS

Gill's Art Galleries, and Springfield Art Association, Springfield, MA, *Fourth Annual Artists' Exhibition*, open by 4 Feb. 1881, no. 30; NGA 1995, no. 100; Reynolda House, Museum of American Art, Winston-Salem, NC, *Winslow Homer: Early Prints and Paintings*, 24 Sept.–28 Nov. 1999

LITERATURE

"Gill's Artists' Exhibition," *Springfield (MA) Daily Republican*, 3 Feb. 1881; "Art Notes," *New-York Times*, 10 Apr. 1881; "Art Notes. Picture Sales of the Month," *(NY) Art Journal* 7 (May 1881): 160; Hendricks 1979, 80; Cikovsky and Kelly 1995, 168

768

Reading by the Brook

1879

Oil, 15¾ × 22½ (40.005 × 57.150)
Inscribed lr: Homer '79

Memphis Brooks Museum of Art, Memphis Park
Commission Purchase, 43.22

PROVENANCE
(Ainslie Galleries, by 1924); (M. A. Newhouse &
Son, St. Louis, 1924); E. M. Stottar, 1924;
(Newhouse Galleries, by 1936); Warner S. McCall,
St. Louis, 1936; (Gimbel's [department store], 1941)

EXHIBITIONS
Parthenon 2000; New Britain 2003; The Newark (NJ)
Museum, *Off the Pedestal: New Women in the Art of
Homer, Chase and Sargent*, 17 Mar.–18 June 2006;
McNay Art Museum, San Antonio, 26 July–15 Oct.
2006; Frick Art and Historical Center, Pittsburgh, 4
Nov. 2006–14 Jan. 2007

No. 768. Reading by the Brook

769

Girl with Laurel

1879

Oil, 22⅝ × 15¾ (57.468 × 40.005)
Inscribed ll: Homer / 1879

The Detroit Institute of Arts, gift of Dexter M.
Ferry, Jr., 40.56

This painting has chiefly attracted attention for the
extraneous issue of an identity for the figure which is
its subject, and the landscape in which she stands. As
with a number of the substantial, finished oil paintings which remained with the Homer family at his
death, it gained the attachment of a quaint story.
The essentials of this tale were that a West
Townsend, Massachusetts, girl posed for the figure at
a time Homer was visiting his brother and sister-in-
law, Charles and Martha French Homer, at their
summer residence in the town; that the girl's father
had asked Homer to paint a portrait of his wife; that
Homer declined, whereupon the disappointed husband and father cut down the laurel plants seen
behind the girl.

In about 1936 LG was told this story by Mrs.
Charles Homer's nurse, who added that the girl still
lived across the street from Mrs. Homer's West
Townsend house. Lois Homer Graham, Mrs.
Charles Homer's great-niece, gave LG a copy of a list
she had compiled of "Winslow Homer Pictures
Belonging to Mrs. Charles S. Homer, 1935" on
which this painting was annotated "Miss Saunders
on Laurel Hill."

Mrs. Homer's nephews clearly provided the
Macbeth gallery with a version of the story when
they placed the painting with the gallery. On its sale
to the Detroit Institute of Arts the story was passed
on to the Institute's Clyde Burroughs by Hazel Lewis
of the Macbeth staff in a letter of 2 August 1940:

> Two interesting bits of information I remember
> hearing Mr. [Robert] Macbeth tell about the pic-
> ture are that the "girl" was in reality a local boy
> named Sanders, who posed for Homer, and that
> the farmer on whose property the laurel grew, was
> very much interested in the painting of the pic-
> ture and asked Homer to paint his portrait.
> Homer replied that he was not a portrait painter
> and therefore could not comply. The next morn-
> ing when Homer went to the spot to continue the
> painting of "girl with Laurel," all the laurel bushes
> had been cut down to the ground for spite.

This conflation of the old story associated with *Girl
and Laurel* and the account told in 1936 by Officer
Keenan of the Belmont, Massachusetts, police force
that, as a boy, he posed for Homer wearing a dress,
may have been concocted by Mrs. Homer's nephews

No. 769. Girl with Laurel   see color illustration, p. 445

when the painting was consigned to the Macbeth
gallery. However it is equally possible Robert
Macbeth or Ms. Lewis confused the tale which
accompanied *Girl and Laurel* and the story provided
with the 1878 watercolor *Waverley Oaks* (No. 739)—
also consigned to Macbeth by Charles L. Homer—
for which Keenan probably did pose.

ABG: Martha French Homer (known in the Homer
family as "Mattie") figures prominently in Richard
N. Smith's history of the town written for the
Townsend Historical Society, published in 1978. Her
father had been a prominent, wealthy citizen of West
Townsend, and it was the fairly grand French family

home she and Charles used as a country retreat. It is clear from Smith's history that even as a seasonal resident, Mattie Homer was an impressive force in the town. In later years her prominence owed much to her philanthropy—and something to the celebrity of her brother-in-law. (Smith captions the illustration of the French family mansion, "Homer House, built in 1823 by the Warren Family and made famous by Winslow Homer and his brother Charles. Charles's wife Martha, born and brought up in Townsend, later gave the Reading Room for literary and social uses.")

Smith recounts the story of *Girl and Laurel*, for its value in demonstrating the famous artist's connection with his subject.

> Winslow Homer made local history at the [Homers's] house in the summer of 1879, when he selected a young village girl, Fannie Sanders, to depict against a background of native laurel. Fourteen years old at the time, Fannie lived long enough to escort her niece to Homer House to view the now-famous painting on Mrs. Homer's wall. "Girl With Laurel" now hangs in Detroit's Institute of Art [*sic*], to which it was sold by Mattie Homer's nephew, Arthur, in 1940.

Apparently, the portion of the story concerning the unlikely destruction of laurel bushes had been lost by the time it got to Smith, or he did not find it credible.

Gordon Hendricks whose Homer monograph was published in the year after publication of Smith's history of Townsend, clearly was acquainted either with the earlier book, or its author, and also the letter from Ms. Lewis held in the Detroit Art Institute's curatorial files. He exercised more skepticism than usual in regard to the notion of a boy having posed in company with the profusion of laurel; he assumed—probably correctly—that the ultimate source of the tale was Mrs. Charles S. Homer, Jr.

Although Hendricks accepts that the girl and laurel bush were both rooted in West Townsend, he decided the painting was derived from nonexistent sketches made in the summer of 1878. He offers two points in support of this conclusion: the first is an unfounded assumption that the group of men Homer sketched in *The Card Game* (No. 664) were playing in the shade of the Charles Homers's West Townsend porch; the second is an unlocated letter he describes as written by Elizabeth Preston of New Ipswich, New Hamphire, in which she mentions Homer then being a guest in her home. Hendricks says the letter was written the day following the date "July 5th 1878" inscribed by Homer on *The Card Game*. However, as he does not give a transcription or facsimile illustration of this letter, his dating it to 6 July 1878 is open to interpretation. The letter may be inscribed with a full date, or only a day and month. As Hendricks imagined *The Card Game* had occurred in West Townsend, he could easily use the drawing to validate putting Homer's July visit to New Ipswich—about eight miles northwest of West Townsend—into the same year. On the other hand, the letter may be fully dated, and have been Hendricks's incentive to place that *Card Game* on the Charles Homers' West Townsend porch.

See commentaries No. 770, and No. 771.

PROVENANCE
Charles S. Homer, Jr., by bequest, 1910; Mrs. Charles S. Homer, Jr., by bequest, 1917; Arthur P. and Charles L. Homer, by bequest, 1937; (William Macbeth, Inc., c. 1937)

EXHIBITIONS
Whitney 1936, no. 18; NGA 1958/MFA, Boston, 1959, no. 43/39

LITERATURE
Richard N. Smith, *Divinity and Dust: A History of Townsend, Massachusetts* (Lancaster, MA: privately printed, 1978), 39, 193; Hendricks 1979, 134, 138, 302; Patricia Hills, in, *American Paintings in the Detroit Institute of Arts, Volume II* (New York: Hudson Hills Press, 1997), 123–24

770
The Shepherdess
1879

Oil, 22¾ × 15½ (57.785 × 39.370)
Inscribed lr: Homer 1879

Private collection

ABG: This *Shepherdess* appears to be the ultimate development of the 1878 drawings No. 700, and No. 701, and watercolors No. 702, and No. 703, which repeat an image of a slight farm girl standing with her staff or crook in a field she shares with a variable number of sheep. These four works on paper are assumed to be products of a visit to Houghton Farm Homer made in the summer of 1878. This culminating conception of those essential subject features has more in common, pictorially, with *Girl with Laurel* (No. 769) than with the 1878 drawings and watercolors. Both oil paintings present well developed young women who dominate the picture space; both are almost encumbered by the profusion of rotund natural forms at their feet: the boulders of a stone wall between the farm girl and the laurel bushes in one, and the wooly bodies of sheep in the other. There is also an affinity between the two paintings in the exceptional articulation of the womens' faces, and that they are made individual to the point of portraiture. Moreover, the features of the two young women are so closely similar, it is arguable that they are based on the same model.

The shepherdess theme of this painting and its descent in the Lawson Valentine family cast it as a scene at the Valentine's Houghton Farm in upstate New York. *Girl with Laurel* has an oral history which places the scene and model firmly in West Townsend, Massachusetts. The resemblance between the two paintings calls these geographical imperatives into question. It is perhaps more instructive to recognize both paintings as imaginative compositions which it is the power of an artist to create from accumulated studies and experience.

In October 1879 Homer exhibited an oil painting under the title *The Shepherdess* in the Century Association's first monthly exhibition of the 1879-1880 season. Three months later, in January 1880 he again contributed an oil to the Century's monthly event under that same title; The Century's ledger record for this event notes this *Shepherdess* was valued at $500. It is unlikely Homer would have shown the same panting twice, especially within such a short period of time. Given Homer's devotion to the theme of the shepherdess in this period, it would seem futile to try to identify either work; however, frequently as this subject appears in his work, it is rarely presented in the oil medium. The only surviving examples are three studies assigned to 1878,

No. 770. The Shepherdess

which are too roughly sketched to be appropriate for introduction in a Century Association exhibition: *Shepherd Girl Resting* (No. 749), *Girl and Sheep* (No. 754), and *Shepherdess* (No. 756); and two fully realized compositions: this painting, and the work known as *Spring: The Shepherdess of Houghton Farm* (No. 772). When Homer showed the latter painting in the 1879 annual exhibition of the National Academy of Design, it was a substantially larger canvas than it is now, and was priced in the exhibition catalogue at $1,500. The *Shepherdess* Homer contributed to the Century in October 1879 was probably the work that had been on view at the National

Academy throughout April and May that year. The other two major oils Homer had shown at the 1879 Academy *Annual* reappeared, sequentially, as his contributions to the November and December 1879 Century Association exhibitions. Consequently, this *Shepherdess* may reasonably be assumed to have been the canvas Homer put on view at the Century in January 1880. It may have attracted Lawson Valentine's attention at that time, or Valentine might already have reserved it.

PROVENANCE
Lawson Valentine, New York, nd; Lucy Houghton Valentine (Mrs. Lawson Valentine), 1891; Almira Valentine Pulsifer (Mrs. Nathan Trowbridge Pulsifer), her daughter, 1911; Lawson Valentine Pulsifer, Mountainville, NY, her son, nd; Alice Pulsifer Doyle and Natalie Pulsifer Byles, his daughters, 1957; (Davis & Long Co., 1978)

EXHIBITIONS
Century Association, New York, 10 Jan. 1880, no. 36 [?]; Storm King 1963, no. 9

No. 771. Woman Driving Geese

see color illustration, p. 444

771

Woman Driving Geese

nd

Oil, 15¹¹⁄₁₆ × 22½ (39.848 × 57.150)

Phoenix Art Museum, gift of Mr. and Mrs. H. L. Pratt, 59.1

LG first examined this painting in February 1937, when it was brought to him on behalf of Dr. Henry B. Boynton, Jr., of West Townsend, Massachusetts. At that time LG recorded an inscription on the center cross bar of the stretcher, noting that it was written in ink, in what was unmistakably Homer's hand. "To Dr Boynton / with the compts of / the Artist Winslow Homer"

Later that year Dr. Boynton placed *Woman Driving Geese* with the Macbeth gallery. Boynton wrote Robert W. Macbeth on 7 August 1937, presumably in response to Macbeth's request for a history of the work he then had in hand to sell.

> The painting which you referred to in your letter of August 2nd [1937] was painted by Mr. Homer in the late 70's. The scene was in Ashby, Mass. Mr. Homer gave this painting to my father the spring of '81 or '82. My father took care of him while he was convalescing after breaking his arm. During this time he lived with us six weeks. I was a small boy at the time. We went fishing together. He was an ardent fisherman, and was very particular about his fishing gear. He would prepare his gut leaders, preferring his own make to anything he could buy. We used to repair to the back waters of the river at 11 a. m. and 3 p.m., fishing for about an hour (for pickerel). I can remember very vividly his skill in casting among the lily pads and his adroitness in playing the fish, which he never failed to land. He was very patient while teaching me to draw. A very lovable and painstaking companion to me; making a life-long impression.

The younger Dr. Boynton was clearly not much engaged by the painting itself; it carried other, more important associations for him. He may be forgiven a natural flaw of memory in thinking his father received this gift in West Townsend at the time Homer was in England. However, the period Homer spent with the Boynton family may have been within the summer of 1878 or 1879, and *Woman Driving Geese* was presented in 1879 or 1880. Ashby is about four miles west of West Townsend.

ABG: In early November 1878, a reporter for the *New York Herald*, making the usual rounds of the studios as the artists returned from their summer absence, paid a visit to Homer. After commenting on "the very admirable water colors and pencil drawings" the artist had made during the summer, the writer went on to notice "some good studies in oil of oaks at Waverley, near Boston, and a scene under a cloudy sky on some hills, near Leeds, Greene county in this State." That "scene under a cloudy sky"—which corresponds to no other oil painting from this period in Homer's surviving oeuvre—may have been this painting, in which case, *Woman Driving Geese* would be a work of the 1878–1879 season.

It should be remembered that Homer routinely paid summer visits to family and friends in various parts of New England; he may well have been in the West Townsend area in 1878, as well as in 1879. Certainly, Dr. Boynton, or his father could have been mistaken in siting the painting to Ashby, but in choosing a work to give the senior Dr. Boynton it is more likely that Homer would—if he could—have it be a subject the doctor would recognize from his neighborhood. If the painting the New York reporter saw in Homer's studio in the autumn of 1878 was *Woman Driving Geese*, he might well have made a patriotic, but erroneous, assumption in placing the scene in one of Homer's favored New York State haunts.

PROVENANCE
Dr. Henry B. Boynton, West Townsend, MA, by gift of Homer, probably 1879; Dr. Henry B. Boynton, Jr., West Townsend, MA, nd; (William Macbeth, Inc., 1937); (Milch Galleries, 1938); Oliver B. James, New York, 1938; (Parke-Bernet Galleries, 7 Jan. 1953, Gallatin et al. sale, no. 85); (Milch Galleries, 1953); H. L. Pratt, Scottsdale, AZ, 1954

EXHIBITIONS
Macbeth 1938, no. 18; University of Arizona 1963, no. 114

LITERATURE
"Fine Arts. Studio Notes," *New York Herald*, 11 Nov. 1878

772

Spring: The Shepherdess of Houghton Farm

1879

Oil, 24½ × 28½ (62.230 × 72.390)
Inscribed ll: Homer / 1879

Private collection

LG heard of this painting from several sources in the 1930s, but did not have an opportunity to examine it until 1940 when it returned from the mid-West to the Findlay Galleries in New York. By that time LG already knew of a Homer letter which confirmed that the painting was one of the three major works the artist had contributed to the National Academy of Design annual exhibition of 1879; and that—some twenty-five years later—Homer, himself, had substantially altered the painting to its present appearance.

LG subsequently acquired the letter, which is dated 3 December 1906, and was written to William Clausen, a New York art dealer. Clausen had apparently carried through some business transaction which was profitable to Homer and gave Clausen occasion to explore his chances of brokering something else by the artist.*

Homer wrote Clausen:

> I received your check on Saturday night for which please find receipt. In regard to some other picture I will send you something that has been a favorite of mine since 1877 - when I commenced it - & in 1878 or 9 - it was in the Academy Exhibition.
>
> Enclosed *sketch*. Please make me a *frame for this*—a very strong frame in color & heavy moulding as the shaddows [*sic*] are quite dark and they are to stay so as I do not care to repaint the whole picture. Have the frame ready *in two weeks*. *Size of Canvas* 24 × 28¼

The enclosure to which Homer referred is a sheet carrying a sketch of this *Shepherdess of Houghton Farm* and a line of text giving the title, dimensions and further pertinent information: "'Spring' 24 × 28¼ (Cut from the center of *a larger picture*) Figure 21½ inches high."

More than six weeks passed before Homer wrote again to Clausen on 22 January 1907:

> Please send me the bill for the frame 24 × 28. I shall send the picture for it soon & will leave it with you for a month. As I am in love with it and have been for thirty years I put a price on it so that it will not be sold at present. I know all the faults in it, but they are useful to the whole thing & I leave them untouched. If you will place some article of furniture in front of this in your Gallery or hang it up high to keep people from smelling of it—and at their proper distance—*three times its width* I should say that would be a good hint to them & something they *should know*.
>
> This must net me $2400.00 as I now can afford to have it hanging in my own house. You see I know how old I am, the amount of money I have in my pocket, & the limit of old age. The years & money are all right but pictures are scarce.

To emphasize his concern that distance between viewer and painting was essential to the work of art being perceived as a whole Homer interrupted the text of his letter with a sketch of a gallery wall with a railing. He abhorred the common practice of examining a painting, as if—and at the same distance from the surface—reading a page of print, which he here referred to as "smelling" the work. Later the same year he again used the image of the nose in a letter to the Knoedler gallery expressing his conviction that *Early Evening* (5:No. 1764), which he was about to send to them, was best seen from the west side of Fifth Avenue. Knoedler's establishment was then located at the northeast corner of Fifth Avenue and 34th Street.

A few days later Homer appeared to act on his sentimental attachment to this painting in mentioning it in a letter of 25 January 1907 to the Pennsylvania collector, William J. Johnson: "Your letter of the 7th at hand. I would say not to be in a hurry to buy one of my pictures but depend upon me to give you one someday. The one [*Shepherdess of Houghton Farm*], I am to send to Clausen is not the thing for you."**

Homer seems disingenuous in protesting his attachment to the work. Early in March 1907, as soon as Clausen's month-long opportunity to sell it had expired, *Shepherdess of Houghton Farm* was received at Knoedler's. As *Spring*, and priced at $2,000. Knoedler's then sent it to annual exhibitions of contemporary American art mounted at the Cincinnati Art Museum; the Art Institute of Chicago; and the Buffalo Fine Arts Academy (shared with the City Art Museum of Saint Louis). Homer kept track of the painting's exposure, and seemed to have expected it to be sold. On 14 August 1907 he wrote the Knoedler gallery: "The painting called 'Spring' representing a girl with sheep must have been returned to you [from Cincinnati] by this time. I should like to have a photograph of it before it is sold and I ask you to have it done by your man who arranges your scrapbook. I should like to know also where it is now."

Perhaps to Homer's disappointment, *Shepherdess of Houghton Farm* came back to him immediately following its showing in Saint Louis. Knoedler's records noted its shipment to the artist on 19 November 1909.

No. 772. Spring: The Shepherdess of Houghton Farm

see color illustration, p. 446

*Homer was represented by the Knoedler gallery at this time. The artist was punctilious in respecting the territorial prerogative of his dealers, and thus, Knoedler would have had first right to offer any new oil in New York. Knoedler probably yielded its privilege in relation to *Shepherdess of Houghton Farm*, as being from an era in Homer's oeuvre which early twentieth century collectors might have found puzzling.

**Quoted in: Nicholas Chilcott, *A Champion of American Art*, privately printed, 1975, 31.

ABG: Homer introduced three major paintings at the National Academy of Design annual exhibition of 1879. The three were: *The Shepherdess of Houghton Farm*; *Sundown* (No. 775), and *Upland Cotton* (No. 776). Each was noted in the *Annual* catalogue as for sale for the extraordinary figure of $1,500, or approximately twice the highest amount Homer had previously placed on his oils. Given the uniformity of price, its amount, and Homer's habit of using supports of repetitious dimensions it is reasonable to speculate that the these three oils were the same

size, and that that size was larger than Homer's norms at the time. Homer, himself, stated that *The Shepherdess of Houghton Farm* as it is now known was "cut from the center of a larger picture;" *Sundown* disappeared within a few years of its creation; the canvas support of *Upland Cotton* alone survives in its original size, and it likely gives the measure of all three works: approximately 50 inches by 30 inches.

The New York press gave considerable attention to all three paintings on their debut at the Academy, but the response probably fell far short of Homer's expectation. His favorite, *The Shepherdess of Houghton Farm*, was the least noticed of the three. Critical opinion of it was unevenly divided with negative comments in the majority, and probably influenced Homer's substantial revisions made many years later.

The *Daily Graphic*'s reaction formed at the exhibition preview was that,

While Mr. Winslow Homer's hand has lost nothing of its old time vigor and individuality his pictures have certainly gained in finish and artistic completeness.... His shepherdess seems like an unsuccessful effort to elaborate one of the pastoral idles exhibited in the water color collection. The Hanging Committee have considerably hidden this canvas away in the small room. The sentiment and refinement which is displayed in the landscape and sheep seems totally wanting in the figure of the girl, which is crude in color and wooden in pose.

The *Independent* expressed its opinion that "'The Shepherdess of Houghton Farm' . . . is incorrect in drawing, absurd in arrangement, and detestable in color." On the other hand, the *World* had referred to the painting as "Mr. Winslow Homer's charming young shepherdess" in its coverage of the preview of the *Annual*, and had not essentially changed its opinion by the time its formal review was published nearly a month later. The *World*'s review also suggests specific guidance to Homer's eventual alteration of the composition.

> Perverse as it may seem to say so, we prefer the "Shepherdess" to [Homer's other two submissions] which the Hanging Committee have treated better. Its whole pictorial treatment, not only its composition and figure-drawing, but the landscape and the soft, clear air which fills it, is more delicate and refined than anything of Mr. Homer's that we remember; and at the same time it is as fresh and breezy as his somewhat similar water-colors exhibited two months or more ago. And when it is remembered that to this delicacy and refinement of both idea and expression, it adds Mr. Homer's other qualities, his vigor, his directness and his picturesqueness, it will be seen that it is one of the few pictures of which it can be said that they mark a perceptible advance in art at the National Academy. To this the ultra-realism of the lower part of the figure is but a slight and unimportant offset.

Susan Carter, in her review for the *Art Journal*, thought "'The Shepherdess of Houghton Farm,' by Mr. Homer, is a charming idyll, full of sentiment and delicate beauty." Marianna van Rennsselaer, in *The American Architect and Building News*, held a quite different opinion: "Mr. Winslow Homer abandons more and more entirely his better manner. The color in his Shepherdess of Houghton Farm is not bad by accident, it would seem, but by deliberate design. Especially may this be said of the rasberry-colored flesh."

The close of the Academy *Annual* on 31 May 1879, also marked the effective end of the 1878–1879 season for art exhibitions. The new season began with the Century Association's October reception and exhibition. For this occasion Homer contributed one watercolor and one oil painting, recorded in the Century's ledger as "The Shepherdess." While that title, alone, does not surely identify the work

exhibited, several factors strongly favor it being *The Shepherdess of Houghton Farm* making its second appearance.

There are four other surviving examples of the shepherdess subject executed in oils in the period of 1878–1879. Three are far too rough studies to be appropriate for introduction in a Century Association exhibition. (See No. 749, No. 754, and No. 756). The fourth is the fully realized, mid-sized *The Shepherdess* (No. 770), which is the likely candidate to be "The Shepherdess" Homer showed—valued at just $500—in the Century Association's monthly exhibition of January 1880.

That it was *The Shepherdess of Houghton Farm* Homer was showing in October at the first worthy opportunity following its appearance in the Academy 1879 *Annual* forms a pattern with his contributing his other two 1879 Academy works to the next succeeding monthly exhibitions at the Century: *Sundown* in November, and *Upland Cotton* in December 1879.

The Shepherdess of Houghton Farm next appeared in Springfield, Massachusetts, in February 1881. Homer had had good success with showing *A Visit from the Old Mistress* (2:No. 603) and *Sunday Morning in Virginia* (No. 620) at Gill's in Springfield in December 1879, and *By the Sea Side* (No. 874) there in February 1880. On this third opportunity to contribute to an exhibition at Gill's Homer sent *Peach Blossoms* (No. 767), which attracted some press notice, and a buyer, and this *Shepherdess*. Although it did not enjoy the same favor as *Peach Blossoms*, the reviewer of Gill's show for the *Springfield Daily Republican* did provide his readers—and posterity—with an extensive description of the subject as Homer originally conceived it.*

> The figure-pieces are numerous and their range of subject considerable. The largest and most boldly challenging is Winslow Homer's "Shepherdess," the buxom young woman of down-East with whom his brush became suddenly enamored about two years ago, and whom it has so effectively put on canvas and paper since. This is on a large canvas, and the girl stands on a breezy summer hill, her strong, free figure fronting the wind which, blowing her gown backwards, defines the contour of her shapely limbs addressed to movement, as she pauses a moment,—her vigorous arms, bare to above the elbow, raised for her hands to grasp her tall staff, and her well-poised head turned lightly to the right. She has a rosy red complexion, an independent and wholesome expression on her face, light hair with a braid down her back, and wears a straw hat with a light blue ribbon; a white [bodice], piqué perhaps, at all events something well-starched and picturesquely frilled and ruffled; a lilac reddish skirt, white stockings and stout calf-skin shoes; a very complete and interesting ensemble, surely, and painted

with appreciative vigor. Not all the artist's pains is bestowed on the shepherdess; her sheep are portrayed characteristically, and especially the cosset bell-wether, that stands looking up adoringly at her. These are all, however; the trees are nebulous, and there is no attempt at the grass, yet the green of them and the soft cloudy sky contribute much to the effect of the figure.

With this evidence that Homer had originally presented his *Shepherdess* at full length, three works of 1878 may be assumed to be particularly relevant to *The Shepherdess of Houghton Farm*. The small watercolor known as *Tending Sheep, Houghton Farm* (No. 734) is a likely prototype for the 1879 oil as it was originally constituted, although in the oil, Homer opted for a vertical format; the oil sketch *Shepherdess* (No. 756) appears to be a preliminary study for the central figure in *The Shepherdess of Houghton Farm*; and *Girl and Sheep* (No. 754), which Homer inscribed "Picture of Value," may be a variant conception for the *Shepherdess of Houghton Farm*.

The Shepherdess of Houghton Farm would have been returned from Springfield about a month before Homer left for his extended stay in England. He stored it safely away—in fact and in memory—for a quarter of a century.

*I am indebted to Martha J. Hoppin for sharing the substantial information on Homer and Springfield resulting from her extensive research in support of cataloguing the collections of Springfield's George Walter Vincent Smith, and Fine Arts museums.

PROVENANCE
Charles S. Homer, Jr., by bequest, 1910; (M. Knoedler & Co., 1912); (Henry Shultheis Co., 1912); (Howard Young Galleries, nd); J. W. Aylor, Kansas City, Mo., nd; (David B. Findlay Galleries, nd); (Robert C. Vose Galleries of Boston, nd); Ralph Chudney, Chicago, nd; (David B. Findlay Galleries, by 1925); Mrs. Ike M. Chubb, Kaw, OK, 1925; (David B. Findlay Galleries, 1940); (Grand Central Art Gallery, 1940); private collection, 1940

EXHIBITIONS
National Academy of Design, New York, *Fifty-fourth Annual Exhibition*, 1 Apr.–31 May 1879, no. 520 (as *Shepherdess of Houghton Farm*); Century Association, New York, 4 Oct. 1879, no. 23 (as *Shepherdess*) [?]; Gill's Art Galleries, and Springfield Art Association, Springfield, MA, *Fourth Annual Artists' Exhibition*, open by 4 Feb. 1881, no. 37 (as *The Shepherdess*); Cincinnati Art Museum, *Fourteenth Annual Exhibition of American Art*, 18 May–16 July 1907, no. 2 (as *Spring*); Art Institute of Chicago, *Annual Exhibition of Oil Paintings and Sculpture by American Artists*, 22 Oct.–1 Dec. 1907, no. 187 (as *Spring*); Buffalo Fine Arts Academy, and City Art Museum

of Saint Louis, *Fourth Annual Exhibition of Selected Paintings by American Artists*, 10 May–30 Aug., and 12 Sept.–[12 Nov.] 1909, no. 92 (as *Spring*); Herron 1911, no. 16 (as *Spring, Shepherdess of Houghton Farm*); Whitney 1944; Worcester 1944, no. 14; Storm King 1963, no. 10

LITERATURE
"The Academy Exhibition. A Creditable Display of the Work of American Artists," *(NY) Daily Graphic*, 29 Mar. 1879; "The Academy Exhibition. I," *(NY) World*, 30 Mar. 1879; "Fifty-Fourth Annual Exhibition of the National Academy of Design. The West and Northwest Galleries," *New York Herald*, 28 Apr. 1879; "The Academy Exhibition," *Appletons' Journal of Literature, Science, and Art* 21 (6 May 1879): 471; [Susan N. Carter], "The Academy Exhibition," *(NY) Art Journal* 5 (May 1879): 158–59; M[arianna] G. Van Rensselaer, "The Spring Exhibitions in New York. The National Academy of Design—The Society of American Artists," *American Architect and Building News* 5 (10 May 1879): 149; "The Two New York Exhibitions," *Atlantic Monthly* 43 (June 1879): 785; "Gill's Artists' Exhibition," *Springfield (MA) Daily Republican*, 3 Feb. 1881

773-R
Beach Scene
[1879]

Charcoal, 7⅛ × 5 (18.098 × 12.700)

Cooper-Hewitt, National Design Museum, Smithsonian Institution, gift of Charles Savage Homer, Jr., 1912-12-251

ABG: This sketch and the more finished drawing, No. 774, of essentially the same subject are likely contributory sources to the unlocated oil painting *Sundown* (No. 775).

PROVENANCE
Charles S. Homer, Jr., by bequest, 1910

773-V
Girls' Legs, Standing; Kites
[1879]
Charcoal

No. 773-R. Beach Scene

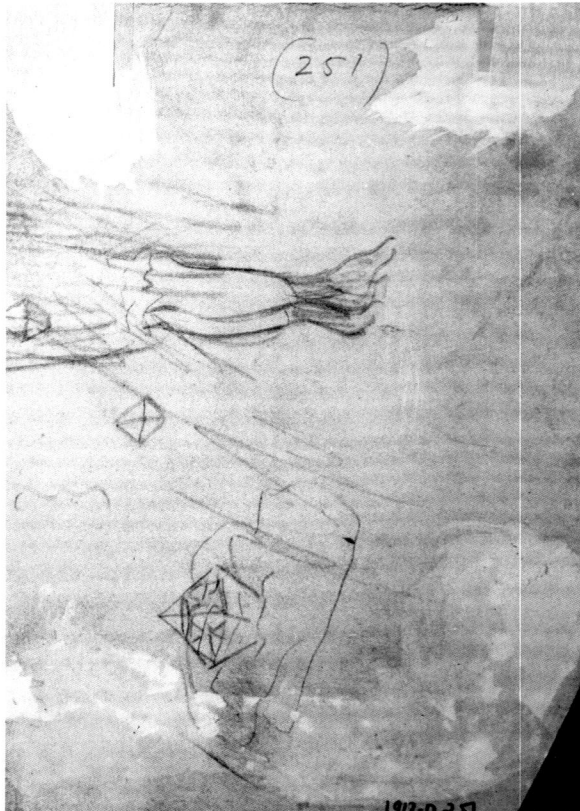

No. 773-V. Girls' Legs, Standing; Kites

No. 774. Girl Holding a Shell

774

Girl Holding a Shell

1879

Charcoal, 12⅜ × 8¹⁄₁₆ (31.433 × 20.480)
Inscribed lr: W. H. / 1879

Cooper-Hewitt, National Design Museum, Smithsonian Institution, gift of Charles Savage Homer, Jr., 1912-12-275

ABG: This drawing and the sketch, No. 773-R, of essentially the same subject are likely contributory sources to the unlocated oil painting *Sundown* (No. 775).

PROVENANCE
Charles S. Homer, Jr., by bequest, 1910

EXHIBITIONS
Academy of Arts & Letters 1953, no. 188; Ogunquit 1954, no. 22; Cooper-Hewitt 1972, no. 41; Columbia/ Telfair 1974, no. 15; Greenville County 1986

775

Sundown

[1879]

Oil

Unlocated

ABG: *Sundown* was one of the three major paintings Homer introduced at the National Academy of Design annual exhibition of 1879. The others were *The Shepherdess of Houghton Farm* (No. 772), and *Upland Cotton* (No. 776). Each of the three was noted in the *Annual* catalogue as for sale for the extraordinary figure of $1,500, or approximately twice the highest amount Homer had previously placed on his oils. Given the uniformity of price, its amount, and Homer's habit of using supports of repetitious dimensions, it is reasonable to speculate that these three oils were the same size, and that that size was larger than Homer's norms at the time. Homer, himself, stated that *The Shepherdess of Houghton Farm* as it is now known was "cut from the center of a larger picture;" *Sundown* disappeared within a few years of its creation; the canvas support of *Upland Cotton* alone survives in its original size, and it likely gives the measure of all three works: approximately 50 inches by 30 inches.

The New York press gave considerable attention to all three paintings on their debut at the Academy, but the response probably fell far short of Homer's expectation. Comment was fairly bland concerning his favorite, *The Shepherdess of Houghton Farm*; *Upland Cotton* was widely and favorably noticed. *Sundown* elicited remarkably virulent objections from a majority of the press. Fortunately, descriptive details on the subject and appearance of this lost painting were liberally entwined in the critical appraisals.

Initial reactions to *Sundown* leaned toward favorable. The *Daily Graphic* admired it on first sight at the press preview of the exhibition.

While Mr. Winslow Homer's hand has lost nothing of its old time vigor and individuality his pictures have certainly gained in finish and artistic completeness. . . . Mr. Homer has certainly exhibited no more original work than the charming seaside idyll which hangs in the large room. The easy and unconventional pose of the figure and the symmetrical disposition of the lines of the composition are particularly pleasing.

The *Herald* also thought well of *Sundow*n.

On the right of the Beckwith is one of the striking pictures of the display, "The Shell" [*sic*] (347) by Winslow Homer. A young girl sits on the seashore at sunset and watches the sparkle of the reflections of the sun's rays in a shell, which she holds.

Behind her the waves break on to a lower level of the beach, which, though not seen, is finely suggested, and in the middle distance is a schooner. In golden sunset tone the picture is admirable; the cold blue of the wave rolling in is very true, and the effect of sunlight on the broken crests and the white sails of the vessel is very real. The sky is undecided in effect and the weakest point in an otherwise admirable work.

The *Evening Post*, while more restrained, was generally positive in its report on the preview.

Mr. Winslow Homer is on the line with an American girl in a dressing gown, seated on the beach alone. The waves roll up toward her, in deep blue and their blue, just before they break, being pierced with a row of what looks like a steamer's round cabin windows. Purplish clouds unwreath themselves, entwine and vanish above the sea, and a stately ship—a piece of significant invention, novel, bold and large in handling.

But a *Times* report on the Academy *Annual* preview suggested what was to come in formal, expansive reviews of the exhibition.

Not many artists avail themselves seriously of the privilege of Varnishing Day, the prevailing idea being that it is best to leave well alone. There are conspicuous exceptions to the rule, however, such as in the case of Mr. Winslow Homer, who finds that his young girl sitting on the sea-beach before a wall of surf, and holding up a shell, is quite out of harmony with everything about it, especially with another young person painted in Brittany by Hovenden, whose harsh, brilliant coloring even takes the eye away from a picture by Homer, and that is saying a good deal. Mr. Homer varnished down his large canvas, and certainly improved it very much; but whether it can ever be improved up to a point worthy of his skill and reputation is quite another matter. To call the line of breakers a wall is perfectly correct. It is as hard as porcelain, and the spots where the edge has crumbled into foam look like napkins hung upon this wall. The picture is out of tune, in spite of that air of individuality which all Mr. Homer's work possesses and which raises him so far out of the crowd of mediocrities.

The *Evening Telegram* held a similar opinion on first viewing *Sundown*: "Winslow Homer's painting, representing a young girl sitting on the sea beach and holding up a sea shell is by no means in his best style. The wave of water has nothing of the characteristic of waves as they are known to ocean, and we can see nothing intrinsically entrancing in the handling of the subject."

The *Evening Mail* went into more detail in expressing much the same objections to the painting.

> Mr. Winslow Homer has this time strayed to the water in one of his three pictures on the walls, but cannot be congratulated on his success. In the picture to which we allude, 347, "Sundown," a young girl is sitting on a beach holding a shell to her ear, while behind breaks the sea. Mr. Homer has well succeeded in giving the steel blue color which ocean breakers sometimes have when they roll in from a long distance over an abruptly shelving bottom, but the water is solid, the yeastly [*sic*] foam might be cut with a knife, and a schooner in the distance, with all sails set, is nailed to the water. The mightiest tempest that ever blew would never budge her.

In reviewing the exhibition, the *New-York Times* had little to say about *Sundown*, only adding to the faults it had noted a week earlier: "Mr. Winslow Homer is also surprisingly weak in perspective, and frequently allows his figures to appear hardly detached from their backgrounds. The girl with the shell in the South Room does not err so much in that way, but her surroundings do."

As full reviews of the Academy *Annual* began to appear in print, a critical distaste for *Sundown* seemed to gather momentum.

Ten days after the public opening of the exhibition the *Independent* gave its opinion:

> Mr. Winslow Homer is represented by three of his peculiarities, the one before us, "Sundown" (347), being exasperatingly bad. It is the figure of a young person of the feminine gender, in a yellow dress, squatting on a seashore and holding a shell in her hand. What it means we don't know; but we do know that such a sea as Mr. Homer has painted never existed, and that his sky is of the sort that never was on sea or land, and never will be. If this enigmatical picture is a joke, the joke is a poor one.

Nearly two weeks later, it was the *Evening Telegram*'s turn to excoriate the painting.

> Winslow Homer's "Sundown" will, in our opinion, do him more harm than he can undo until a singularly favorable hour of redemption arrives. It represents a young girl in yellow, half kneeling upon the gray seashore, her back turned to a wall of dark blue waves fringed with wedding-like foam and holding in her hand a large pearl-tinted shell. Neither the girl's face nor form is comely, the attitude is not graceful, nor is the contrast of color harmonious. Why Mr. Homer should choose

such a subject for a picture intended to be at least partially representative of his powers is more than we can explain. It will probably be admired by a small circle of eccentrics and uniques.

The *Daily Tribune* had its say a few days later.

> But what to say of the audacity of Mr. Winslow Homer who sends his picture "Sundown" into an assembly such as this is supposed to be; and what to say of the Academy that gives it a conspicuous place upon the line in the best room! . . . . There can, however, be no doubt about the reality of Mr. Homer's young woman. How, on a beach that evidently, like all other beaches, slopes down to the water, this uncommonly heavy being can sit with her back to the breakers; where she got on a beach hereabouts—and she is, no doubt, a hereabout girl, we take her for no gay creature of the element—a pearl shell like this; these and some other questions come naturally to the mind on seeing for the first time this most extraordinary performance. It is so unnatural, so ugly, so wanting in taste, in sentiment, in meaning of any sort, and here's the rub—it might have been so pretty, or beautiful, or grand, according to the artist's mood or capacity, that we have no patience to discuss it.

Where a writer for the *Daily Graphic* found *Sundown* a "charming seaside idyll" on viewing it a few days before the public opening of the Academy exhibition, a little over a month later the newspaper included it among a small number of works to be ridiculed in the voice of a fictitious "Amateur" visitor to the Academy.

> No. 347, "Sundown." Young lady in yellowish dress suggestive of mandarin's robe, reclining on a brown beach and back against a very blue ocean and clouds; crests of waves, inclined to be cream color, with a suspicion of red tinge. Young lady holds in her hand a mother of pearl, or abalone shell, found in great numbers in tropical latitudes. Have assisted in loading a schooner with them. Fish boiled and then dried in the sun. Chinese make soup of them. Hard as gutta-percha vulcanized. Make excellent soup. Only one shell. Fish holds on to rocks by suction. Pry them off with cold chisels. Wet work in heavy surf. Loaded the Henry with forty ton cured. Losing business 1856. Small Chinese war with England. Abalones in Canton market went down to nothing. Can't see where this young woman found one of those shells on a sand beach. Always found on rock beaches in low latitudes.

Reviewers for the periodical press were more temperate in expressing their opinions of *Sundown*, but hardly more approving. *Appletons' Journal* tried to cushion its negative reaction to the one work with a vague compliment for Homer's total representation in the exhibition.

Of "Sundown," Mr. Homer's third picture, one can not speak with confidence. It is a seashore scene, with sky and sea bathed in deep indigo—a study of effect of light that may be true, but which seems to us an excessive exaggeration. Nor do we like the composition. The surf is a rigid wall with breaks that look like land-slides. The girl on the sand looks out of the picture, and holds up a shell as if it were a mirror to reflect the visages of the spectators. But it is original in thought, and, taken with Mr. Homer's other subjects, is valuable as indicative of the many resources of expression which he possesses.

Marianna van Rennsselaer, writing for the *American Architect and Building News* simply dismissed the painting with few, but, cutting words: "Mr. Winslow Homer abandons more and more entirely his better manner . . . . Sundown is comical rather than affecting." In contrast, *The Nation's* reviewer was ambivalent.

The [Hanging] Committee-members having thus fulfilled their annual mission of tickling each other, but with less boldness than common, the other National Academicians have been shown to their places on the coveted line. The selections for this honor which seem to be unobjectionable are . . . Mr. Homer's, N. A., "Sundown," a painful paint-problem of vivisection, not pursued out of any sympathy with the heroine, but to show how the hot rays of sunset are cutting into the sclerotic coats of her eyes.

Art Amateur also contrived to admire and reject *Sundown* within one paragraph.

Mr. Winslow Homer is a realist of the realists, with a kind of haughty and half-grudged poetry breaking out from him against his will. He is never commonplace, and is never insincere. That he despises composition, and never idealizes anything is his peculiar form of artistic virtue. In "Sundown" (347) we have a sea-beach; the vaulted wall of a coming wave; a stretch of sand, whose rapid descent shows just that steepness of beach where the largest breakers form; and a girl sitting on it holding up a pearly shell to reflect the last red ray. The light catches on the gleaming enamel of her eyes as she smiles at the play of colors. Her yellow dress turns orange in the sunset. It is a scientific rather than a beautiful picture. Full of serious study, and careful to apply the supposed conditions of the light to every part of the composition, it is yet so abrupt in its massive forms, the silhouette of the figure is so inlaid against

the porphyry wave which stands motionless in act to devour the beach, that we think rather of mosaic-work than of painting—mosaic-work where the stony nature of the vehicle has got into the pictorial effect.

Susan Carter, writing for the *Art Journal* was nearly alone in giving the painting general approval.

"Sundown" (no. 347), is a girl on the seashore, which is much more strong in effect than [Upland Cotton], and is painted with a very great range in the scale of colour and light and shade. Perhaps many of our readers will have observed the violent effect of sunset from the seashore, when against a bank of dark clouds, which dims into an indigo-colour the long line of the ocean, out of the darkness, like magic, sails and near objects on the seashore start into life—when the glancing beams of the setting sun strike upon them, and sails of ships near and distant, and bits of rock and any stray figure wandering on the beach, appear as if transfigured. This sudden and fierce glow has the splendour of a stage effect under calcium-light, but it is, nevertheless, a true effect of one of the phases of Nature. Such a moment as this is that which Mr. Homer has caught and fixed upon his canvas, and out of the dark, indigo sea and sky, cold with the breeze of the nearing night, a ship, with its sails set, the curling, white crests of the great rollers breaking on the beach, and a solitary woman holding a sea-shell in her hand, shine with lurid brightness as a last sunbeam touches them.

The 1878–1879 season effectively ended with the close of the National Academy of Design *Annual* 31 May 1879. Apparently Homer worked very little in oil that spring and early autumn for instead of showing new works in the last months of 1879 he reprised his representation in that spring's *Annual* at the Century Association's monthly exhibitions. In October, the first of the 1879–1880 season, he showed *The Shepherdess [of Houghton Farm]*. In November he showed *Sundown*; and in December, *Upland Cotton*.

Sundown was possibly seen once again, if it was the *On the Beach* Homer put for sale with Daniel A. Mathews in early January 1880. The New York *Evening Post* reported that "Two good collections of pictures are now exhibiting down town and will be sold by auction on Thursday and Friday afternoons at 1 o'clock. . . . In the Mathews Gallery in Cedar street the American pictures are the chief attraction. Here the visitor with his catalogue will probably note . . . . Winslow Homer's original, odd and striking 'On the Beach,'"

The *Post's* comment and a titling of *On the Beach* is equally applicable to *By the Seaside* (No. 874), a subject which has much in common with *Sundown*, as described by the critics. It is questionable, however, whether Homer would have introduced *By the Seaside*, his only—and possibly, still wet—"serious" oil of the season, in an unexceptional auction. It is more believable that *By the Seaside* was held back—or finished just in time—for the more promising venue of the annual exhibition produced by Gill's Art Galleries in Springfield, Massachusetts, and *Sundown* was the work being offered at Mathews Gallery.

Sundown was surely last seen at the Century Association in November 1879. Even if it was the work put up for auction in January 1880, there is no assurance it found a buyer, so it is quite possible Homer eliminated the painting, as he had the equally disliked *Low Tide* (2: No. 358) a decade earlier. Homer gave considerable attention in 1878 to the image of fashionable young women positioned on dramatically lighted beaches, with vast seas receding behind them (see No. 655 through No. 660); this theme would culminate in *By the Seaside* of 1880. While these works are clearly closely related to *Sundown*, none provides a sure approximation of the missing painting's appearance.

See No. 773-R, No. 774, No. 876.

EXHIBITIONS

National Academy of Design, New York, *Fifty-fourth Annual Exhibition*, 1 Apr.–31 May 1879, no. 347; Century 1879, no. 28; Daniel A. Mathews Art Gallery, New York, [auction], c. 12–16 Jan. 1880 (as *On the Beach*) [?]

LITERATURE

"The Academy Exhibition. A Creditable Display of the Work of American Artists," *(NY) Daily Graphic*, 29 Mar. 1879; "Fine Arts. Fifty-Fourth Annual Exhibition of the Academy of Design—Important Pictures—First Notice," *New York Herald*, 30 Mar. 1879; "Preparing the Pictures. The Artists Varnishing Day," *New-York Times*, 30 Mar. 1879; "The Academy Exhibition. First Impression and a Hasty Tour of the Galleries," *(NY) Evening Post*, 30 Mar. 1879; "The Academy Exhibition," *New York Evening Mail*, 1 Apr. 1879; "The Spring Exhibition. National Academy of Design. First Notice," *Art Interchange* 2 (2 Apr. 1879): 50; "Artists and Their Works. Around the Galleries. A Stroll Through the Academy of Design," *New-York Times*, 7 Apr. 1879; "Fine Arts. National Academy," *The Independent* 31 (10 Apr. 1879): 13; "The Academy Pictures. Further View of More Prominent Works," *(NY) Evening Telegram*, 22 Apr. 1879; "Academy of Design. Fifty-fourth Annual Exhibition. Fourth Article," *New-York Daily Tribune*, 26 Apr. 1879; "The Academy Exhibition. III," *(NY) World*, 27 Apr. 1879; "The Academy Exhibition," *Appletons' Journal of Literature, Science, and Art* 21 (6 May 1879): 471; [Susan N. Carter], "The Academy Exhibition," *(NY) Art Journal* 5 (May 1879): 158–59; "An Amateur at the Academy," *(NY) Daily Graphic*, 3 May 1879; M[arianna] G. Van Rensselaer, "The Spring Exhibitions in New York. The National Academy of Design—The Society of American Artists," *American Architect and Building News* 5 (10 May 1879): 149; "Fine Arts. The Fifty-Fourth Exhibition of the Academy of Design," *The Nation* 28 (15 May 1879): 341; "The Two New York Exhibitions," *Atlantic Monthly* 43 (June 1879): 785; [Earl Shinn], "The Art Gallery. The National Academy of Design. First Notice," *Art Amateur* 1 (June 1879): 4

776
Upland Cotton
[1879]

Oil, 49 × 29¼ (124.460 × 74.295)
Inscribed ll: Winslow Homer N A / 1879
[overwritten] Homer / 1879-'95

Weil Brothers Cotton, Inc., Montgomery, AL

ABG: Homer introduced three major paintings at the National Academy of Design annual exhibition of 1879. The three were on distinctively different themes. *The Shepherdess of Houghton Farm* (No. 772) was the culmination of the pastoral images which had preoccupied Homer from 1877. *Sundown* (No. 775) featured a young woman seated on a dramatically lighted beach, and probably was developed from a composition Homer had rendered in several variations in 1878. *Upland Cotton* was clearly a reprise of *The Cotton Pickers* (2:No. 602) which had some reputation, having been highly admired by the few who saw it at the Century Association in March 1876 before it was removed to England by its purchaser. Each of the three was noted in the *Annual* catalogue as for sale for the extraordinary figure of $1,500, or approximately twice the highest amount Homer had previously placed on his oils.

The New York press gave considerable attention to all three paintings on their debut at the Academy, which is especially fortunate because none is now known in its original form. Homer altered the composition of *The Shepherdess of Houghton Farm* by cutting down the canvas to its present size. *Sundown* probably did not survive much more than a few years from its creation. Homer may have made some change in *Upland Cotton* in the mid-1890s; and certainly, some time in the last decade of his life, obliterated much of the upper two-thirds of the composition apparently in preparation to repaint virtually the entire work. He carried this intention no further than applying a heavy layer of lead white over the area he had apparently cleared by scraping away his original design.

Homer seems to have had *Upland Cotton* in process by late 1877, at least. Early in January 1878 the New York *Daily Graphic* reported, "Winslow Homer, whose original and forcible method is so readily recognizable, is completing a Southern scene representing cotton pickers at work. The bursting buds of the plant and the moving character of the figures—colored women—are enhanced by the background of positive sky." The *Graphic* admired the painting again fifteen months later when reporting on the preview of the National Academy of Design annual exhibition of 1879, but gave no descriptive detail.

The representative of the *New-York Times* who attended the preview did give his readers some idea of the subject features of *Upland Cotton* as he admired its qualities.

[following discussion of *Sundown*] Fortunately, [Homer] retrieves himself, not merely in this exhibition, but upon the opposite wall of the same room. His scene of negro women picking cotton is both fresh and modern as well as national in subject. It is also well managed in its hues, notwithstanding the slight character of the sky. This sky may not be exactly out of harmony with the trellis of cotton plants and the negro women at work behind it, but a finer sense of the relations of tones in the painter would possibly have lent it a severer character. Be that as it may, here is a picture that a cotton millionaire, or say the Cotton Exchange, ought to buy as a graceful tribute to the plant which has made so many fortunes. It will always be worth more than the price paid for it.

The *New York Herald* was of much the same opinion: "In Winslow Homer's 'Upland Cotton' all is to be praised, except the incoherent sky. The cotton plants are treated with great knowledge, and the good figures of the two negresses are well introduced." And so was the *Evening Telegram*:

Winslow Homer's "Upland Cotton" has been very much praised and justly. The theme has evidently been deeply studied and reproduced with a nice fidelity that is indeed rare. Against him the complaint cannot be urged that he does not choose modern and American subjects. The sky shows less masterful handling than anything else in the picture, but the cotton plants and the negresses at work at them are singularly true to nature and will be instantly recognized and appreciated by any one familiar with such scenes.

Susan Carter provided the most detailed description of the subject features of *Upland Cotton*, as visitors to the Academy in 1879 experienced it, in her review of the *Annual* in the *Art Journal*.

A picture by Winslow Homer, "Upland Cotton" (no. 393), a scene on a Southern plantation, is a remarkable penetration of Japanese thought into American expression. The cotton-plants are straggling across a footpath, in which are two negro women, with their heavy, Oriental figures clad in strong, rich colours. One woman stands upright, with her turbaned head swung back, outlined against a thin, hot sky. The other woman is stooping over and gathering the cotton-pods, and her rounded back seems to bear the burden of all the toil of her race. Down close into the foreground of the canvas the cotton-plant is painted, and for crispness and delicacy of drawing, and in the variously developed cotton-pods, from where the wool hangs out of the dry pod, to the half-opened and still unclosed buds, each pod is painted as if

Upland Cotton as it has appeared since about 1950.

doing it was all the artist had ever cared for. The picture is a superb piece of decoration, with its deep, queer colours like the Japanese dull greens, dim reds, and strange, neutral blues and pinks. Japanese art is not gorgeous, like the Turkish and Persian, but its peculiar artistic subtlety has been assimilated precisely by Mr. Homer. This picture seems to us original and important as an example of new thought.

Besides her useful factual information, Carter's perception of *Upland Cotton* as a decorative conception, and her suggestion of intentional affinity with Japanese aesthetic, is revealing in itself, and has long intrigued scholars of Homer's work.

Carter was not alone in seeing the painting as decorative. The *Appletons' Journal*'s critic had no doubt of Homer's compositional intent:

"Upland Cotton," being almost without perspective, and painted nearly flat, must be recognized by the spectator as purely a decorative picture if he is to understand it. It represents two negro women in a field gathering cotton. Nothing could

be more delicate and perfect than the painting of the cotton-pods in this picture—nothing more truly expressive within the design of the artist than the whole composition, which is brilliant and unique, and viewed with a knowledge of the limitations of its purpose, is excellent.

The Nation, in the first installment of its review of the *Annual* also thought, "Mr. Homer's 'Upland Cotton' (393), a beauty and an original, with figures seen through a lattice of wayward plants, where the pods and flowers occur in the finest possible decorative arrangements." The *Nation* seemed to think praise of the painting was worth repeating the following week in its second article on the *Annual*: "Mr. Homer's best contribution is the 'Upland Cotton' (393), thoroughly individual and unborrowed in its effect of dusky figures seen through a tracery of intricate plants which quite enlace the canvas."

Response to the painting was remarkably consistent in its admiration, and in the characteristics on which attention focused. *Scribner's Monthly* noted, "Mr. Winslow Homer exhibited a singular and very pleasing study of the upland cotton plant, with negresses picking cotton. The sky of this picture has been criticized for its color and thinness, but people were pretty much at one as to its merits."

The *Atlantic Monthly* recorded the work they called "Cotton-Pickers" as a "field of tall cotton-plants, crossed and tangled in front, and spotted with the large, soft, white pods, with two women of the African race half shrouded in the midst, is very decorative; and there is made to be something mysterious and sphinx-like about the women against the sky."

The 1878–1879 season effectively ended with the close of the National Academy of Design *Annual* on 31 May 1879. Apparently Homer worked very little in oil that spring and early autumn for instead of showing new works in the last months of 1879, he reprised his representation in that Spring's *Annual* at the Century Association's monthly exhibitions. In October, the first of the 1879–1880 season, he showed *The Shepherdess [of Houghton Farm]*. In November he showed Sundown; and in December, *Upland Cotton*.

The Shepherdess of Houghton Farm and *Sundown* were then effectively retired. However just three months following its appearance at the Century, Homer placed *Upland Cotton* in a Union League Club exhibition where it again attracted critical attention. The *Times* writer's description of the features of the *Upland Cotton* he saw at the Union League Club is consistent with those given in the spring of 1879, when the painting was at the National Academy. He had no patience with Homer's retreat from anecdotal genre.

The most conspicuous loan to the monthly exhibition last night was Winslow Homer's picture of two negro women at work in a cotton-field. Like most of Mr. Homer's work, this has its fine places and its crude. The stalks and bolls of the plants form an original kind of trellis, through which the cotton-pickers in their colored gowns show pleasantly enough, so far as the colors go. But one may not be overcritical, and yet ask why it is that Mr. Homer should have placed his cotton-pickers in such ungraceful attitudes. Were it possible to give a reason, the ungainliness of the figures might be accepted, but there appears to be nothing in the situation which warrants either the crouching position of the one or the upright pose of the other. Why should they take the poses they do, rather than any of a thousand others. Art is supposed to exhibit the quintessence of design; but these women show no design; they might have been anywhere else in the picture and yet have done quite as well. The fact that the painting is an able one does not suffice to protect it from criticism on that side; on the contrary, its very excellence forces one to demand of the painter that he shall move a step further than the mere placing of two dark-skinned women in juxtaposition with certain cotton plants, and devote this large canvas and this fine initial conception to the telling of some story, such story being either openly descriptive of something read with ease by him who runs, or else having a meaning of finer quality and one to be perceived only by those who devote time and thought to pictures. No one has a better foundation for such a progress in his art than Mr. Homer, for no one unites just his proportion of experience, industry and originality.... Mr. Homer's cotton field wants a drama, or comedy, or some story.

The New York *Evening Mail*'s comment, appearing on the same day, was far less verbose, but just as intent on pointing out faults: "Mr. Winslow Homer's "Picking Cotton" [*sic*] in last year's Academy Exhibition is equally conspicuous for its merits and its faults. The theme is broadly treated, the scene is painted with fidelity, and the expression of the figures full of meaning. But the latter are not well drawn, the stooping woman being out of all proportion from her neck to where the body begins to curve, and the color is in parts inadequate."

Homer exhibited the painting again just at the end of 1880, in Brooklyn, and with its purchase price somewhat discounted to $1,200. The work had worn out its novelty, as the *Art Journal*'s coverage demonstrated.

The Brooklyn Art Association began its forty-first semi-annual exhibition on [December] 7th, having had its reception and private view the evening before.... A good many of the best pictures have been seen before, as is always true of the Brooklyn Exhibition, which, since it depends largely upon the same painters as the National Academy Exhibition, is obliged, of course, to attempt no rivalry, but to remain content with following in

Photograph of a detail of *Upland Cotton* made in 1939 by Robert Macbeth of the Macbeth gallery. Macbeth chose to concentrate on the altered portion of the painting rather than stand farther from his subject and capture an image of the whole canvas. That portion is here placed within an outline representing its position within the full painting.

its more important contemporary's footsteps. For examples, among the pictures hitherto exhibited either at the Academy or elsewhere, and tolerably familiar to persons interested in the Fine Arts, are Mr. Winslow Homer's "In the Cotton Field," an important decorative work, to which the public were introduced in the spring of 1879.

Upland Cotton did not find a buyer in Brooklyn, and then was presumably stored away with *The Shepherdess of Houghton Farm* as Homer prepared to go abroad in March 1881. Like *Shepherdess*, Homer brought it out again many years later, in its case because an especially apt exhibition opportunity presented itself: the *Cotton States and International Exposition* organized by the city of Atlanta, and held there from mid-September through December 1895.

Homer would surely have thought *Upland Cotton* needed what he referred to as "overlooking" by this time, some fifteen years since it had been put out on public display. To Homer "overlooking" a painting certainly meant light cleaning with a sponge and clear water, and touching up where natural thinning of paint layers had revealed some rejected formal detail, or put value relationships out of balance. Whether Homer substantially altered the painting, and, if so, how, are questions which can never be answered because of his later obliteration of a large area of the work.

The revision of the line of inscription from "Winslow Homer N A / 1879" applied in black paint, to "Homer / 1879 - '95" in brown paint—the "1879" being overwritten in brown on the black characters—may be assumed to have been done in connection with sending the painting to Atlanta. The addition of "'95" implies a significant change made at the time. However, in 1936, Miss Alice Burditt of Prout's Neck recalled for LG having seen "a picture of two negro women picking cotton" in Homer's studio at the time it was about to go to, or had just returned from, an exhibition. This would suggest no radical change was made in *Upland Cotton* in 1895. Homer was particularly given to altering the skies of those of his earlier works which remained in his possession in his later years (e. g., *Answering the Horn* [2:No. 599]), and in light of the critics' dissatisfaction with just this part of the subject in 1879, speculation that he repainted that area of *Upland Cotton* before sending it to Atlanta is reasonable—but can be no more than speculation.

Updating the inscription to the year of the Atlanta exhibition could have had more to do with Homer's sense of public relations then a marker of creative change. Critics and viewers were not engaged by anything deemed old, and thereby "used." Also, the Atlanta public might well have been offended if it were perceived the now-famous Homer had sent them a work from his past.

If such slight misdirection had any part in Homer expanding his inscription, than he may have been gratified by *The Nation*'s comment on the art exhibition at the Atlanta fair: "Many of the best American painters, both at home and abroad are represented. . . . 'Upland Cotton,' a new work by Winslow Homer." And that of the *Art Amateur*: "One may also see here 'Upland Cotton,' a picture by Winslow Homer, not yet exhibited in the North."

Gustav Reichard, Homer's New York dealer apparently managed the presentation of *Upland Cotton* in Atlanta. The inscription "Reichard, 18th St. & 5th Ave." could be seen on the back of the stretcher in 1936 and was still visible in 1958. Although Reichard had given up his gallery in Manhattan at just the time of the Atlanta fair, he maintained an affiliation with the M. Knoedler gallery. This explains the notation in Knoedler's records: "March 1896. Cotton Pickers [*sic*]. G. Reichard, Phila. $1,000. March 1896 returned." Apparently the canvas was shipped from

Georgia to Reichard's attention at Knoedler, which, in turn sent it to Homer in Prout's Neck.

The next time the canvas was seen in public was in Maine, on the occasion of the centenary exhibition mounted by the Prout's Neck Association for a few weeks in July 1936. The exhibition was assembled almost exclusively from what remained of Homer's estate in the possession of Mrs. Charles S. Homer, Jr. It was installed at the Association's premises, but, as the public was being admitted to the Homer studio for this special event, a few objects were informally put out on view there. Among them was *Upland Cotton* in the condition Homer had left it: inscription and cotton plants intact at the sides and along the lower portion of the canvas, and a blank expanse of white above. LG examined it there. On Mrs. Homer's death in 1937 *Upland Cotton* passed to Homer's nephews, Arthur Patch Homer and Charles Lowell Homer. In 1939, in connection with settling Mrs. Homer's estate, Robert Macbeth recorded and photographed the canvas at Prout's Neck.

In a letter of 15 January 1942 Charles L. Homer wrote to Robert McIntyre of the Macbeth gallery:

> If by chance you see Goodrich, you might tell him that the big canvas I asked him about at the W. H. studio—the one with the cotton plants and great deal of white lead—is developing into something very fine. There are two figures in the place he was positive there were none. . . . By the removal of the white lead two very fine negro pickers are gradually coming out.

Charles L. Homer's confidence proved to be premature. Giovanni Castano, a Boston dealer and "restorer," was working on the painting. Castano wrote C. L. Homer on 20 July 1942, "In regard to the cotton-picking painting, I regret very much to say that there is nothing further I can do with it as I find that the picture was scraped before your uncle repainted it. It is now in my studio in Boston and if you wish to have it back you may call for it at any time." C. L. Homer replied on 21 September 1942: "Sorry not to have picked up the painting before . . . I expect to come up at the end of this week—will get it at that time. . . . . Sorry that we could not have made a masterpiece out of this. It looked like real money."

But C. L. Homer did not take *Upland Cotton* out of Castano's studio in the autumn of 1942. He was writing Castano about its disposition in June 1946, and in a letter of 15 December 1946 told him, "In regard to 'Upland Cotton' hang onto it as my family, who will cash in on this after my death, are moving to Boston in a couple of months. I do not want it down here [in Prout's Neck]."

It is only possible to speculate on what might have been done with the painting between late 1942 and mid-1946. In light of C. L. Homer's report of the two "pickers gradually coming out" as the coating of lead white was being removed, it seems likely some indication of the scale and placement of the two figures as they appeared in 1879 remained despite Homer having scraped down his original work. When C. L. Homer was next in Castano's studio following the discovery of that scraping, the men may have decided that instead of abandoning the canvas, it should be reconstructed.

Apparently having learned it was Castano who had *Upland Cotton* in hand, LG wrote him 3 June 1943, requesting information on the condition of the painting and a photograph of it, presumably with the newly emerged figures. Castano never acknowledged this request; however, on 21 June 1943, he wrote LG asking for a photograph of the *Cotton Pickers* of 1876, stating Charles B. Guinn had given permission for Castano to get a photo. Guinn, who lived in Carthage, Missouri, had then owned *Cotton Pickers* for about thirty years. LG provided the photograph. Sometime in the summer of 1943 Castano purchased *Cotton Pickers* from Dr. Guinn; in September 1943 Castano sold it to the Wildenstein gallery. Castano, thus had had the company—probably for several months—of the one surviving work which could serve as the model for "restoration" of *Upland Cotton.*

While Homer's hand is evidently absent from a large portion of the present surface of the painting, the most conspicuous incongruity is the standing woman at the right of the composition. Apparently, Homer's scraping was so thorough in this area that nothing remained on which to reconstruct the figure, so she was replaced with a precise copy of the figure at the right in *Cotton Pickers.* She is not "clad in strong, rich colours," nor is her head "turbaned" or "swung back," as vividly described by Susan Carter in the May 1879 *Art Journal.*

Charles L. Homer died in 1955. Castano sold *Upland Cotton* on behalf of his widow on 22 March 1956. Castano wrote her on the same date concerning remuneration due him for his efforts in disposing of works by Homer for the estate. In partial support of his taking a fifty percent share in the sale of the painting, rather than a commission, he stated that it had taken him "exactly one year to do the restoration work on the painting 'Upland Cotton.'"

An exhaustive technical examination of *Upland Cotton* carried out in February 1963 for the Munson-Williams-Proctor Institute by Richard Buck, director of the Intermuseum Conservation Association laboratory in Oberlin, Ohio, confirmed that the portion of the painting seen in the Macbeth photograph to be obscured by the white coating is the work of a modern hand. The hand may reasonably be assumed to be that of Giovanni Castano. Buck's report also confirmed that except for minor touches, the inscription and the cotton plants at the sides and along the lower portion of the canvas remain as Homer created them in the late 1870s, and which, some twenty years later, he retained to be incorporated into a new composition.

*The letters here quoted between Giovanni Castano and Charles L. Homer are in the Castano papers held by the Archives of American Art, Smithsonian Institution, Washington, DC.

PROVENANCE
Charles S. Homer, Jr., by bequest, 1910; Mrs. Charles S. Homer, Jr., by bequest, 1917; Arthur P. and Charles L. Homer, by bequest, 1937; Mrs. Charles L. Homer, by bequest, 1955; (Giovanni Castano, Boston, 1956); (Hirschl & Adler Galleries, 1956); Alastair Bradley Martin, Glen Head, NY, 1956; Munson-Williams-Proctor Institute, Utica, NY, partial gift, 1958; (Hirschl & Adler Galleries, 1964); (Adam A. Weschler & Son, Washington, DC, 2 Nov. 1970, sale, no. 988)

EXHIBITIONS
National Academy of Design, New York, *Fifty-fourth Annual Exhibition,* 1 Apr.–31 May 1879, no. 393; Century Association, New York, 6 Dec. 1879, no. 12; Union League Club, New York, 11–13 Mar. 1880; Brooklyn Art Association, 7 Dec. 1880–1 Jan. 1881, no. 74; *Cotton States and International Exposition,* Atlanta, 18 Sept.–31 Dec. 1895; Prout's Neck 1936 (as *Cotton Blossoms,* not in catalogue); NGA 1958/MFA, Boston, 1959, no. 42a/38; Vermont Art Center 1964, no. 19; Hamilton 1964, no. 4; Menil 1988, no. 32

LITERATURE
"The Academy Exhibition. A Creditable Display of the Work of American Artists," *(NY) Daily Graphic,* 29 Mar. 1879; "Fine Arts. Fifty-Fourth Annual Exhibition of the Academy of Design—Important Pictures—First Notice," *New York Herald,* 30 Mar. 1879; "Preparing the Pictures. The Artists Varnishing Day," *New-York Times,* 30 Mar. 1879; "The Academy Paintings. A Better Display Than Has Been Seen for Years," *(NY) Evening Telegram,* 31 Mar. 1879; "The Spring Exhibition. National Academy of Design. First Notice," *Art Interchange* 2 (2 Apr. 1879): 50; "The Academy Exhibition. III," *(NY) World,* 27 Apr. 1879; "The Academy Exhibition," *Appletons' Journal of Literature, Science, and Art* 21 (6 May 1879): 471; [Susan N. Carter], "The Academy Exhibition," *(NY) Art Journal* 5 (May 1879): 158-59; "Fine Arts. The Fifty-Fourth Exhibition of the Academy of Design," *The Nation* 28 (15 May 1879): 341; "Fine Arts. Exhibition of the Academy of Design. II," *The Nation* 28 (22 May 1879): 359; "The Academy of Design," *Scribner's Monthly* 18 (June 1879): 312; "The Union League Club. The Monthly Display of Paintings," *New-York Times,* 12 Mar. 1880; "Fine Arts. Pictures at the Union League," *New York Evening Mail,* 12 Mar. 1880; "Art Notes," *(NY) Art Journal* 7 (Jan. 1881): 32; William A. Coffin, "The Atlanta Exhibition," *The Nation* 61 (7 Nov. 1895): 325; "The Atlanta International Fair," *Art Amateur* 34 (Dec. 1895): 4

No. 777. Yoke of Oxen

777
Yoke of Oxen
1879

Graphite, 6¹¹⁄₁₆ × 9¹⁵⁄₁₆ (16.988 × 25.243)
Inscribed lr: W. H. '79

Cooper-Hewitt, National Design Museum,
Smithsonian Institution, gift of Charles Savage
Homer, Jr., 1912-12-261

PROVENANCE
Charles S. Homer, Jr., by bequest, 1910

EXHIBITIONS
Carnegie 1937, no. 172

778
A Rural Couple
[1879]

Graphite, 8¾ × 7 (22.225 × 17.780)

A. Alfred Taubman, Bloomfield Hills, MI

This is one of seven drawings brought to LG in June
1936 by H. H. Pierce. LG noted from close examination that this and three others of the drawings were
"drawn quite heavily in the main lines with the pencil
pressing so hard into the paper that on the reverse
side one can actually feel the raised lines. Also these
lines on the reverse are dark, not from the pencil
showing through the paper, but evidently from pressing against a surface which transferred a tone to the
lines, like carbon paper, though not so dark [as was
carbon paper in the 1930s]. The color of this transferred tone [on the reverse of *A Rural Couple*] is black."

Three of the seven, including this drawing, were
brought to LG again in January 1960: "I examined
them carefully, using a magnifying glass. The lines
on the front of the drawings are fresh and direct, with
no sign of being drawn over other lines, or of the lines
being gone over as they would have been if Homer
had first made a drawing, then gone over it with carbon paper beneath it. It seems evident that he made
the drawings directly with carbon paper beneath."

PROVENANCE
Mrs. Louis Prang, Boston, nd; (Frances Tarbox,
1924); (Kennedy Galleries, 1960); (Park Gallery,
Detroit, 1960); (James Goodman Gallery, Buffalo,
nd); Harold K. Hochschild, New York, c. 1966;
(Sotheby Parke-Bernet, 22 Oct. 1981, sale 4707M,
no. 16); (Frank Fowler, Lookout Mountain, TN,
1981); (Sotheby's, 28 May 1987, sale 5584, no. 100)

No. 778. A Rural Couple

779
Early Morning
nd

Ink, 3⅞ × 4⅞ (9.843 × 12.383)
Inscribed lc: Early Morning

Private collection

PROVENANCE
Frank Rokowski, Scarborough, ME, c. 1900;
J. Frank Rokowski, Scarborough, ME, his son, by
bequest, 1962; (Sally Turner, Plainfield, NJ, 1963);
(Jack Tanzer, c. 1966); Mrs. Victor H. Neirinckx,
New York, by 1971; (Sotheby's, 23 Sept. 1988,
Arcade sale, no. 56A)

No. 779. Early Morning

780-R
Noon-day Rest
[1879]

Graphite, watercolor, 5¼ × 13¹⁄₁₆ (13.335 × 33.180)
Inscribed lr: W H

Private collection

ABG: See commentary No. 782.

PROVENANCE
Mr. Beard, c. 1895; Bessie W. Beard, Cambridge,
MA, his daughter, before 1936; (William Macbeth,
Inc., 1936); James W. Fosburgh, New York, 1938;
Pieter W. Fosburgh, Cherry Plain, NY, his brother,
by gift, before 1970; (Kennedy Galleries, 1972);
private collection, c. 1973

EXHIBITIONS
Macbeth 1936, no. 12

LITERATURE
John Wilmerding, "Winslow Homer's Creative
Process," *The Magazine Antiques* 108 (Nov. 1975):
965–71

No. 780-R. Noon-day Rest

No. 780-V. Two Men Scything

780-V
Two Men Scything
[1879]

Graphite, watercolor

ABG: From the sharp truncation of these figures
at about knee-height, it would appear the sheet
supporting this double-sided drawing was originally
substantially larger. Considering the placement
of his initialling on the recto of the drawing, it
seems likely Homer trimmed the sheet himself,
and favored his drawing of the reclining scyther.

213

No. 781. Man Scything

781

Man Scything

[1879]

Graphite, watercolor, 5⅝ × 4⅜ (14.288 × 11.113)

Private collection

PROVENANCE
Mr. Beard, c. 1895; Bessie W. Beard, Cambridge,
MA, his daughter, before 1936; (William Macbeth,
Inc., 1936); Mrs. Robert Wheelwright, Wilmington,
DE, 1937; Renee Meeds Geary (Mrs. William J.
Geary), Littleton, CO, her daughter, by bequest,
c. 1965

EXHIBITIONS
Macbeth 1936, no. 11

No. 782. Man with a Scythe

782

Man with a Scythe

[1879]

Graphite, watercolor, 5⁹⁄₁₆ × 14¹⁄₁₆ (14.130 × 35.720)

Cooper-Hewitt, National Design Museum,
Smithsonian Institution, gift of Charles Savage
Homer, Jr., 1912-12-258

ABG: In listing "Homer Drawings in the [Cooper-
Hewitt] Museum's Collection which are Studies
for Paintings or Illustations" Charles S. Hathaway
categorized this truncated sketch known as *Man
with a Scythe* as having been used by Homer in
designing the illustration, "Making Hay" published
in *Harper's Weekly*, 6 July 1872.

John Wilmerding initiated identification of this
drawing as a specific and pivotal study for the oil
Veteran in a New Field (2:No. 271), thus assuming a
dating of not later than 1865. As he found the paper
on which Homer executed the double-sided drawing
Noon-day Rest and *Two Men Scything* (No. 780-R
and No. 780-v) to be similar to that of the Cooper-
Hewitt's *Man with a Scythe*, he extended his assumption of the purpose and dating of these sketches to an
immediate relationship to *Veteran* and execution in
the mid-1860s. Unfortunately, the basis for coupling
the Cooper-Hewitt drawing with *Veteran* seems to
be only the similarilty of appearance of central
figures engaged in the same activity. Discrepancies
in pose, costume, and especially in style combined
with the substantial group of drawings—several
inscribed with an 1879 date—of the same model
make a dating to that year more probable.

See also No. 781, No. 783, No. 784, No. 785, and No. 786.

PROVENANCE
Charles S. Homer, Jr., by bequest, 1910

EXHIBITIONS
Ithaca 1971, no. 17; Cooper-Hewitt 1972, no. 22; Greenville County 1986; FAM San Francisco 1988, no. 15a

LITERATURE
Calvin S. Hathaway, "Drawings by Winslow Homer in the Museum's Collections," *Chronicle of the Museum for the Arts of Decoration of Cooper Union* 1 (Apr. 1936): 61; John Wilmerding, "Winslow Homer's Creative Process," *The Magazine Antiques* 108 (Nov. 1975): 965–71

783+

Man with Scythe
1879

Graphite, charcoal, watercolor, 10 × 12½ (25.400 × 31.750)
Inscribed ll (apparently erased): Homer; ur: W. H. / 1879

Bowdoin College Museum of Art, Brunswick, ME, gift of Shorey M. Armstrong, 1991.44

PROVENANCE
James Alexander Miller, nd; John P. Armstrong; Shorey M. Armstrong (Mrs. John P. Armstrong), nd

No. 783. Man with Scythe

784

Boy with Scythe
1879

Graphite, 8⅛ × 12⅜ (20.638 × 31.433)
Inscribed lr: Homer 1879

Private collection

PROVENANCE
Edward W. Hooper, Boston, nd; Ellen Sturgis Hooper Potter (Mrs. John Briggs Potter), Boston, his daughter, by bequest, 1901

EXHIBITIONS
MFA, Boston, 1911

LITERATURE
Downes 1911, op. 60

No. 784. Boy with Scythe

No. 785. The Reaper

No. 785.5. The Reaper in His Field

785

The Reaper

1879

Graphite, watercolor, 9 × 14¼ (22.860 × 36.195)
Inscribed ll: Winslow Homer 1879

Private collection

PROVENANCE
(Wm. A. Butters & Co., Chicago, 10 Dec. 1879,
Homer sale) [?]; Eda Hurd Lord (Mrs. George S.
Lord), Evanston, IL, nd [?]; (J. W. Young Galleries,
Chicago, by 1923); Mrs. Woodruff J. Parker,
Chicago, 1923; Mrs. George A. Martin, Cleveland,
before 1938; (Parke-Bernet Galleries, 18–19 Oct.
1946, sale 795, no. 113); (Wildenstein & Co., 1946);
private collection, 1957

EXHIBITIONS
Butters, Chicago, 1879 [?]; Wildenstein 1947, no. 96;
Wildenstein 1948, no. 8; Wildenstein 1949, no. 20;
Houston 1952, no. 31; Knoedler 1986, no. 29

785.5+

The Reaper in His Field

1879

Watercolor, 8½ × 12⅝ (21.590 × 32.068)
Inscribed lr: Homer 1879

Private collection

ABG: Of Homer's two closely similar versions of
this subject in graphic media, No. 784 and No. 785,
he clearly chose the former as model for this watercolor version.

There is no information on the history of the
work before the earlier twentieth century; however,
it is appropriate to imagine the watercolor's first
owner acquiring it from Homer's large sale of drawings and watercolors under the auspices of Daniel A.
Mathews held in early March 1880.

PROVENANCE
Mrs. Lida T. Nugent, Brooklyn, NY, nd

786+

Man Reaping

[1879]

Graphite, watercolor, 9½ × 13⅜ (24.130 × 33.973)
Inscribed lr: Winslow Homer N. A.

Bowdoin College Museum of Art, Brunswick, ME,
gift of Elizabeth McLaren Stovel, Anne McLaren
Griffin, and Donald McLaren in memory of their
parents, Thayer McLaren and Madeleine Skinner
McLaren, 1991.105

ABG: This drawing is closely related to Homer's
drawing known as *Bob's Dilemma* (No. 1016), which,
in turn, was the source for the illustration captioned
"Hallo! What's up now? Are your babies in there?"
published in the July 1881 issue of the *St. Nicholas*
magazine.

Frederick Stuart Church (1842–1924), the earliest
known owner of this drawing, was an active participant in the New York art scene. He was a prolific
illustrator for the popular press, including *St.
Nicholas*, as well as a painter. Augusta Valentine
Nelson, besides being the recipient of Church's gift
of this work, was the older sister of Lawson and
Henry Valentine.

PROVENANCE
Frederick S. Church, New York, nd; Augusta
Valentine Nelson, by gift, nd; Thayer McLaren,
Essex Falls, NJ, her grandson, before 1977; children
of Mr. and Mrs. Thayer McLaren, nd

No. 786. Man Reaping

787

Bossy

nd

[Graphite]

Unlocated

By the end of the 1870s illustrated publications were no longer dependent on hand-cut blocks; technology based on photographic reproduction of artists' works, without intervention of the engraver was commonplace, and several drawings by Homer were published in popular journals by this method. "Bossy" appeared, independent of any literary context, in the issue of the *Art Interchange* published a few days before Christmas 1880. However, in what apparently was a departure from its habit the *Interchange* made editorial comment on the artists represented in the issue—saving Homer for the finale of the column.

> A chat about the different artists who have contributed to this Holiday number is so eminently *apropos* that we make no apology for its insertion.... Of Winslow Homer, the artist of "Bossy," it is hard to know what not to say. Ranking, as he does, among the foremost and most original of American painters, he commands the admiration of all critics. Few men would introduce such lines in a picture as appear in "Bossy," and not one in a thousand would dare to concentrate attention, as here, all in one corner. This, however, is characteristic of the man; for he

is *posé* in the extreme, and affects eccentricities of manner that border upon gross rudeness. To visit him in his studio, is literally bearding a lion in his den; for Mr. Homer's strength as an artist is only equalled by his roughness when he does not happen to be just in the humor of being approached.

The drawing which was photographically reproduced in the *Interchange* is unlocated and likely has not survived. It probably was executed in graphite, and was only slightly larger than the 6⅞ inches by 8⅞ inches size of the image in reproduction.

LITERATURE

"The Studio. Art Interchange Artists," *Art Interchange* 5 (22 Dec. 1880): 129, 130

788

Man with Horse and Plow

[1879]

Graphite, 8⅝ × 9⅝ (21.908 × 24.448) sight
Inscribed lr: Homer

Private collection

This drawing was one of two photographically reproduced to illustrate an article by G. W. Sheldon first published in the April 1880 issue of the *Art Journal*. It also is clearly an immediate source for the central image in the watercolor *Man and Plow Horse* (No. 789) of 1879, and is also related to the watercolor *Boy and Horse Plowing* (No. 873) of 1880.

ABG: The very close resemblance of this drawing to the central image in the watercolor, *Man and Plow Horse* (No. 789), is obvious, and prompts the question of how intimately they are linked. The drawing has been inaccessible for many years, so it is not possible to prove absolutely that it is an example of Homer's occasional practice in 1879 and 1880 of drawing over carbon paper, thus creating a master, and one or more sheets with the major outline of subject features pre-sketched and ready for elaboration, generally as a watercolor painting. However, recent professional examination of the watercolor, No. 789, provides enough evidence to support speculation that this drawing was the master in one such of Homer's carbon paper "sandwichs."
See commentary No. 789.

PROVENANCE

(William Macbeth, Inc., 1902/1907); Mrs. Francis S. Smithers, Greenwich, CT, 1909; Austin Smithers, Greenwich, CT, her son, by gift, 1935; Mrs. Austin Smithers (later Mrs. Henry Sears), Greenwich, CT, by bequest, 1936

Illustration: "Bossy," "The Studio. Art Interchange Artists," *Art Interchange* 5 (22 Dec. 1880): 129

No. 788. Man with Horse and Plow

EXHIBITIONS
Fogg 1936, no. 5; Baltimore 1978, no. 24

LITERATURE
[George William Sheldon], "Sketches and Studies. II. From the Portfolios of A. H. Thayer, William M. Chase, Winslow Homer, and Peter Moran," *(NY) Art Journal* 6 (Apr. 1880): 109. Reprinted in, G. W. Sheldon, *Hours with Art and Artists* (New York: D. Appleton and Company, 1882), 137

789

Man and Plow Horse

1879

Watercolor, 12$\frac{1}{16}$ × 19$\frac{1}{8}$ (30.640 × 48.578)
Inscribed lr: Homer 1879

Private collection

ABG: See commentary No. 788.

In 2007 Martha Tedeschi, curator in the Art Institute of Chicago department of prints and drawings, and Kristi Dahm, paper conservator at the Institute had the opportunity to make a thorough study of this watercolor. They report that traces of carbon lines as well as graphite underlie the pigment. Using the *Art Journal* illustration, Ms. Dahm created a model of the drawing, No. 788, on a transparent sheet. This sheet was placed over the central image of the watercolor; the outlines of the grouping of man, horse and plow in the watercolor precisely duplicate the drawing.

The composition and essential features of this watercolor are repeated in *Boy and Horse Ploughing* (No. 873) of 1880, but there are sufficient discrepancies in the posture of the central characters and style of execution in the two paintings to make it clear the later work was not also developed over a carbon copy of drawing, No. 788. The two paintings also differ notably in color: this version of the image is rendered entirely in shades of gray and brown, whereas Homer chose to use vivid color in No. 873.

PROVENANCE
(Wm. A. Butters & Co., Chicago, 10 Dec. 1879, Homer sale) [?]; Eda Hurd Lord (Mrs. George S. Lord), Evanston, IL, nd; Thomas Lord, Evanston, IL, her son, by gift, c. 1920; private collection, 1951

EXHIBITIONS
Butters, Chicago, 1879 [?]; AI Chicago 2008

No. 789. Man and Plow Horse

see color illustration, p. 447

No. 790. Harrowing

790

Harrowing

1879

Watercolor, 12 × 19 (30.480 × 48.260) sight
Inscribed lr: Homer '79

Private collection

See No. 791.

PROVENANCE
(Wm. A. Butters & Co., Chicago, 10 Dec. 1879,
Homer sale) [?]; Eda Hurd Lord (Mrs. George S.
Lord), Evanston, IL, nd; Robert O. Lord, New York,
her son, probably 1938; Museum of Modern Art,
New York, by gift of the estate of Robert O. Lord,
1969; (Kennedy Galleries, 1972); James Titleman,
Hollidaysburgh, PA, 1972

EXHIBITIONS
Butters, Chicago, 1879 [?]; Whitney 1973, no. 89;
NGA 1986, no. 20

791

Boy Seated on a Plow

1879

Graphite, 6⁵⁄₁₆ × 10⅝ (16.035 × 26.988) sight
Inscribed ul: Homer 1879

Private collection

This drawing is the source for the image at the right
side of the watercolor *Harrowing* (No. 790).

PROVENANCE
(William Macbeth, Inc., 1902/1907); Mrs. Francis S.
Smithers, Greenwich, CT, 1909; Austin Smithers,
Greenwich, CT, her son, by gift, 1935; Mrs. Austin
Smithers (later Mrs. Henry Sears), Greenwich, CT,
by bequest, 1936

EXHIBITIONS
Fogg 1936, no. 4; Baltimore 1978, no. 23

No. 791. Boy Seated on a Plow

No. 792. Blossom Time in Virginia

792

Blossom Time in Virginia

nd

Watercolor, 14 × 20 (35.560 × 50.800)

The Detroit Institute of Arts, bequest of Robert H. Tannahill, 70.259

The earliest record of this watercolor is the Macbeth gallery's notation of Charles L. Homer placing it for sale with them in November 1931, under the title *Blossom Time in Virginia*, with a dating of "c. 1878." Charles L. Homer would have been the source of Macbeth's record that the previous owner had been his father, Arthur B. Homer. The fact that the younger Homer could put the painting up for sale tends to confirm this provenance, as he and his brother did not come into possession of Homer's remaining estate by inheritance from their aunt, Mrs. Charles S. Homer, Jr., until 1937. No work which fits the subject of *Blossom Time in Virginia* was among the Homers Arthur B. Homer lent to the Portland, Maine, art museum in 1912. Nor was it described by William Howe Downes as hanging in "Kettle Cove" cottage, which had been given, with its contents, to Arthur B. Homer by Charles S. Homer, Jr. shortly before Downes visited it in late

autumn 1910. However, neither source of information on the Homers in his younger brother's possession should be assumed to be comprehensive. It is most likely Arthur B. Homer acquired the watercolor with "Kettle Cove."

Theodore Bolton's 1932 checklist of Homer watercolors is the first publication of the painting: "Blossom Time in Virginia. A negro boy driving an ox hitched to a plow. A fruit tree in blossom in the back." Bolton placed the painting as a work of 1876, and credited ownership to "Mr. Arthur T. Homer," presumably a misunderstanding of Arthur P. Homer's middle initial.

LG's only opportunity to examine the watercolor was when it was hanging in the Carnegie Institute's 1937 Homer exhibition. He described the figure as "a negro boy, probably about fourteen, striding along behind a plow." LG's notes on the style of execution, and his opinion on dating, written at that time were: "Painted very sketchily, in the peculiar matted, blotted, impressionistic style that one finds in some of his Gloucester watercolors of about 1880, but even more so. No high finish or great precision, as in the Houghton Farm work. The drawing is fairly precise and definite, and well-constructed, but the execution is quite impressionistic. The color is applied loosely, in staccato blobs and dabs, very much in the impressionist manner, though without the division into pure colors. . . . The whole effect is unusual for him (or at least an extreme manifestation of a style he sometimes showed) . . . . I should say he did this about the time he did the *Boy and Horse Plowing* [No. 873] in the R. I. School of Design."

Yet when LG noted the upper corner of his manuscript catalogue pages to place them chronologically, he assigned it to "probably 1875."

ABG: This watercolor is routinely grouped with Homer's 1875 watercolors and oils conspicuously featuring an African-American boy: *Contraband* (2:No. 587), *A Flower for the Teacher* (2:No. 588), *The Busy Bee* (2:No. 589), *Two Boys in a Cart* (2:No. 590), *The Unruly Calf* (2:No. 592), and *Weaning the Calf* (2:No. 593), presumably because of the geographic determinism of its title and the dark hue of the boy's one visible hand and the exposed portion of his face. However, the title was assigned, probably by Charles L. Homer and probably in 1931, when he first put the painting into the Macbeth gallery's hands. The dark skin coloration—which is Homer's device for rendering the shadow of the hat on the suntanned skin of a working farmer—likely inspired the arbitrary decision to place the scene in Virginia. (The same darkened coloring of a head shaded by a hat brim may be seen on the *Boy in a Dory* [No. 944] in Gloucester waters.) The specification to Virginia scenery, in turn, reinforces the perception of the boy as African-American. Neither the identification to race or to site has any factual or circumstantial basis.

Nearly fifty years after LG's ambiguous reflections on dating *Blossom Time in Virginia*, Helen Cooper seems to have had much the same difficulty in reconciling its assumed Southern context and its stylistic character. Although Cooper introduces *Blossom Time in Virginia* as "one of a series of watercolors from his trip to Virginia in 1875," her specific comment on the work concerns Homer having "scraped away the painted surface to expose the white paper beneath, thereby creating a lighter, brighter white in the blossoms." This technique would be unusual for Homer as early as 1875, just two years after he took up watercolor as a painting medium. The illustration of *Blossom Time in Virginia* in Cooper is juxtaposed with images of *Harrowing* (No. 790) and *Boy Seated on a Plow* (No. 791), both works of 1879.

Separated from the implications of an assigned title, this watercolor finds its best fit in context with Homer's farm subjects of the late 1870s.

PROVENANCE

Charles S. Homer, Jr., by bequest, 1910; Arthur B. Homer, by gift, 1910; Arthur P. and Charles L. Homer, by bequest, 1916; (William Macbeth, Inc., 1931 and 1933); Robert H. Tannahill, Grosse Point Farms, MI, 1934

EXHIBITIONS

Carnegie 1937, no. 118

LITERATURE

Theodore Bolton, "Water Colors by Homer: Critique and Catalogue," *Fine Arts* 18 (Apr. 1932): 20; National Gallery of Art, Helen A. Cooper, *Winslow Homer Watercolors* (Washington, DC, 1986, 32–33, 34, 50 n. 33; The Menil Collection, "Winslow Homer's Images of Blacks," by Peter H. Wood and Karen C. C. Dalton, in *Winslow Homer's Images of Blacks: The Civil War and the Reconstruction Years* (Houston, 1988), 73–74

No. 793. Boy and Girl on a Plow

793

Boy and Girl on a Plow

[1879]

Graphite, 8¼ × 10⅜ (20.955 × 26.353)

Cooper-Hewitt, National Design Museum, Smithsonian Institution, gift of Charles Savage Homer, Jr., 1912-12-73

PROVENANCE

Charles S. Homer, Jr., by bequest, 1910

EXHIBITIONS

Slater 1952; Academy of Arts & Letters 1953, no. 178; Ogunquit 1954, no. 23

794
Girl Seated on Plow
[1879]

Graphite, 5⅞ × 9¼ (14.923 × 23.495)

Cooper-Hewitt, National Design Museum, Smithsonian Institution, gift of Charles Savage Homer, Jr., 1912-12-74

PROVENANCE
Charles S. Homer, Jr., by bequest, 1910

EXHIBITIONS
Academy of Arts & Letters 1953, no. 177; Ogunquit 1954, no. 20

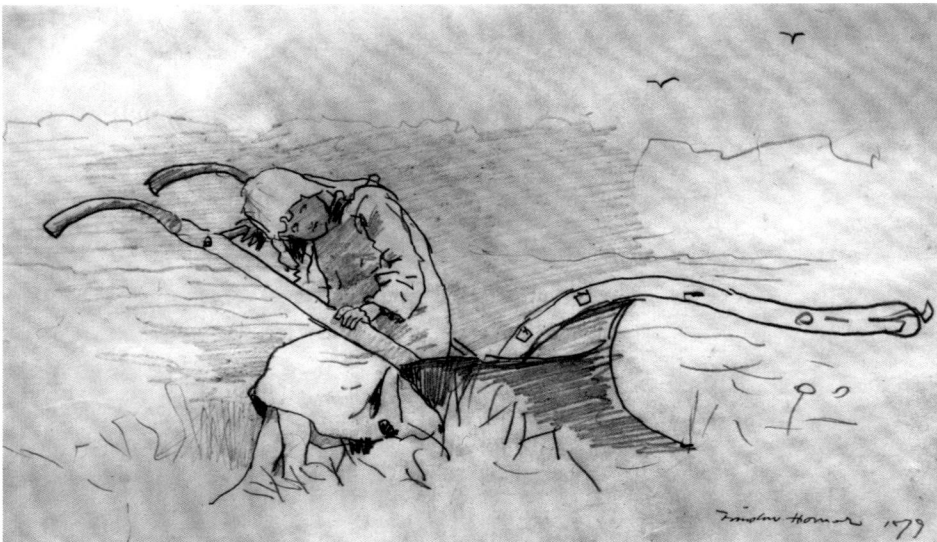

No. 794.5. Girl Seated on a Plow

794.5+
Girl Seated on a Plow
1879

Graphite, 5⅞ × 9⅝ (14.923 × 24.448)
Inscribed lr: Winslow Homer '79

Private collection

ABG: This drawing was introduced to the Homer catalogue raisonné in 2006 with the quaint tale attached that Homer had given it to the six-year old Frederick Rundlet in 1879 while the two were on a beach in Gloucester, Massachusetts; young Frederick's father, Taylor Rundlet, was with him at the time. Even if such a transaction had occurred in Gloucester, then the year would almost surely have been 1880.

There are several obstacles to accepting the story at face value. To do so it is necessary to believe Homer was carrying around on his person some quantity of his previous summer's work, and further, that he was casually giving away items from his saleable inventory. It is also necessary to believe that a six-year old would have been pleased to receive a drawing—and one of a girl—as a present, let alone, that he would have taken good care of it.

However, this story does encourage speculation that Homer made some opportunity to show and sell some of his work during the months he was in Gloucester in the summer of 1880, and that Frederick was with his father when the senior Rundlet made a purchase directly from the artist.

PROVENANCE
Taylor Parker Rundlet, c. 1880; Frederick Taylor Rundlet, his son, nd; private collection, c. 1959; (Skinner, Inc., Boston, MA, 15 Sept. 2006, sale 2329, no. 377)

795
Girl Seated on a Tree-trunk
[1879]

Graphite, 8⅜ × 10¼ (21.273 × 26.035)

Cooper-Hewitt, National Design Museum, Smithsonian Institution, gift of Charles Savage Homer, Jr., 1912-12-66

PROVENANCE
Charles S. Homer, Jr., by bequest, 1910

796
Girl Seated on a Rail Fence
[1879]

Graphite, watercolor, 6⅝ × 8 (16.828 × 20.320)

Brooklyn Museum, Frederick Loeser Fund, 28.210

PROVENANCE
(Andre Rueff, Brooklyn, nd)

EXHIBITIONS
Metropolitan/Brooklyn 1972, no. 52; Lowe, Syracuse, 1979, no. 17

No. 796. Girl Seated on a Rail Fence

797
Boy and Girl on a Wood Scoot
1879

Graphite, 7⅝ × 10⅛ (19.368 × 25.718)
Inscribed lr: Homer '79

Private collection

This is one of seven drawings brought to LG in June 1936 by H. H. Pierce. LG noted from close examination that this and three others of the drawings were "drawn quite heavily in the main lines with the pencil pressing so hard into the paper that on the reverse side one can actually feel the raised lines. Also these lines on the reverse are dark, not from the pencil showing through the paper, but evidently from pressing against a surface which transferred a tone to the lines, like carbon paper, though not so dark [as was carbon paper of the 1930s]. The color of this transferred tone [on the reverse of *Boy and Girl on a Wood Scoot*] is dark blue."

No. 797. Boy and Girl on a Wood Scoot

PROVENANCE
Mrs. Louis Prang, Boston, nd; (Frances Tarbox, 1924); (Henry H. Pierce, Reading, MA, 1936); (Gilbert Brouillette, Boston, probably 1936); (William Macbeth, Inc., 1938); Edith Wetmore, New York, 1939; Frank D. Duncan, Middletown, RI, by gift, before 1966; (M. Knoedler & Co., 1967)

EXHIBITIONS
Farnsworth 1970, no. 45; Farnsworth 2006

No. 798. Boy with a Stick

No. 799. A Stump Speech

798

Boy with a Stick

1879

Boy Frightening Birds

Graphite, watercolor, 9 × 12 (22.860 × 30.480)
Inscribed lr: Homer '79

Private collection

PROVENANCE
Horace D. Chapin, Boston, nd; Margaret Chapin
Osgood (Mrs. Robert B. Osgood), Boston, his sister,
c. 1936; private collection, 1957

EXHIBITIONS
MFA, Boston, 1911 (as *Boy with a Stick*)

799

A Stump Speech

1879

Watercolor, 8⅞ × 11½ (22.543 × 29.210)
Inscribed lr: Homer '79

Private collection

PROVENANCE
James Craig Nicoll, New York, nd; Emily Nicoll,
New York, his daughter, by bequest, 1918; (Milch
Galleries, 1919); Warren P. King, Willoughby, Ohio,
1919; Mrs. Warren P. King, Willoughby, OH, nd

800

Boys on a Hillside

[1879]

Watercolor, 8⅜ × 11½ (21.273 × 29.210)

Private collection

PROVENANCE
Edward W. Hooper, Boston, nd; Mary Hooper
Warner (Mrs. Roger Sherman Warner), Boston, his
daughter, by bequest, 1901; Roger Sherman Warner,
Jr., Washington, DC, her son, by bequest, 1972;
Sturgis Warner, Washington, DC, his brother, by
bequest, 1978

EXHIBITIONS
MFA, Boston, 1936; Boston Symphony 1937; MFA,
Boston, 1959, no. 83

No. 800. Boys on a Hillside

801

Boy and Fallen Tree

[1879]

Watercolor, 8⅛ × 11⅛ (20.638 × 28.258)

Museum of Fine Arts, Boston, bequest of Katherine
Dexter McCormick, 68.570

LG examined Mrs. Katherine Dexter McCormick's
five watercolor paintings and three drawings by
Homer in her Boston home, in September 1938.
(The other seven works are 2:No. 464, No. 713,
No. 744, No. 803, No. 814, No. 825, and No. 861.)
Mrs. McCormick said they all had been acquired
by her mother, Mrs. Wirt Dexter, at an auction
in Chicago "in 1876." Mrs. McCormick or Mrs.
Dexter's memory was evidently slightly imperfect:
all their Homers date from 1878 or 1879, excepting
2:No. 463, an 1873 drawing.

PROVENANCE
(Wm. A. Butters & Co., Chicago, 10 Dec. 1879,
Homer sale) [?]; Mrs. Wirt Dexter, Chicago,
probably 1879; Katherine Dexter McCormick
(Mrs. Stanley McCormick), Boston, her daughter,
probably 1937

EXHIBITIONS
Butters, Chicago, 1879 [?]; MFA, Boston, 1959
(not in catalogue); University of Arizona 1963,
no. 75; MFA, Boston, 1977, no. 48

No. 801. Boy and Fallen Tree

No. 802. On the Hillside

802

On the Hillside

[1879]

Watercolor, 7½ × 11½ (19.050 × 29.210)

Unlocated

PROVENANCE
(M. A. Newhouse & Son, St. Louis, before 1924);
Laura Davidson Sears Academy of Fine Arts,
Elgin, IL, 1924

803

Driving Cows to Pasture

1879

Watercolor, 8%6 × 13%6 (21.750 × 34.450)
Inscribed ll: Homer '79

Museum of Fine Arts, Boston, bequest of Katherine
Dexter McCormick, 68.569

LG examined Mrs. Katherine Dexter McCormick's
five watercolor paintings and three drawings by
Homer in her Boston home, in September 1938.
(The other seven works are 2:No. 464, No. 713,

No. 744, No. 801, No. 814, No. 825, and No. 861.)
Mrs. McCormick said they all had been acquired by
her mother, Mrs. Wirt Dexter, at an auction in
Chicago "in 1876." Mrs. McCormick or Mrs.
Dexter's memory was evidently slightly imperfect:
all their Homers date from 1878 or 1879, excepting
2:No. 463, an 1873 drawing.

PROVENANCE
(Wm. A. Butters & Co., Chicago, 10 Dec. 1879,
Homer sale) [?]; Mrs. Wirt Dexter, Chicago,
probably 1879; Katherine Dexter McCormick
(Mrs. Stanley McCormick), Boston, her daughter,
probably 1937

EXHIBITIONS
Butters, Chicago, 1879 [?]; NGA 1958/MFA,
Boston, 1959, no. 97/89; University of Arizona 1963,
no. 76; MFA, Boston, 1977, no. 47; MFA, Boston,
1993/1996, no. 49/10

LITERATURE
Museum of Fine Arts, "Driving Cows to Pasture,"
by Sue Welsh Reed, in *Awash in Color: Homer,
Sargent, and the Great American Watercolor* (Boston,
1993), 104–5

No. 803. Driving Cows to Pasture

804

Boys on Fallen Tree

[1879]

Graphite, watercolor, 7⅛ × 11¼ (18.098 × 28.575)
Inscribed lr: W H

Private collection

PROVENANCE
(Wm. A. Butters & Co., Chicago, 10 Dec. 1879,
Homer sale) [?]; Eda Hurd Lord (Mrs. George S.
Lord), Evanston, IL, nd; (J. W. Young Galleries,
Chicago, c. 1920); (M. Knoedler & Co., 1944); pri-
vate collection, c. 1955; (Hirschl & Adler Galleries,
1959)

EXHIBITIONS
Butters, Chicago, 1879 [?]

No. 804. Boys on Fallen Tree

No. 805. Boys Fishing from a Rock

805

Boys Fishing from a Rock

[1879]

Crayon, watercolor, 7⁵⁄₁₆ × 10⅜ (18.575 × 26.353)

Mead Art Museum, Amherst (MA) College, gift of Professor Emeritus and Mrs. Charles H. Morgan, 1971.55

PROVENANCE

(William Macbeth, Inc., by 1955); Charles H. Morgan, Amherst, MA, 1955

EXHIBITIONS

Vermont Art Center 1957, no. 20; University of Arizona 1963, no. 92

806

Three Boys on a Raft

1879

Graphite, 7¾ × 11 (19.685 × 27.940)
Inscribed lr: Homer '79

Private collection

The the figure of the seated boy at left remains alone as the *Boy on a Raft* (No. 807), a watercolor which may be presumed to have been based on this drawing.

PROVENANCE

(Doll & Richards, Boston, 1879–1880) [?]; Edward W. Hooper, Boston, nd; Mabel Hooper La Farge (Mrs. Bancel La Farge), Boston, his daughter, by bequest, 1901; Edward H. La Farge, Providence, RI, her son, c. 1945; private collection, nd

No. 806. Three Boys on a Raft

807

Boy on a Raft

1879

Watercolor, 7⅜ × 12½ (18.733 × 31.750) sight
Inscribed ll: Homer '79

Private collection

See No. 806, a source for this figure of a boy.

PROVENANCE
Hamilton Cole, New York, c. 1880; the Misses Cole,
New York, his sisters, by bequest, c. 1889; Marie
Torrey Copp, New London, CT, their great-niece,
by bequest, 1925; private collection, c. 1955

No. 807. Boy on a Raft

808

Youth of S. T. Preston

1879

Watercolor, 5¼ × 8⅝ (13.335 × 21.908)
Inscribed ll: Homer; lc: The Youth of S. T. Preston;
lr: W H / 1879

Fayez Sarofim

ABG: Samuel Thorndyke Preston was a first cousin
of Martha French Homer, Winslow Homer's sister-
in-law. Preston came to New York from the Preston
family home, New Ipswich, New Hampshire, in
about 1877 or early 1878. The New York Directory
identified his business as "skins" or, later, "hides."
For some time (probably not more than a year) after
his arrival in New York, Preston lived with Martha
and Charles S. Homer, Jr. on the west side of
Washington Square. New Ipswich was only a few
miles from West Townsend, Massachusetts, Martha
Homer's family home and place of summer retreat.
It is likely Homer visited the Prestons in New Ipswich
in July 1879. About a year later, Homer and Preston
would be sharing an apartment in the Benedick
building on Washington Square.

No one of the boys in this watercolor was modeled
by Thorn Preston, who was a full grown man when
it was executed. The legend applied to the painting,
itself, may be presumed to be some facetious allusion, understood between friends. Some years earlier
Homer had made the same sort of personal reference
in inscribing "The Youth of C. S. H. Jr." on the
drawing known as *Beetle and Wedge* (2:No. 416).

No. 808. Youth of S. T. Preston

see color illustration, p. 448

PROVENANCE
Samuel Thorndyke Preston, New York, by gift of
Homer, nd; George W. Preston, Saint Paul, MN, his
brother, c. 1898; Anna M. Preston (Mrs. George W.
Preston), Saint Paul, MN, by 1937; John Preston,
New Ipswich, NH, her great-nephew, by purchase,
by 1960; (Coe Kerr Gallery, nd); Mr. and Mrs.
Charles Ireland, Birmingham, AL, c. 1980; (Adelson
Gallery, c. 1990)

EXHIBITIONS
Vermont Art Center 1964, no. 21

809

Boy Swinging on a Bough

1879

Graphite, watercolor, 17 × 8⅜ (43.180 × 21.273)
Inscribed lr: Homer / 1879

Private collection

See No. 810.

PROVENANCE
(Wm. A. Butters & Co., Chicago, 10 Dec. 1879,
Homer sale); Mrs. Eliphalet Wickes Blatchford,
Chicago, 1879; Edward W. Blatchford, Jerusalem,
and Chicago, her son, by gift, by 1938

EXHIBITIONS
Butters, Chicago, 1879; Knoedler 1986, no. 27

No. 810. Boy in a Bough

810

Boy in a Bough

1879

Carbon tracing, 8¾ × 11⅛ (22.225 × 28.258)
Inscribed lr: W. H. '79

Cooper-Hewitt, National Design Museum,
Smithsonian Institution, gift of Charles Savage
Homer, Jr. Presumed destroyed, formerly 1912-12-280

In 1941 when LG made an exhaustive examination
and record of the Homers given by Charles S.
Homer, Jr., to the Cooper Union Museum (now
the Cooper-Hewitt Museum) he noted seven works
which were apparently "carbon copies" made by
Homer as he was executing drawings; all seven dated
to 1879. Although these are termed "carbon tracings,"
they show no evidence of having been made by
re-drawing under heavy pressure the essential lines
of a previously completed drawing. That is, they
are not *ex post facto* tracings, but instead were made
simultaneously with a principal drawing. They
not only demonstrate an unconventional technique
with which Homer was experimenting, but are
symptomatic of his exploration of methods by which
he could increase his output by means other than
a printing press. Of the seven, the Cooper-Hewitt
is now only able to locate *Two Girls* (No. 817) and
Girl with Pail (No. 818). LG's descriptions and—
in several cases—sketches, therefore may be all that
remain of this drawing, and of No. 823, No. 828,
No. 835, and No. 840.

LG's description of this work is: "In blue carbon
on white paper. A boy clinging to a bough of a tree.
Body full face, head, half turn left. The boy clings
to the bough with hands and feet. He wears a round
brimmed hat, shirt, suspenders, long pants, bare
feet. Branch has large leaves. The boy's body takes up
about three-fifths the height of the paper [approxi-
mately 5¼ inches]." LG obviously immediately
recognized the resemblance of this carbon tracing
to *Boy Swinging on a Bough* (No. 809); his record
continues:

I compared the photo of [No. 809] with the
Cooper Union drawing. They are very close but
not identical. The lines differ a little everywhere;
not just in accents and character; but in the
positions of the lines, their shapes; so that it is
evident that the Cooper Union drawing is not a
carbon copy of [No. 809], unless the latter has
been gone over and altered, of which there is no
sign in the photo. The actual position of some
objects (the direction of the short branch on
which the boy leans his left arm, for example) is
slightly different, but enough different to make it

impossible that the Cooper Union drawing is a carbon of [No. 809].

On the other hand they are so close that it is obvious that there is a very close relationship between them. Looking at the photo of [No. 809] again, it seems possible that this drawing might originally have been the same as the Cooper Union carbon, but was drawn over, the lines reinforced and altered.

LG noted that the sheet on which this carbon tracing was made was used horizontally, whereas No. 809 is formatted vertically. However, as the image in both works is so nearly the same, that discrepancy is irrelevant.

PROVENANCE
Charles S. Homer, Jr., by bequest, 1910

No. 811. Girls at a Well

811

Girls at a Well

[1879]

Graphite, watercolor, 7⅝ × 8¹/₁₆ (19.368 × 20.480)
Inscribed lr: W. H.

Brooklyn Museum, Frederick Loeser Fund, 28.212

PROVENANCE
(Andre Rueff, Brooklyn, nd)

EXHIBITIONS
Metropolitan/Brooklyn 1972, no. 53; Lowe, Syracuse, 1979, no. 6

No. 812. Two Girls in Sunbonnets at a Well

812

Two Girls in Sunbonnets at a Well

1879

Graphite, watercolor, 9⅛ × 14¾ (23.178 × 37.465)
Inscribed ll, on well: Homer / 1879

Private collection

PROVENANCE
Allan A. Morrill, Chicago, nd; Donald Morrill,
Winnetka, IL, his son, nd; Ophelia Morrill (Mrs.
Donald Morrill), Winnetka, IL, by bequest, c. 1956;
Dr. Wayne P. Bryer, Hampton, NH, 1963; (Vose
Galleries of Boston, 1984); private collection, 1985

813

Two Girls Blackberrying

nd

Graphite, watercolor, 5¾ × 8¼ (14.605 × 20.955)
Inscribed lr: W. H.

Private collection

PROVENANCE
Mrs. Louis Prang, Boston, nd; (Frances Tarbox,
1924); (Henry H. Pierce, Reading, MA, 1936);
(Gilbert Brouillette, Boston, probably 1936);
(William Macbeth, Inc., 1938); Mr. and Mrs.
Thomas N. Metcalf, Boston, c. 1939; private
collection, by 1962

813.5+

Two Young Girls Carrying a Pail

Graphite, watercolor, 7¹¹⁄₁₆ × 11⅞ (19.528 × 30.163)
Inscribed ll: WH '79

Private collection

PROVENANCE
Edward W. Hooper, Boston, nd; Louisa Chapin
Hooper Thoron (Mrs. Ward Thoron), Boston,
his daughter, nd; Faith Thoron Knapp, her daughter,
by gift, 1976;

No. 813. Two Girls Blackberrying

No. 813.5. Two Young Girls Carrying a Pail

No. 814. Going Berrying

814

Going Berrying

1879

Chalk, watercolor, 8⅜ × 13¼ (21.273 × 33.655)
Inscribed ll: Homer / 1879

Museum of Fine Arts, Boston, bequest of Katherine
Dexter McCormick, 68.573

LG examined Mrs. Katherine Dexter McCormick's
five watercolor paintings and three drawings by
Homer in her Boston home, in September 1938.
(The other seven works are 2:No. 464, No. 713,
No. 744, No. 801, No. 803, No. 825, and No. 861.)
Mrs. McCormick said they all had been acquired by
her mother, Mrs. Wirt Dexter, at an auction in
Chicago "in 1876." Mrs. McCormick or Mrs.
Dexter's memory was evidently slightly imperfect:
all their Homers date from 1878 or 1879, excepting
2:No. 463, an 1873 drawing.

PROVENANCE
(Wm. A. Butters & Co., Chicago, 10 Dec. 1879,
Homer sale) [?]; Mrs. Wirt Dexter, Chicago,
probably 1879; Katherine Dexter McCormick
(Mrs. Stanley McCormick), Boston, her daughter,
probably 1937

EXHIBITIONS
Butters, Chicago, 1879 [?]; MFA, Boston, 1959
(not in catalogue); MFA, Boston, 1977, no. 49

No. 815. Going Berrying

815
Going Berrying
1879

Watercolor, 9½ × 12¼ (24.130 × 31.115)
Inscribed ll: Winslow / Homer / 79

Private collection

ABG: This work was stolen from its owner's home in 1969. It was reclaimed in 1995, having remained in the sphere of the thief or thieves throughout the previous twenty-six years. However, at some time in that period the work was cut down, presumably in hopes of disguising it for possible introduction into the art market. The removal of 2½ inches at the left edge of the sheet exactly eliminated Homer's quite distinctive inscription at the lower left corner. The 1½ inches trimmed from the top edge of the sheet removed the profile of trees which defined the background as a wooded hillside.

PROVENANCE
Horace D. Chapin, Boston, probably 1880; Margaret Chapin Osgood (Mrs. Robert B. Osgood), Boston, his sister, c. 1936; private collection, 1957

EXHIBITIONS
MFA, Boston, 1911; Copley Society 1921, no. 28; MFA, Boston, 1924; Fogg 1932, no. 25; Fogg 1936, no. 2; MFA, Boston, 1959, no. 88

LITERATURE
Downes 1911, op. 118

Going Berrying as it has appeared since about 1970.

No. 816. Picking Berries

816
Picking Berries
[1879]

Watercolor, 11⅛ × 7³⁄₁₆ (28.258 × 18.258)
Inscribed lr: Homer

Private collection

PROVENANCE
Edward F. Lenihan, Cleveland, nd; Michael
Lenihan, New York, his son, nd; (Hirschl & Adler
Galleries, 1981); private collection, 1981; (Hirschl &
Adler Galleries, 1994)

817
Two Girls
[1879]

Carbon tracing, 7⁷⁄₁₆ × 4⁷⁄₁₆ (18.893 × 11.273)

Cooper-Hewitt, National Design Museum,
Smithsonian Institution, gift of Charles Savage
Homer, Jr., 1912-12-71

In 1941 when LG made an exhaustive examination
and record of the Homers given by Charles S.
Homer, Jr., to the Cooper Union Museum (now the
Cooper-Hewitt Museum) he noted seven works
which were apparently "carbon copies" made by
Homer as he was executing drawings; all seven dated
to 1879. Although these are termed "carbon tracings,"
they show no evidence of having been made by
re-drawing under heavy pressure the essential lines
of a previously completed drawing. That is, they are
not *ex post facto* tracings, but instead were made
simultaneously with a principal drawing. They not
only demonstrate an unconventional technique with
which Homer was experimenting, but are symptomatic of his exploration of methods by which he
could increase his output by means other than a
printing press. Of the seven, the Cooper-Hewitt is
now only able to locate this drawing and *Girl with
Pail* (No. 818). LG's descriptions and—in several
cases—sketches, therefore may be all that remain of
No. 810, No. 823, No. 828, No. 835, and No. 840.

ABG: In the course of her discussion of Joseph
Pennell's lectures and articles (composed in the
later 1890s) on "'various methods of making and
reproducing drawings for book and newspaper
illustrations,'" Floramae McCarron-Cates cites this
drawing as an example of Homer employing a
method described by Pennell of transferring an image
for wood engraving. Ms. McCarron-Cates states
that Pennell's instruction was to sandwich an original
drawing between sheets of "transfer paper" (below)
and tracing paper (above): Thus "allowing the artist
to have both a tracing and a transfer while still
retaining the original without additional markings.
In many cases, it explains how both a wood engraving
and an original drawing can remain intact."
In Ms. McCarron-Cates scenario the image made
by tracing over "transfer paper"—that is, carbon
paper—was made in service of the engraver, and,
therefore, had either been traced directly onto a
wood block, or to a paper attached to a block; its
function was to allow the original drawing to survive,
and was not, itself, expected to remain viable. The
survival of seven carbon tracing drawings by Homer
would, alone, suggest they had not been created as
models for wood engravers. However, Ms. McCarron-
Cates's explanation for the exceptional medium of

Two Girls is further called into question by the facts that by the mid-1870s Homer had essentially ceased to produce images for translation by means of wood engraving into illustration in the popular press; and that none of the seven carbon tracing drawings once registered by the Cooper-Hewitt has a twin in a published illustration.

PROVENANCE
Charles S. Homer, Jr., by bequest, 1910

EXHIBITIONS
Academy of Arts & Letters 1953, no. 164b; Ogunquit 1954, no. 25a; Cooper-Hewitt 1972, no. 43; Columbia/Telfair 1974, no. 17

LITERATURE
Cooper-Hewitt, National Design Museum, "The Best Possible View: Pictorial Representation in the American West," by Floramae McCarron-Cates, in *Frederic Church, Winslow Homer and Thomas Moran: Tourism and the American Landscape* (New York, 2006), 106

No. 818. Girl with a Pail

No. 817. Two Girls

818

Girl with a Pail

[1879]

Carbon tracing, 8⁵⁄₁₆ × 4³⁄₁₆ (21.115 × 10.638)

Cooper-Hewitt, National Design Museum, Smithsonian Institution, gift of Charles Savage Homer, Jr., 1912-12-72

See commentary No. 817.

PROVENANCE
Charles S. Homer, Jr., by bequest, 1910

EXHIBITIONS
Academy of Arts & Letters 1953, no. 173b; Ogunquit 1954, no. 25b; Cooper-Hewitt 1972, no. 44; Columbia/Telfair 1974, no. 18

No. 819. The Berry Picker

819

The Berry Picker

nd

Graphite, watercolor, 12¾ × 7¾ (32.385 × 19.685)
Inscribed cr: W. H.

Private collection

ABG: The image of this little girl and her frivolous headgear represented with little variation in No. 819 and No. 820 are placed here because she appears again in No. 821, a drawing Homer presumably executed late in 1879 or early 1880 for an illustration which was published in April 1880. The two drawings in which the child is the sole subject were not necessarily executed at approximately the same time, nor in the same year as the work done for illustration.

PROVENANCE
Charles Whitmore, Boston, before 1902; Whitmore descendant, c. 1902; Pavy, J., Birmingham, MI, 1945; (P. Budrose, Marblehead, MA, c. 1970); (Curt Deininger, Boston, 1970); Arthur G. Altschul, New York, 1971; (Sotheby's, 4 Dec. 2002, sale 7854, no. 14)

EXHIBITIONS
Whitney 1973, no. 168

No. 820. Girl Carrying Berry Pail

820

Girl Carrying Berry Pail

nd

Graphite, watercolor, 9⅞ × 8¹⁄₁₆ (25.083 × 20.480)
Inscribed lr: Homer

Montclair (NJ) Art Museum, gift of Mr. and Mrs. William W. Skinner, 1961.5

ABG: See commentary No. 819.

PROVENANCE
David Mitchell, New York, nd; Sarah Olive Cogswell Mitchell (Mrs. David Mitchell), New York, by bequest, 1900; Mrs. Grace Mitchell Frambach, Paramus, NJ, her daughter, by gift, nd; Mr. and Mrs. William W. Skinner, Montclair, NJ, 1960

No. 821. Gathering Wild Blackberries

821

Gathering Wild Blackberries

nd

Ink, watercolor, 9 × 13⅞ (22.860 × 35.243)

Private collection

Homer's unusual use of black ink, and aggressive outlining of forms are indications that he executed this drawing specifically to be reproduced in publication. The drawing illustrated the article "Success With Small Fruits" by Edward Payson Roe, published in the *Scribner's Monthly* of April 1880. It appeared again in Roe's book of the same title, published by Dodd, Mead and Co. in the same year.

PROVENANCE
Arthur B. Davies, New York, nd; (American Art Association, 17 Apr. 1929, A. B. Davies estate sale, no. 376); Lillian Guyer Timkin (Mrs. William R. Timkin), New York, 1929; (Parke-Bernet Galleries, 18 May 1960, sale 1976, no. 11)

LITERATURE
Edward Payson Roe, "Success with Small Fruits," *Scribner's Monthly* 19 (Apr. 1880): 806

No. 822. Girl on a Swing

822

Girl on a Swing

1879

Graphite, 7¾ × 10⅞ (19.685 × 27.623)
Inscribed lr: W. H. '79

Hunter Museum of American Art, Chattanooga, TN, gift of Mr. and Mrs. Gary M. Brower, by exchange, 1987.18

This is one of seven drawings brought to LG in June 1936 by H. H. Pierce. LG noted from close examination that this and three others of the drawings were "drawn quite heavily in the main lines with the pencil pressing so hard into the paper that on the reverse side one can actually feel the raised lines. Also these lines on the reverse are dark, not from the pencil showing through the paper, but evidently from pressing against a surface which transferred a tone to the lines, like carbon paper, though not so dark [as was carbon paper of the 1930s]. The color of this transferred tone [on the reverse of *Girl on a Swing*] is dark blue."

Three of those four drawings were brought to him again in January 1960; he then expanded on his observations: "The lines on the front of the [three] drawings are fresh and direct, with no sign of being drawn over other lines, or of the lines being gone

over as they would have been if Homer had first made a drawing, then gone over it with carbon paper beneath it. It seems evident that he made the drawings directly, with carbon paper beneath."

This *Girl on a Swing* was the fourth drawing of the original group of seven which LG supposed had carbon-line dopplegangers. Although it was not before him in 1960 as he continued recording his thoughts on Homer's use of carbon paper, it was the example foremost in his mind:

Why would [Homer] have done this? Perhaps to keep a record of the drawings so that he could repeat them, or use them in watercolors or other mediums. (Note that [this drawing, No. 822] is very much like the drawing [No. 825] and the watercolor [No. 826].) [No. 825] is almost identical, except for the difference in technique (being on gray paper with a good deal of Chinese white) although there are a few differences in detail. [No. 826] is a little different from the two drawings, especially in the background and the branch of the tree. It seems likely that [this drawing, No. 822] came first, then [No. 825], then [No. 826]. It is quite possible that a carbon copy of [this drawing No. 822] was used in either of the other drawing or the watercolor. Judging by the sizes recorded, the figure is a little larger in [No. 825] than in [this drawing, No. 822]. But the two drawings (and to some extent the watercolor) are so close in detail that Homer must have used one of them in doing the others.

When LG thus speculated on the relationship and sequence of execution of two drawings and one watercolor of this little girl in full swing in 1960, he did not know of the existence of the watercolor now in the Hunter Museum of Art collection (No. 824); that painting did not come to light until 1972. In 1960, LG also apparently did not recall the carbon-tracing version of this same image, No. 823, Which he had seen—but not photographed—in the Cooper Union collection twenty years earlier.

ABG: There are a number of examples of closely repetitive images in Homer's oeuvre in the late 1870s, but the five recorded variants of a little girl in full, exuberant swing are the most numerous such grouping known to have survived. (The five are No. 822, No. 823, No. 824, No. 825, and No. 826.) In 1941 when LG made a careful comparison of No. 822 and the carbon traced drawing, No. 823—now missing from the Cooper-Hewitt Museum—it was his judgement that they had been executed simulta-neously as the product of a carbon paper sandwich. By 1960, without an image of No. 823 to refresh his memory, he speculated that No. 824 or No. 825 might have been developed from the carbon-traced outlines of No. 822. Of those two, the watercolor, No. 824, seems to resemble No. 822 more closely. If either No. 824 or No. 825 had been initiated on a foundation created as No. 822 was drawn, then the question remains: did Homer make more than one carbon duplication as he executed a single principal drawing, or was No. 823 the under sheet of a now unknown *sixth* representation of this playful little girl?

PROVENANCE
Mrs. Louis Prang, Boston, nd; (Frances Tarbox, 1924); (Victor Spark, nd); Mr. and Mrs. Lawrence A. Fleischman, Detroit, 1955; (Kennedy Galleries, by 1968); (Christie's, 5 Dec. 1986, sale 6288, no. 92b); (Douglas James, Fort Pierce, FL, 1986)

823
Girl on a Swing
[1879]

Carbon tracing, 8¾ × 10⅞ (22.225 × 27.623)

Cooper-Hewitt, National Design Museum, Smithsonian Institution, gift of Charles Savage Homer, Jr. Presumed destroyed, formerly 1912-12-281

In 1941 when LG made an exhaustive examination and record of the Homers given by Charles S. Homer, Jr., to the Cooper Union Museum (now the Cooper-Hewitt Museum) he noted seven works which were apparently "carbon copies" made by Homer as he was executing drawings; all seven dated to 1879. Although these are termed "carbon tracings," they show no evidence of having been made by re-drawing under heavy pressure the essential lines of a previously completed drawing. That is, they are not *ex post facto* tracings, but instead were made simultaneously with a principal drawing. They not only demonstrate an unconventional technique with which Homer was experimenting, but are symptomatic of his exploration of methods by which he could increase his output by means other than a printing press. Of the seven, the Cooper-Hewitt is now only able to locate *Two Girls* (No. 817) and *Girl with Pail* (No. 818). LG's descriptions and—in several cases—sketches, therefore may be all that remain of this drawing, and of No. 810, No. 828, No. 835, and No. 840.

LG described this drawing as "a young girl in a sunbonnet, swinging towards us and left," and noted, "It looks to me exactly like the drawing owned by Miss Francis Tarbox [*Girl on a Swing* (No. 822)]." LG returned to the Cooper Union Museum with his photograph of No. 822; his comparison of it with this work confirmed that the carbon drawing is—or was—a duplicate of No. 822. On this visit he amplified his description: "The Cooper Union drawing is not signed and dated as is the Tarbox drawing. This is the only point on which they differ. The overall paper of the Cooper Union drawing includes a little more at the edges than the Tarbox drawing, but very little more—perhaps a half inch at each side."

ABG: See commentary No. 822.

PROVENANCE
Charles S. Homer, Jr., by bequest, 1910

824

Girl on a Swing

[1879]

Watercolor, 9⅜ × 13⅛ (23.813 × 33.338)
Inscribed lr: Homer

Hunter Museum of American Art, Chattanooga,
TN, gift of Edgar M. Jolley, by exchange, 1987.17

ABG: No catalogue survives of the sale of recent
work Homer mounted in New York in March 1880.
However, the New York press gave it ample coverage,
allowing identification of a few of the lots. The *Times*
summarized the event: "Seventy-one of Winslow
Homer's water-colors were sold at auction yesterday
by Daniel A. Mathews, at No. 55 Cedar-street. The
attendance of art-lovers was large and the pictures
were sold at fair prices;" the *Times*. went on to give a
sampling of the prices, including "'Full Swing,' $21."

The *World*'s article of the previous day provides a
description of the work which probably was being
titled "Full Swing:" "As if in contrast to [the plump
and pretty maiden seated on 'The Convent Wall'
(No. 643) . . . disclosing a bit of scarlet stocking] is a
still younger girl swinging 'like mad'—the main
effect of the picture it should be noted is in its 'go'—

with the same red stockings, but a thoroughly lank,
awkward and ugly object as girls at the awkward age
are apt to be in configuration."

Of the two surviving examples of this subject
executed in color, only this *Girl on a Swing* wears
red stockings.

PROVENANCE
(Daniel A. Mathews Art Gallery, 4 Mar. 1880,
Homer sale) [?]; Ruth Thorne Douglas Davis (Mrs.
T. Preston Davis), Palm Beach, FL, nd; Joy Plummer
Findlay (Mrs. Donald R. Findlay), Palm Beach, FL,
her daughter, by gift, 1951; (Kennedy Galleries,
1973); (Christie's, 5 Dec. 1986, sale 6288, no. 92a);
(Douglas James, Fort Pierce, FL, 1986)

EXHIBITIONS
Mathews 1880 (as *Full Swing*) [?]

LITERATURE
"Water-Colors by Winslow Homer," *(NY) World*, 4
Mar. 1880; "Winslow Homer's Water-colors,"
New-York Times, 5 Mar. 1880

No. 824. Girl on a Swing

825

Girl on Swing

1879

Graphite, watercolor, 8¼ × 12⁹⁄₁₆ (20.955 × 31.910)
Inscribed lr: W. H. '79

Museum of Fine Arts, Boston, bequest of Katherine
Dexter McCormick, 68.574

See commentary No. 822.
    LG examined Mrs. Katherine Dexter McCormick's
five watercolor paintings and three drawings by
Homer in her Boston home, in September 1938.
(The other seven works are 2:No. 464, No. 713,
No. 744, No. 801, No. 803, No. 814, and No. 861.)
Mrs. McCormick said they all had been acquired
by her mother, Mrs. Wirt Dexter, at an auction
in Chicago "in 1876." Mrs. McCormick or Mrs.
Dexter's memory was evidently slightly imperfect:
all their Homers date from 1878 or 1879, excepting
2:No. 463, an 1873 drawing.

PROVENANCE
(Wm. A. Butters & Co., Chicago, 10 Dec. 1879,
Homer sale) [?]; Mrs. Wirt Dexter, Chicago, probably
1879; Katherine Dexter McCormick (Mrs. Stanley
McCormick), Boston, her daughter, probably 1937

EXHIBITIONS
Butters, Chicago, 1879 [?]; MFA, Boston, 1959 (not
in catalogue); MFA, Boston, 1977, no. 50

826

The Swing

[1879]

Watercolor, 7³⁄₁₆ × 9⅝ (18.258 × 24.448)
Inscribed lr: Homer

Worcester Art Museum, gift of Mrs. Howard W.
Preston in memory of Dr. and Mrs. Loring Holmes
Dodd, 1969.128

PROVENANCE
James F. Sutton, New York, nd; Dr. Edward J. Davin,
before 1936; (American Art Association, 23 Jan. 1936,
sale 4227, no. 5); (E. C. Babcock Art Galleries, 1936);
(Robert C. Vose Galleries of Boston, 1936); Dr. and
Mrs. Loring Holmes Dodd, Worcester, MA, 1936;
Mrs. Howard W. Preston, Cranston, RI, 1968

No. 825. Girl on Swing

No. 826. The Swing

EXHIBITIONS
Worcester 1944, no. 29; Worcester 1987, no. 60;
Worcester 1998

LITERATURE
Helen Cooper, "The Swing," in Susan E. Strickler,
ed., *American Traditions in Watercolor: The Worcester
Art Museum Collection* (New York: Abbeville Press,
1987), 84.

827

Boy on a Swing

1879

Graphite, 10¼ × 8⅞₁₆ (26.035 × 21.433)
Inscribed ll: H 79

Cooper-Hewitt, National Design Museum,
Smithsonian Institution, gift of Charles Savage
Homer, Jr., 1912-12-65

PROVENANCE
Charles S. Homer, Jr., by bequest, 1910

EXHIBITIONS
Cooper-Hewitt 1972, no. 46; Columbia/Telfair 1974,
no. 20; Lowe, Syracuse, 1979, no. 13

828

Girl Resting Head on A Swing

1879

Carbon tracing, 8¾ × 10½ (22.225 × 26.670)
Inscribed ll: W. H. '79

Cooper-Hewitt, National Design Museum,
Smithsonian Institution, gift of Charles Savage
Homer, Jr. Presumed destroyed, formerly 1912-12-282

In 1941 when LG made an exhaustive examination
and record of the Homers given by Charles S. Homer,
Jr., to the Cooper Union Museum (now the Cooper-
Hewitt Museum) he noted seven works which were
apparently "carbon copies" made by Homer as he
was executing drawings; all seven dated to 1879.
Although these are termed "carbon tracings," they
show no evidence of having been made by re-drawing
under heavy pressure the essential lines of a previously
completed drawing. That is, they are not *ex post facto*
tracings, but instead were made simultaneously with
a principal drawing. They not only demonstrate an
unconventional technique with which Homer was
experimenting, but are symptomatic of his exploration
of methods by which he could increase his output
by means other than a printing press. Of the seven,
the Cooper-Hewitt is now only able to locate *Two
Girls* (No. 817) and *Girl with Pail* (No. 818). LG's
descriptions and—in this case—a sketch, therefore
may be all that remain of this drawing, and of
No. 810, No. 823, No. 835, and No. 840.

In addition to recording the subject of this drawing
in a sketch, LG described its features: "A young girl
in a sunbonnet, seated on grass, half turn left, resting
her head on the wooden seat of a swing, eyes closed."

PROVENANCE
Charles S. Homer, Jr., by bequest, 1910

Sketch of *Girl Resting Head on A Swing* made by Lloyd Goodrich as part of his
catalogue record of the "carbon tracing" drawing formerly in the collection of
the Cooper-Hewitt, National Design Museum, Smithsonian Institution.

829

Two Girls on a Swing

[1879]

Graphite, 6¾ × 4⅛ (17.145 × 10.478)

Cooper-Hewitt, National Design Museum, Smithsonian Institution, gift of Charles Savage Homer, Jr., 1912-12-61

PROVENANCE
Charles S. Homer, Jr., by bequest, 1910

EXHIBITIONS
Lowe, Syracuse, 1979, no. 16

830

Girl Seated on a Swing

1879

Graphite, 10 × 8¾ (25.400 × 22.225)
Inscribed lr: W. H. '79

Private collection

This is one of seven drawings brought to LG in June 1936 by H. H. Pierce. LG noted from close examination that this and three others of the drawings were "drawn quite heavily in the main lines with the pencil pressing so hard into the paper that on the reverse side one can actually feel the raised lines. Also these lines on the reverse are dark, not from the pencil showing through the paper, but evidently from pressing against a surface which transferred a tone to the lines, like carbon paper, though not so dark [as was carbon paper of the 1930s]. The color of this transferred tone [on the reverse of *Girl Seated on a Swing*] is dark blue."

Three of the seven, including this drawing, were brought to LG again in January 1960: "I examined them carefully, using a magnifying glass. The lines on the front of the drawings are fresh and direct, with no sign of being drawn over other lines, or of the lines being gone over as they would have been if Homer had first made a drawing, then gone over it with carbon paper beneath it. It seems evident that he made the drawings directly with carbon paper beneath."

PROVENANCE
Mrs. Louis Prang, Boston, nd; (Frances Tarbox, 1924); (Kennedy Galleries, 1960)

No. 829. Two Girls on a Swing

No. 830. Girl Seated on a Swing

831

Girl on a Swing

1879

Graphite, 8⅜ × 5¼ (21.273 × 13.335)
Inscribed ll: Homer / 1879

Cooper-Hewitt, National Design Museum,
Smithsonian Institution, gift of Charles Savage
Homer, Jr., 1912-12-64

PROVENANCE
Charles S. Homer, Jr., by bequest, 1910

EXHIBITIONS
Slater 1952; Academy of Arts & Letters 1953, no.
169a; Ogunquit 1954, no. 27b; Ithaca 1971, no. 24b

No. 831. Girl on a Swing

No. 832. Girl on a Swing

see color illustration, p. 449

832

Girl on a Swing

[1879]

Watercolor, 12⅜ × 9⅜ (31.433 × 23.813)
Inscribed ll: Homer; lr: Homer

Private collection

ABG: The New York *World*'s reviewer of the
large Homer sale held at the Mathews gallery in
March 1880 may be presumed to be referring to
this painting in his comment: "In such a picture,
however, as that of the girl in a swing holding to
one of the ropes, and relieved against a background
of russet leafage, the charm is distinctly poetic; the

attitude is delightful in grace and ease of poise, and the color of the whole is as bright and buoyant as the action of the figure."

PROVENANCE
(Daniel A. Mathews Art Gallery, 4 Mar. 1880, Homer sale); Mr. and Mrs. Robert P. McDougal, Orange, NJ, nd; (Sotheby's, 4 Dec. 1986, sale 5524, no. 87)

EXHIBITIONS
Mathews 1880

LITERATURE
"Water-Colors by Winslow Homer," (NY) World, 4 Mar. 1880

833

Girl Standing on a Swing

[1879]

Graphite, 10⅜ × 8⅜ (26.353 × 21.273)

Cooper-Hewitt, National Design Museum, Smithsonian Institution, gift of Charles Savage Homer, Jr., 1912-12-63

PROVENANCE
Charles S. Homer, Jr., by bequest, 1910

No. 833. Girl Standing on a Swing

834

Girl on a Swing

[1879]

Graphite, 7½ × 5⅛ (19.050 × 13.018)

Cooper-Hewitt, National Design Museum, Smithsonian Institution, gift of Charles Savage Homer, Jr., 1912-12-62

PROVENANCE
Charles S. Homer, Jr., by bequest, 1910

EXHIBITIONS
Slater 1952; Academy of Arts & Letters 1953, no. 169b; Ogunquit 1954, no. 27a; Ithaca 1971, no. 24a

No. 834. Girl on a Swing

835

Girl Holding a Swing

[1879]

Carbon tracing, 8¾ × 6¾ (22.225 × 17.145)

Cooper-Hewitt, National Design Museum, Smithsonian Institution, gift of Charles Savage Homer, Jr. Presumed destroyed, formerly 1912-12-279

In 1941 when LG made an exhaustive examination and record of the Homers given by Charles S. Homer, Jr., to the Cooper Union Museum (now the Cooper-Hewitt Museum) he noted seven works which were apparently "carbon copies" made by Homer as he was executing drawings; all seven dated to 1879. Although these are termed "carbon tracings," they show no evidence of having been made by re-drawing under heavy pressure the essential lines of a previously completed drawing. That is, they are not *ex post facto* tracings, but instead were made simultaneously with a principal drawing. They not only demonstrate an unconventional technique with which Homer was experimenting, but are symptomatic of his exploration of methods by which he could increase his output by means other than a printing press. Of the seven, the Cooper-Hewitt is now only able to locate *Two Girls* (No. 817) and *Girl with Pail* (No. 818). LG's descriptions and—in several cases—sketches, therefore may be all that remain of this drawing, and of No. 810, No. 823, No. 828, and No. 840.

LG had no need to sketch this carbon traced drawing, as he described it as being:

> identical with 1912-12-62 [No. 834]. (Young girl in sunbonnet holding to two ropes of swing.) I compared them; they are identical, line for line, except that the present drawing is rather fainter and all the lines do not appear. This drawing is in blue on white paper. I should say that this is a carbon copy of 1912-12-62, and that it was made at the same time that the latter was drawn, as the lines are absolutely identical, and there is no sign that 1912-12-62 was gone over after the first drawing was done.

PROVENANCE
Charles S. Homer, Jr., by bequest, 1910

836+

Girl on a Swing

1879

Charcoal, watercolor, 16½ × 8 (41.910 × 20.320) sight
Inscribed ll: Homer '79

Private collection

PROVENANCE
(Wm. A. Butters & Co., Chicago, 10 Dec. 1879, Homer sale) [?]; Susan Walbridge Hamill (Mrs. Davisson Hamill), Chicago, nd; Frances Hamill Phelps, Chicago, her daughter, nd; Charlotte Phelps Dodge, Washington, DC, her daughter, nd; unidentified daughter-in-law of Mrs. Dodge, by gift, nd; (Sotheby's, 25 May 1988, sale 5721, no. 65)

EXHIBITIONS
Butters, Chicago, 1879 [?]

No. 836. Girl on a Swing

837

The Swing

[1879]

Watercolor, 11½ × 8½ (29.210 × 21.590)
Inscribed lr: Homer

Private collection

PROVENANCE
Private collection, nd; (Coe Kerr Gallery, 1982)

No. 837. The Swing

838

Girl Seated on a Porch Step

[1879]

Graphite, 6⅝ × 5⁹⁄₁₆ (16.828 × 14.130)

Cooper-Hewitt, National Design Museum,
Smithsonian Institution, gift of Charles Savage
Homer, Jr., 1912-12-78

PROVENANCE
Charles S. Homer, Jr., by bequest, 1910

EXHIBITIONS
Cooper-Hewitt 1972, no. 45; Columbia/Telfair 1974,
no. 19; Lowe, Syracuse, 1979, no. 14; Greenville
County 1986

No. 838. Girl Seated on a Porch Step

No. 839. Girl Seated on a Step

839

Girl Seated on a Step

1879

Graphite, 8⅜ × 9¹⁵⁄₁₆ (21.273 × 25.243)
Inscribed lr: W. H. / Aug 20th '79

Cooper-Hewitt, National Design Museum,
Smithsonian Institution, gift of Charles Savage
Homer, Jr., 1912-12-69

PROVENANCE
Charles S. Homer, Jr., by bequest, 1910

EXHIBITIONS
Lowe, Syracuse, 1979, no. 12

840

Children Picking Fruit from a Tree

[1879]

Carbon tracing, 8¾ × 9¼ (22.225 × 23.495)

Cooper-Hewitt, National Design Museum,
Smithsonian Institution, gift of Charles Savage
Homer, Jr. Presumed destroyed, formerly 1912-12-278

In 1941 when LG made an exhaustive examination
and record of the Homers given by Charles S.
Homer, Jr., to the Cooper Union Museum (now
the Cooper-Hewitt Museum) he noted seven works
which were apparently "carbon copies" made by
Homer as he was executing drawings; all seven dated
to 1879. Although these are termed "carbon tracings,"
they show no evidence of having been made by
re-drawing under heavy pressure the essential lines
of a previously completed drawing. That is, they
are not *ex post facto* tracings, but instead were made
simultaneously with a principal drawing. They
not only demonstrate an unconventional technique
with which Homer was experimenting, but are
symptomatic of his exploration of methods by which
he could increase his output by means other than
a printing press. Of the seven, the Cooper-Hewitt
is now only able to locate *Two Girls* (No. 817) and
Girl with Pail (No. 818). LG's descriptions and—
in several cases—sketches, therefore may be all that
remain of this drawing, and of No. 810, No. 823,
No. 828, and No. 835.

PROVENANCE
Charles S. Homer, Jr., by bequest, 1910

Sketch of *Children Picking Fruit from a Tree* made by Lloyd
Goodrich as part of his catalogue record of the "carbon tracing"
drawing formerly in the collection of the Cooper-Hewitt, National
Design Museum, Smithsonian Institution.

841

Three Little Girls Perched on a Fence

nd

Graphite, 6¼ × 7 (15.875 × 17.780)
Inscribed lr: W.

Private collection

PROVENANCE
Mrs. Louis Prang, Boston, nd; (Frances Tarbox, 1924); (Henry H. Pierce, Reading, MA, 1936); James L. Plaut, Boston, 1936; (Frank Fowler, Lookout Mountain, TN, 1978)

EXHIBITIONS
MFA, Boston, 1936; IMA, Boston, 1941, no. d-12; MFA, Boston, 1959 (not in catalogue); Farnsworth 2006

No. 841. Three Little Girls Perched on a Fence

842

Girl with Chickens

[1879]

Graphite, 5½ × 8 (13.970 × 20.320)
Inscribed ll: Homer

Private collection

In 1948 Mrs. Mabel Blanchard transcribed for LG a label which was then still attached to the frame backing of this drawing: "American Water Color Society / Winslow Homer - Scarboro, Maine / William Macbeth / 450 Fifth Avenue." On several occasions in the first years of the twentieth century Homer sent William Macbeth substantial groups of his drawings done in the 1870s and early 1880s. Homer had been a regular contributor to American Water Color Society annual exhibitions from 1874 through the 1880s and in 1891. Thereafter, the rare appearances of his work in these annuals was apparently instigated by dealers. Although not identified as "lender" of the works, watercolor paintings included in the 1905 and 1906 Society annuals may be presumed to have been placed by the Knoedler gallery; and the five drawings by Homer shown in the 1909, and two in the 1910 exhibitions, may be presumed to have been placed by the Macbeth gallery and have come from its stock of earlier works. *Girl with Chickens* may be presumed to have been one of those exhibited in 1909, or—a little more likely—1910. However, as all were identified in the Society catalogues simply as "Drawing," it is not possible to give a specific exhibition reference.

No. 842. Girl with Chickens

PROVENANCE
(William Macbeth, Inc., 1902/1907); Richard de Wolfe Brixey, New York, 1935; Mabel F. Blanchard (Mrs. C. Ford Blanchard), Virginia, 1936; Mrs. Smith, her niece, nd; The sons of Mrs. Smith, nd; (Sotheby's, 21 Sept. 1994, sale 6595, no. 31); (Jordan-Volpe Gallery, 1994)

No. 843. Over the Garden Wall

843
Over the Garden Wall
[1879]

Graphite, 5¹³⁄₁₆ × 5⅛ (14.765 × 13.018)
Inscribed lr: W H

Private collection

PROVENANCE
(William Macbeth, Inc., 1902/1907); Mahonri
Young, New York, 1936; Brigham Young University,
Provo, UT, by gift, nd; Dion O'Wyatt, New York,
nd; (Hirschl & Adler Galleries, 1969)

No. 844. Young Girl in an Orchard

844+
Young Girl in an Orchard
[1879]

Graphite, 6¼ × 8¾ (15.875 × 22.225)
Inscribed ll: W. H.

Private collection

PROVENANCE
Mr. and Mrs. Dean W. Barnett, Balmville, NY, nd;
(Thomas Colville Fine Art, LLC, New Haven, 1992)

845

Girl (Adelaide Cole)

1879

Graphite, 10¹⁄₁₆ × 9⁷⁄₁₆ (25.560 × 23.973)
Inscribed lr: Homer / 1879

The University of Michigan Museum of Art, Ann
Arbor, bequest of Margaret Watson Parker, 1955/1.104

The adult Adelaide Cole Chase (1868–1944) was a
successful portraitist, maintaining her studio in
Boston. She was the daughter of Joseph Foxworth
Cole. Cole and Homer had been friends from their
days working together at Bufford's lithography shop
in Boston. Cole spent lengthy periods of time in
France developing his career as a landscape painter
in the Barbizon mode; he was living in Paris at the
same time in 1867 that Homer was there. In 1877 he
settled permanently in Winchester, Massachusetts,
and in the summer of 1879, when Adelaide was
eleven or twelve years old, Homer was a visitor in
the Cole home.

Although LG's catalogue record does not explain
when or how Mrs. Chase was introduced to this
drawing and recognized herself as its central character,
it may have been from a photograph LG sent to
her. In a letter of 6 February 1941, Miss Esther
Williams gave LG a transcription of a pertinent
portion of a letter her cousin, Mrs. Chase, had
written to a family member:

> I really couldn't have given Mr. Goodrich
> any definite information about Winslow Homer
> as I was too young at the time. It was when we
> lived on Mystic Avenue in Winchester, and I only
> remember having posed quite a little for him,
> looking very much like a French child according
> to the drawing Mrs. Walter Parker bought.

PROVENANCE
(Wm. A. Butters & Co., Chicago, 10 Dec. 1879,
Homer sale) [?]; (J. W. Young Galleries, Chicago,
nd); Margaret Watson Parker (Mrs. Walter R.
Parker), Detroit, nd; Dr. Walter R. Parker, Detroit,
her husband [in trust], nd

EXHIBITIONS
Butters, Chicago, 1879 [?]; University of Arizona
1963, no. 81; Knoedler 1986, no. 28

No. 845. Girl (Adelaide Cole)

846

Girl Holding a Branch of an Apple Tree

[1879]

Graphite, 7¹¹⁄₁₆ × 5¹¹⁄₁₆ (19.528 × 14.448)

Cooper-Hewitt, National Design Museum, Smithsonian Institution, gift of Charles Savage Homer, Jr., 1912-12-70

PROVENANCE
Charles S. Homer, Jr., by bequest, 1910

EXHIBITIONS
Academy of Arts & Letters 1953, no. 183; Ogunquit 1954, no. 21a; Cooper-Hewitt 1972, no. 32; Columbia/Telfair 1974, no. 10; Lowe, Syracuse, 1979, no. 1; Cooper-Hewitt 2006

No. 846. Girl Holding a Branch of an Apple Tree

No. 847. Under the Apple Boughs

847

Under the Apple Boughs

[1879]

Graphite, watercolor, 9 × 14½ (22.860 × 36.830) sight
Inscribed ll: Homer

Private collection

PROVENANCE
(Wm. A. Butters & Co., Chicago, 10 Dec. 1879,
Homer sale) [?]; (Findlay Galleries, Chicago, c. 1946);
(Wildenstein & Co., 1948); Joan Hutton Patterson,
New York, c. 1960; (Davis & Long Co., c. 1970)

EXHIBITIONS
Butters, Chicago, 1879 [?]; Wildenstein 1948, no. 5;
Wildenstein 1949, no. 19; Houston 1952, no. 29

848

Young Woman Carrying a Basket

1879

Graphite, 12³⁄₁₆ × 7¾ (30.958 × 19.685)
Inscribed lr: Homer / 1879

Cooper-Hewitt, National Design Museum,
Smithsonian Institution, gift of Charles W. Gould,
1916-15-1

PROVENANCE
Charles W. Gould, New York, nd

EXHIBITIONS
Whitney 1936, no. 107; Carnegie 1937, no. 203;
Cooper-Hewitt 1972, no. 37; Columbia/Telfair
1974, no. 13; Lowe, Syracuse, 1979, no. 4; Cooper-
Hewitt 2006

No. 848. Young Woman Carrying a Basket

No. 849. Through the Fields

849

Through the Fields

1879

Graphite, watercolor, 10⅛ × 15¼ (25.718 × 38.735) sight
Inscribed ll: Winslow Homer / 1879

Private collection

ABG: See No. 851.

PROVENANCE
(Wm. A. Butters & Co., Chicago, 10 Dec. 1879, Homer sale) [?]; Eda Hurd Lord (Mrs. George S. Lord), Evanston, IL, nd [?]; (J. W. Young Galleries, Chicago, before 1923); Mrs. Woodruff J. Parker, Chicago, 1923; Mrs. George A. Martin, Cleveland, before 1938; (Parke-Bernet Galleries, 18–19 Oct. 1946, sale 795, no. 114); (Wildenstein & Co., 1946); Charles W. Engelhard, Far Hills, NJ, 1959

EXHIBITIONS
Butters, Chicago, 1879 [?]; Wildenstein 1947, no. 97; Wildenstein 1948, no. 7; Wildenstein 1949, no. 21; Houston 1952, no. 32

No. 850. Girls Strolling in an Orchard

850

Girls Strolling in an Orchard

1879

Watercolor, 9¾ × 13¼ (24.765 × 33.655)
Inscribed lr: Winslow Homer / 1879

Private collection

ABG: See No. 851.

PROVENANCE
(Wm. A. Butters & Co., Chicago, 10 Dec. 1879, Homer sale) [?]; James H. Dole, Chicago, by 1881; George S. Dole, Galesburg, IL, his son, 1902; Mrs. George S. Dole, Galesburg, IL (later Minneapolis), 1934; John J. Foley, Minneapolis, a relative of Mrs. Dole, nd; (Kennedy Galleries, 1963); Madison H. Lewis, New York, 1963; Elizabeth Sanford Lewis (Mrs. Madison H. Lewis, later Mrs. W. Leicester Van Leer), New York, by bequest, by 1980; (Christie's, 6 Dec. 1991, sale 7380, no. 44); (Debra Force Fine Art, Inc., by 1999)

EXHIBITIONS
Butters, Chicago, 1879 [?]; Inter-State Industrial Exposition of Chicago, *Ninth Annual Exhibition*, 7 Sept.–22 Oct. 1881, no. 211 (as *The Walk*); Inter-State Industrial Exposition of Chicago, *Twelfth Annual*

Exhibition, 3 Sept.–18 Oct. 1884, no. 432 (as *Blossoms*); Inter-State Industrial Exposition of Chicago, *Fifteenth Annual Exhibition*, 7 Sept.–23 Oct. 1887, no. 489 (as *Blossoms*); Inter-State Industrial Exposition of Chicago, *Eighteenth Annual Exhibition*, 3 Sept.– 18 Oct. 1890, no. 408 (as *Under the Apple Trees*)

851

Two Girls in a Field

1879

Graphite, 9³⁄₁₆ × 9¹⁵⁄₁₆ (23.338 × 25.243)
Inscribed lr: Winslow Homer / 1879; across lower edge: Copyright given to D. Appleton and Co.; across left edge (not in Homer's hand): 9251 1 Jan 3xxx / 5″ high

Cooper-Hewitt, National Design Museum, Smithsonian Institution, gift of Charles Savage Homer, Jr., 1912-12-80

This drawing was one of two photographically reproduced to illustrate an article by G. W. Sheldon first published in the April 1880 issue of the *Art Journal*.

The image is illustrated in Albert Ten Eyck Gardner's book on Homer. Doubtless because of editorial confusion the caption identifies the illustration as being the original drawing, and in the collection of the Metropolitan Museum of Art. Presumably its source was a copy of the April 1880 issue of the *Art Journal* held in the Metropolitan's library.

ABG: The subject of this drawing is repeated in the more developed drawing *Through the Fields* (No. 849), and watercolor *Girls Strolling in an Orchard* (No. 850). Although it would seem reasonable to assume Homer made this drawing specifically for the *Art Journal*'s use, in which case it would likely have been executed later than those two, it may just as well have been something Homer had on hand, and had already served as a source for No. 849 and No. 850.

Comparison of this drawing and its reproduction in the *Art Journal* demonstrates the manipulation possible by the photographic technology. Homer's inscribed signature and date, is placed well to the right of the figural group in the drawing; in the *Art Journal* illustration it has been shifted to the left to reduce the gap between it and the right-hand figure, thus making for a tighter composition—and one which needed less space on the vertically formatted journal page

PROVENANCE
Charles S. Homer, Jr., by bequest, 1910

No. 851. Two Girls in a Field

EXHIBITIONS
Carnegie 1937, no. 178; Cooper-Hewitt 1972, no. 42; Columbia/Telfair 1974, no. 16; Lowe, Syracuse, 1979, no. 10

LITERATURE
[George William Sheldon], "Sketches and Studies. II. From the Portfolios of A. H. Thayer, William M. Chase, Winslow Homer, and Peter Moran," *(NY) Art Journal* 6 (Apr. 1880): 108. Reprinted in, G. W. Sheldon, *Hours with Art and Artists* (New York: D. Appleton and Company, 1882), 136; Albert Ten Eyck Gardner, *Winslow Homer American Artist: His World and His Work* (New York: Clarkson N. Potter, Inc., 1961), 67

No. 852. Two Girls in a Field

852

Two Girls in a Field

1879

Graphite, 9¾ × 8¼ (24.765 × 20.955)
Inscribed lr: W. H. '79

Brooklyn Museum, Frederick Loeser Fund, 28.211

PROVENANCE
(Andre Rueff, Brooklyn, nd)

EXHIBITIONS
Metropolitan/Brooklyn 1972, no. 51; Lowe, Syracuse, 1979, no. 18

No. 853. Two Girls Seated on a Bank

853

Two Girls Seated on a Bank

[1879]

Graphite, 8³⁄₁₆ × 4¹⁵⁄₁₆ (20.798 × 12.543)

Cooper-Hewitt, National Design Museum, Smithsonian Institution, gift of Charles Savage Homer, Jr., 1912-12-77

PROVENANCE
Charles S. Homer, Jr., by bequest, 1910

EXHIBITIONS
Academy of Arts & Letters 1953, no. 173a; Ogunquit 1954, no. 21b; Cooper-Hewitt 1972, no. 33; Columbia/ Telfair 1974, no. 11; Lowe, Syracuse, 1979, no. 2; Cooper-Hewitt 2006

No. 854. Two Young Girls

No. 855. Two Young Girls in a Field

854
Two Young Girls
[1879]

Charcoal, watercolor, 10⅜ × 7⅜ (26.353 × 18.733)
Inscribed ll: Homer

Cooper-Hewitt, National Design Museum,
Smithsonian Institution, gift of Charles Savage
Homer, Jr., 1912-12-276

PROVENANCE
Charles S. Homer, Jr., by bequest, 1910

EXHIBITIONS
Whitney 1936, no. 105; Carnegie 1937, no. 207;
Cooper-Hewitt 1972, no. 36; Lowe, Syracuse, 1979,
no. 3; Greenville County 1986; Cooper-Hewitt 2006

855
Two Young Girls in a Field
[1879]

Graphite, 9³⁄₁₆ × 3⅝ (23.338 × 9.208)

Cooper-Hewitt, National Design Museum,
Smithsonian Institution, gift of Charles Savage
Homer, Jr., 1912-12-256

PROVENANCE
Charles S. Homer, Jr., by bequest, 1910

EXHIBITIONS
Lowe, Syracuse, 1979, no. 15

No. 856. Two Girls on a Hillside

856+

Two Girls on a Hillside

1879

Watercolor, 6⅞ × 9⅞ (17.463 × 25.083)
Inscribed lr: Homer '79

Private collection

PROVENANCE
Edward A. Kimball, Boston, nd; Wallace Davidson
Kimball, Middle Haddam, CT, his son, nd;
Madeleine Kimball Crowdus, Laguna Beach, CA,
his daughter, nd; private collection, by 1976;
(Spanierman Gallery, LLC, 1990)

857

The Strollers

[1879]

Graphite, 8¼ × 8⅛ (20.955 × 20.638)

Private collection

PROVENANCE
Mrs. Louis Prang, Boston, nd; (Frances Tarbox,
1924); (Kennedy Galleries, 1960)

No. 857. The Strollers

858
Two Girls
1879

Graphite, 9⅛ × 9¹¹⁄₁₆ (23.178 × 24.608) sight
Inscribed lr: W. H. 79 / Winslow Homer

Private collection

ABG: Among the records of works described as by
Homer, which LG was unable to trace was a *Study of
Two Young Girls* in the sale of the estate of the artist,
Arthur B. Davies. The American Art Association
catalogue of this sale did not illustrate the work, but
provided the following description: "the two young
girls with their arms entwined about each other
are walking from the spectator, in a suggestion of
undulating landscape. Signed at lower right: Winslow
Homer. Pencil drawing. Height 10 inches; length
10½ inches." The buyer of record was identified as
a Mrs. John Stambaugh, without address.

It is likely, but unproven, that this drawing is the
Study of Two Young Girls once owned by Davies.

PROVENANCE
Arthur B. Davies, New York, nd [?]; (American
Art Association, 17 Apr. 1929, A. B. Davies estate sale,
no. 368)[?]; Mrs. John Stambaugh, 1929[?]; private
collection, nd; (Hirschl & Adler Galleries, 1982)

No. 858. Two Girls

859
Girls on Hillside
1879

Graphite, 7¼ × 13 (18.415 × 33.020)
Inscribed ll: Winslow Homer 1879

Unlocated

PROVENANCE
(Wm. A. Butters & Co., Chicago, 10 Dec. 1879,
Homer sale) [?]; Cornelia Lunt, Evanston, IL,
probably 1879; Anne Evans, by bequest, nd; Denver
Art Museum, by bequest, 1941; (M. Knoedler &
Co., 1951)

EXHIBITIONS
Butters, Chicago, 1879 [?]

No. 859. Girls on Hillside

No. 860. Listening to the Birds

860

Listening to the Birds
nd

Watercolor, 5½ × 11¼ (13.970 × 28.575)
Inscribed ll: W H

Private collection

PROVENANCE
(Wm. A. Butters & Co., Chicago, 10 Dec. 1879,
Homer sale) [?]; Charles D. Hamill, Chicago,
probably 1879; Mrs. Dudley, Chicago, by gift, 1882;
Katherine Dudley, Paris, her daughter, by bequest,
c. 1935; (Weyhe Gallery, c. 1935); (Milch Galleries,
1950); Frank W. Spencer, Morristown, NJ, 1950;
(Douglas James, Signal Mountain, TN, 1972);
(Anthony Olivo, Providence, RI, 1974); (Stephen
Straw Company, Inc., Newburyport, MA, 1974)

EXHIBITIONS
Butters, Chicago, 1879 [?]

861

Two Girls Looking at a Book
nd

Watercolor, 5⅜ × 8¹¹⁄₁₆ (13.653 × 22.068)

Museum of Fine Arts, Boston, bequest of Katherine
Dexter McCormick, 68.572

LG examined Mrs. Katherine Dexter McCormick's
five watercolor paintings and three drawings by
Homer in her Boston home, in September 1938. (The
other seven works are 2:No. 464, No. 713, No. 744,
No. 801, No. 803, No. 814, and No. 825.) Mrs.
McCormick said they all had been acquired by
her mother, Mrs. Wirt Dexter, at an auction in
Chicago "in 1876." Mrs. McCormick or Mrs.
Dexter's memory was evidently slightly imperfect:
all their Homers date from 1878 or 1879, excepting
2:No. 463, an 1873 drawing.

PROVENANCE
(Wm. A. Butters & Co., Chicago, 10 Dec. 1879,
Homer sale) [?]; Mrs. Wirt Dexter, Chicago,
probably 1879; Katherine Dexter McCormick
(Mrs. Stanley McCormick), Boston, her daughter,
probably 1937

EXHIBITIONS
Butters, Chicago, 1879 [?]; MFA, Boston, 1959 (not
in catalogue); University of Arizona 1963, no. 78;
MFA, Boston, 1977, no. 42

No. 861. Two Girls Looking at a Book

862

Girl in Black Reading

[1879]

Watercolor, 7½ × 9¼ (19.050 × 23.495)
Inscribed lr: Homer

Colby College Museum of Art, Waterville, ME,
The Lunder Collection

PROVENANCE
(Wm. A. Butters & Co., Chicago, 10 Dec. 1879,
Homer sale) [?]; Mr. and Mrs. Frank Allport,
DeKalb, IL, probably 1879; Mrs. Walter Allport,
Chicago, Mrs. Frank Allport's sister-in-law, by
purchase, c. 1900; Mrs. Sidney Haskell, Geneva, IL,
Mrs. Walter Allport's daughter, by bequest, 1950;
Mrs. Haskell's four children, by bequest, 1968;
(Hirschl & Adler Galleries, 1982); private collection,
1983; (Hirschl & Adler Galleries, 1994)

EXHIBITIONS
Butters, Chicago, 1879 [?]; AI Chicago 2008

No. 862. Girl in Black Reading

863

Girl with a Letter

1879

Watercolor, 8½ × 8⅜ (21.590 × 21.273)
Inscribed ll: [Hom]er '79; ur: Homer 1879

Private collection

PROVENANCE
Edward W. Hooper, Boston, nd; Mabel Hooper
La Farge (Mrs. Bancel La Farge), Boston, 1901;
Thomas Sergeant La Farge, her son, 1944

EXHIBITIONS
MFA, Boston, 1911; Carnegie 1937, no. 133; Whitney
1944; Worcester 1944, no. 28; Maynard Walker 1953,
no. 15; NGA 1958, no. 96; Whitney 1973, no. 90;
NGA 1986, no. 35 (as *Girl Seated*)

No. 863. Girl with a Letter

see color illustration, p. 450

No. 864. Houses on a Hillside

see color illustration, p. 451

864

Houses on a Hillside

1879

Oil, 15¾ × 22½ (40.005 × 57.150)
Inscribed lr: Homer 1879

Private collection

This painting is clearly seen in one of the two formal "portrait" photographs made of the rooms in the Benedict building on New York's Washington Square shared by Homer and Samuel T. Preston for part of 1880 and 1881, and again following Homer's return in late 1882 from his extended stay in England. Gordon Hendricks published copies of both photographs, and in captioning the appropriate image, brusquely dismissed *Houses on a Hillside* as "one at upper right, is not by Homer." Hendricks may have made this conspicuously unfounded judgement from the combination of the painting then being in an obscure private collection (public collections and the market essentially defined the boundaries of his research), and its subject being uncommon in Homer oeuvre.

ABG: In discussing this work in her catalogue for the Halff collection exhibition, Eleanor Jones Harvey embeds it in a charming scenario, which unfortunately is factually flawed. She states: "Over the years Winslow repaid [his brother] Charles's generosity with numerous gifts of oils and watercolors. *Houses on a Hillside* was one such gift and captures the essence of a summer spent together in West Townsend, Massahcusetts."

Homer was as much a man of business as his brothers. He rarely gave away the product by which he earned his living. He certainly did give paintings to Charles, but they were very few. However, Charles was his brother's sole heir, and thereby became the first owner of record of hundreds of working sketches, and in lesser quantities, finished drawings and paintings. There is no basis for supposing *Houses on a Hillside* came into Charles's possession as other than part of that bequest.

All that can be relied upon concerning Homer's summer itineraries through this period of his life is that he surely vacated New York; that he did not settle in one location for the full summer, although often revisiting favored locales; and that he spent some of the time with his parents at whatever resort they were passing the hot months. For most of the decade of 1870s hints in the press, references in letters, or inscriptions on drawings allow piecing together a probable arc of Homer's summer travels. The summer of 1879 is the exception; there are no such clues by which his whereabouts may be positively determined. It seems likely Homer was in Mountainville, New York, the neighborhood of Lawson Valentine's Houghton Farm. It seems very likely he passed some time in the Townsend area, although not necessarily for the sole purpose of enjoying the company of his brother and sister-in-law, nor necessarily living at their West Townsend home the whole time.

At some time in this summer of 1879 Homer was in Winchester in the Boston area. If he held to his usual practice, he would have gone to Maine to visit his parents at one of Prout's Neck's summer hotels. The setting and atmospheric character of *Houses on a Hillside* are so inconsistent with the farm subjects which dominate Homer's surviving work from this summer, that it invites speculation that he might have found its houses, surrounding landscape and vibrant sky along the southern coast of Maine.

Harvey further suggests that the minimally articulated figure seated on the edge of the hill at the right may be identified as a fourteen year-old girl, Fannie Sanders. Richard N. Smith, the author of a history of Townsend Massachusetts, written for the local historical society, and published in 1978, recounts a story he was told of Miss Sanders having said she posed for *Girl with Laurel* (No. 769). Even if *Houses on a Hillside* could be reliably located to Townsend, it seems improbable Homer would have needed a model for such a staffage figure, or logical that he would feel he needed to be exclusive in who served that function.

Harvey also defines this work as small and intimate in scale, whereas the 15 inches by 22 inches dimensions of the canvas put it in company with almost all Homer's few oils dating from 1879, and with many others of this period. It was his favored size for "medium" scaled oils. In 1879, only the three paintings (No. 772, No. 775, and No. 776) he placed in the National Academy of Design annual exhibition are larger. At what, for Homer at the time, was a substantially proportioned work, it may be assumed he had in mind putting out *Houses on a Hillside* for exhibition and sale. No indication that he did so is presently known from contemporary records.

PROVENANCE
Charles S. Homer, Jr., by bequest, 1910; Mrs. Charles S. Homer, Jr., by bequest, 1917; Arthur P. and Charles L. Homer, by bequest, 1937; (William Macbeth, Inc., 1938); Bartlett Arkell, New York, 1940; Elizabeth Campbell Wilson (Mrs. Stephen A. Wilson), New York, his step-daughter, nd; (Hirschl & Adler Galleries, 1976); (James Maroney, Inc., 1978); private collection, 1980; (Christie's, 31 May 1985, sale 5906, no. 85)

EXHIBITIONS
Vermont Art Center 1957, no. 27; Vermont Art Center 1964, no. 8; NGA 1995, no. 102

LITERATURE
Richard N. Smith, *Divinity and Dust: A History of Townsend, Massachusetts* (Lancaster, MA: privately printed, 1978), 193; Hendricks 1979, 169; Smithsonian American Art Museum, "Winslow Homer. Houses on a Hillside," by Eleanor Jones Harvey, in *The Impressionist Sensibility: The Halff Collection* (Washington, DC, 2006), 18–20

865
Summer
[1879–1880]

Oil

Unlocated

ABG: Very few oil paintings by Homer assigned to, or inscribed 1879 survive in fact or in contemporary reports; only one oil is known from 1880. Homer's disengagement from the premier painting medium in this period seems reflected in his submission for the National Academy of Design annual exhibition of 1880, which opened at the end of March. He may well have expected *By the Sea Side* (No. 874, better known as *Promenade on the Beach*) to be back in time from its February exhibition at Gill's Art Galleries in Springfield, Massachusetts. However, it would seem that had he been seriously concerned about having a "fresh" and impressive work to show in the *Annual*, he would have held that canvas—his only 1880 work—in reserve. As it was, *By the Sea Side* sold to one of Springfield's principal collectors. The quick sale of this major work may have left Homer having to improvise in choosing his representation at the Academy that year.

He probably had planned to make this the occasion to introduce *Visit from the Old Mistress* (2:No. 603) and *Sunday Morning in Virginia* (No. 620) to a general New York audience, who knew of them only from reports of their favorable reception at the Paris *Exposition Universelle* of 1878. Although the pair had been briefly shown at the Union League Club in January 1880—just two months before the *Annual* opened—the Academy was probably willing to suspend its disapproval of works previously shown at private clubs being offered for the *Annual*, when, as in this case, the celebrity of the paintings could be expected to attract visitors.

Apparently Homer did not consider any of the few canvases now known from the 1878–1879 and 1879–1880 seasons to be appropriate for the 1880 *Annual*. Bypassing these, he sent *Camp Fire* (No. 627), a work of 1877, possibly already inscribed to date it to 1880. He completed his choices for the 1880 Academy *Annual* with *Summer*, a work which cannot now be identified.

All four of his contributions were for sale: the pair of Southern scenes for $600, each, and the significantly larger Adirondack subject for $800. That *Summer* was a less imposing work than the other three—in size, and probably also in the character of its subject—may be gauged by the price Homer placed on it: $300. Other than that speculation, all that is known of *Summer* is what the New York press wrote of it.

Late in January 1880 a New York *Evening Post* reporter made the rounds of the studios to preview the artists' planned submissions to the upcoming Academy *Annual*, and told his readers:

> To the Academy exhibition [Mr. Homer] will send two companion scenes in American farm life—one warmish and the other coolish in tone. The latter, a sweetly serious girl of sixteen, walking in plain, short, rude and slight frock under a large tree in an open lot, reminds one of the late Mr. William M. Hunt's remark to his pupils: "There's going to be painting that's perfectly simple—the simple expression of simple forms. To do this a man must be tremendously strong." With the exception of his powerful negro studies recently in the gallery of the Union League Club, Mr. Homer has never done a more sterling bit of work.

Either the reporter misunderstood Homer's intentions, or the artist changed his plans by the time he delivered four canvases to the Academy. The image of the "sweetly serious girl of sixteen" the *Post*'s man so much admired may have been *Summer*, however his description is not exactly echoed in the reviews of the Academy's 1880 exhibition which mention the painting. The *New-York Times* noted "Mr. Homer has two more pictures here, which as usual, form little oases in the desert of mediocrity. 'Summer' is a painting of a real and freckled country girl in an orchard. The shadows over her face are very pleasantly managed, and the scene reminds one of the water colors for which Mr. Homer received so much praise

two years ago." The subject of *Summer* was described by the *Andrews American Queen* as "a miss wearing a sun-bonnet and light summer dress, with a flower sprig in one hand . . . walking down a grassy slope."

S. G. W. Benjamin's review of the Academy exhibition published in the *American Art Review* corroborates these reports.

> A little piece by [Homer], called "Summer," is a capital example of the extreme naturalness which characterizes the out-of-door combinations of landscape and figure in which he excels. A young girl is seen descending a rapid slope. If one reflects a moment, he shall realize that the action of such a figure must be very difficult to seize. But in Mr. Homer's picture this is so well represented that we actually see the motion. He reaches his effects with a simplicity and suppression of details that almost make them seem like trickery.

From these descriptions there is no question *Summer* was a realization in oil of the bucolic themes which pervade his many watercolors and drawings of the previous two years. There is no further report of any work placed on exhibition or for sale which might have been *Summer*. Generally, Homer soon put out again paintings left in his hands after being shown in an Academy exhibition. That *Summer* has no further history, suggests it was purchased from the *Annual*.

EXHIBITIONS
National Academy of Design, New York, *Fifty-fifth Annual Exhibition*, 30 Mar.–29 May 1880, no. 235

LITERATURE
"Fine Arts," *(NY) Evening Post*, 26 Jan. 1880; "Artists and Their Work. Pictures in the Academy. The Negro in American Art—Winslow Homer—Marines by Bunce, Quartley, Edward Moran, and de Haas," *New-York Times*, 9 Apr. 1880; "Glimpses of Studios and Galleries," *Andrews American Queen* 3 (24 Apr. 1880): 254, as quoted in Franklyn Kelly et al., *American Paintings of the Nineteenth Century, Part I* (Washington, DC: National Gallery of Art, 1996), 321, n. 20; S[amuel] G[reen] W[alker] Benjamin, "The Exhibitions V. National Academy of Design Fifty-fifth Exhibition. Opened March 30 closed May 29," *American Art Review* 1 (part 2. 1880): 308

866+

Untitled

nd

Ceramic, 8 × 8 (20.320 × 20.320)
Inscribed cr: Homer

Private collection

ABG: This tile came to light in 2000 in company
with eight others. There was no cohesion to the
group, suggesting individual tiles had been acquired
as opportunity dictated, rather than having been
created as a set. Therefore, that two of the nine tiles
are dated 1878 is not relevant to dating the others.
Seven members of the Tile Club accounted for eight
of the squares; the artist of the ninth, J. Macdonough,
is not recognized as a member.

    Homer's surviving tiles are almost all carefully
designed and executed works clearly done under
studio conditions. The rough and sketchy character
of this scene suggests it may be a survivor of one of
the Tile Club's convivial Wednesday evening meetings.
Its subject matter invites association with Homer's
wash drawing, *The Music Lesson* (No. 898), of 1880.

PROVENANCE
(Sotheby's, 15 Mar. 2000, sale 7441, no. 78 [part 9])

No. 866. Untitled

867

Girl at Garden Wall

1879

Oil on ceramic, 16¾ (42.545) diameter
Inscribed ll: Homer / 1879

Bowdoin College Museum of Art, Brunswick, ME,
gift of Davis Pratt, 1991.65

LG had known of this unglazed ceramic plaque, but
first got its quaint history in full from a letter of 7
January 1960 from Davis Pratt. Mr. Pratt, who had a
summer home in Prout's Neck, Maine, described his
acquisition as follows.

    About 1947 I walked into the carpentry shop of
    Bill Googins in Scarborough, Maine. I saw the
    Homer plate hanging on the wall with a fox skin
    over it. It was so dirty I could hardly make it out.
    It was given to Mr. Googins by Clint Harmon
    who was once a trash collector at Prout's when
    Homer was still alive. I knew Harmon well as I
    have known Googins for years. Clint found this
    plate out with Homer's trash one morning so he
    carted it away and gave it to Googins as Googin's
    wife "was interested in painting." Bill gave it to

No. 867. Girl at Garden Wall

me not only because we are old friends but, as he put it at the time, "You better get it out of here before it gets broken."

ABG: This departure from the standard manifestation of Homer's participation in the decorative art "craze" of the 1870s, the eight inch square tile, may be explained by a passage from a *Harper's Weekly* article recounting the history of the Tile Club.

During the winter of 1878–79 the club became conscious of a plethora of tiles. Even the most sanguine member could not convince himself that he should ever become possessed of a sufficient amount of household to use up his decorative material, and a change was decided upon. Plaques were substituted for tiles, and a more liberal method of treatment was adopted.

PROVENANCE
William Googins, Scarborough, ME, nd; Davis N. Pratt, Boston, and Cornish Flat, NH, c. 1947

LITERATURE
"The Tile Club," *Harper's Weekly* 24 (31 Jan. 1880): 75

868

Girl and Sheep
1880

Watercolor, 8¾ × 13⅜ (22.225 × 33.973)
Inscribed lr: Winslow Homer 1880

Museum of Art, Rhode Island School of Design, Providence, bequest of Isaac C. Bates, 13.813

PROVENANCE
Isaac Comstock Bates, Providence, RI, 1880

EXHIBITIONS
Providence (RI) Art Club, [loan collection of paintings], 11 Feb. 1881

No. 868. Girl and Sheep

869

The Shepherdess

1880

Watercolor, 11 × 9¼ (27.940 × 23.495)
Inscribed lr: Winslow Homer 1880

Private collection

ABG: The 1878 sketches, No. 740-R and No. 741, are the source of the images of sheep in this watercolor.

PROVENANCE
Hamilton Cole, New York, nd; the Misses Cole, New York, his sisters, by bequest, c. 1889; Mrs. Gurdon Bidwell, Norwich, CT, their niece, by bequest, 1925; (William Macbeth, Inc., 1939); Bartlett Arkell, New York, 1939; Mrs. Bartlett Arkell, New York, by bequest, 1946; Elizabeth Campbell Wilson (Mrs. Stephen A. Wilson), New York, her daughter, by bequest, 1970

EXHIBITIONS
Vermont Art Center 1957, no. 28; Vermont Art Center 1964, no. 9

870

The Shepherdess

1880

Watercolor, 6⅜ × 12 (16.192 × 30.480)
Inscribed lr: Winslow Homer 1880

Unlocated

ABG: This watercolor is a variation on *Shepherdesses Resting* (No. 759), a watercolor of 1879 in which two young women, wearing the fancy dress shepherdess costume, face each other, in the same reclining posture as the girl in this painting; a line of sheep appears on the distant horizon. In this 1880 version, Homer essentially replaced the shepherdess' companion, by bringing the line of sheep into the near middle ground.

PROVENANCE
Mr. and Mrs. William Crary Brownell, New York, probably c. 1880; William Crary Brownell, New York, nd; Virginia Swinburne Hale, Carmel, CA, Mrs. Brownell's niece, by bequest, 1928; Dorothy Hale (Mrs. Gardner Hale), her sister-in-law, by gift, c. 1934; (M. Knoedler & Co., 1934); (Goodman, Walker, Boston, 1940); Donald B. Willson, Medford, MA, 1940; (M. Knoedler & Co., c. 1962)

EXHIBITIONS
Boston Symphony 1937; University of Arizona 1963, no. 70

No. 869. The Shepherdess   see color illustration, p. 452

No. 870. The Shepherdess

No. 871. Daydreaming

871

Daydreaming

1880

Watercolor, 13⅜ × 19⅜ (33.973 × 49.213)
Inscribed ll: Winslow Homer 1880; lr: To Mrs
Chapman / with compts of the artist 1882
Private collection

ABG: Homer has here placed the relaxed young
woman seen in the drawing, *Shepherdess* (No. 681),
into a segment of the landscape seen in the watercolor, *Autumn, Mountainville, New York* (No. 743),
both works of 1878.

    Helen Cooper identified the Mrs. Chapman
of this inscription as Mrs. William Chapman,
wife of the owner of the Huddleston Arms Hotel
in Cullercoats. As Homer was making a gift of
this watercolor—derived from work of 1878, but
executed in 1880—in 1882, then it may be presumed
he had brought it with him to England in 1881.

PROVENANCE
Mrs. William Chapman, Cullercoats, England, 1882;
unidentified descendant of Mrs. Williams, England,
by 1981; (Christie's, 24 Apr. 1981, sale 5049, no. 75);
(Richard L. Feigen & Co., 1981); private collection,
nd; (Christie's, 26 May 1993, sale 7684, no. 53)

LITERATURE
National Gallery of Art, Helen A. Cooper, *Winslow
Homer Watercolors* (Washington, DC, 1986), 87

872

Spring Lamb

[1880]

[ink]

Unlocated

Like "Pumpkins among the Corn" and "The Sower" which appeared in *Scribner's Monthly* in August 1878, and the uncaptioned illustration published in the April 1880 issue of *Scribner's*, "Spring Lamb," the illustration on the first page of the June 1880 issue of *Scribner's*, would have been made by photographic transfer from a drawing by Homer to the wood block to be cut by a skilled engraver. Homer's drawing for this illustration should have survived, however, it is unknown. (Although the central image of sheep in the illustration is nearly the same as the 1879 drawing *Sheep in a Meadow* (No. 761), it is not identical, and therefore cannot be accounted an immediate source in the production process.)

The illustration is signed in the image at lower right: Homer, and by the engraver at left: "King Sc."

ABG: See commentary No. 761.

LITERATURE
Clarence Cook, "Spring Hereabouts," *Scribner's Monthly* 20 (June 1880): 161

No. 873. Boy and Horse Ploughing

873

Boy and Horse Ploughing
1880

A Halt in the Furrow

Watercolor, 9⅜ × 13⁷⁄₁₆ (23.813 × 34.133)
Inscribed lr: Homer 1880

Museum of Art, Rhode Island School of Design, Providence, bequest of Isaac C. Bates, 13.812

ABG: This watercolor repeats the composition and essential features of the 1879 watercolor, *Man and Plow Horse* (No. 789), but is not a true replication of the earlier example. Besides variations in the posture and scale of the central figural group, the two paintings differ notably in color: No. 789 is rendered entirely in shades of gray and brown, whereas Homer chose to use vivid color in this version of the image. Both watercolors relate to the drawing, No. 788, for their central motive.

PROVENANCE
Isaac Comstock Bates, Providence, RI, nd

EXHIBITIONS
RISD 1931, no. 24; Fogg 1932, no. 38; NE Museums 1936; Albright-Knox 1966, no. 13; AI Chicago 2008

Illustration: "Spring Lamb," Clarence Cook, "Spring Hereabouts," *Scribner's Monthly* 20 (June 1880): 161

874

By the Sea Side

1880

Promenade on the Beach

Oil, 20¼ × 30⅛ (51.435 × 76.518)
Inscribed lr: Winslow Homer 1880

Museum of Fine Arts, Springfield, MA, gift of the Misses Emily and Elizabeth Mills in memory of their parents, 36.06

When the daughters of Isaac Mills gave *By the Sea Side* to the Museum of Fine Arts, Springfield, they told the Museum that their father had purchased it from the artist the same year it was painted, but that George Walter Vincent Smith had handled the transaction for Mr. Mills, working through the Springfield dealer, James Gill. The Misses Mills also presented the Museum with the letter of 3 March 1880 from Homer to George W. V. Smith which may have been the source of their assumption Smith had been acting for their father.

> My Dear Mr. Smith
>
> My picture represents the Eastern Shore at sunset. The long line from the girls is a shadow from the sun.
>
> The girls are "somebody in particular" and I can vouch for their good moral character. They are looking at anything that you wish to have them look at, but it must be something at sea and a very proper and appropriate object for girls to be interested in. The schooner is a Gloucester Fisherman.
>
> Hoping this will make everything clear, believe me most,
>
> Respectfully Yours
> Winslow Homer

Just following the first sentence of this letter Homer interposed a neat diagrammatic map of the mid-section of Massachusetts, bounded by the coastline around Boston's South Shore. Springfield and Boston were positioned on this map, as were two marks representing the ladies on the beach, and beyond them, a little three-sailed vessel. Homer also noted the words "Sun" "West" and "East" at appropriate sides of the page.

We do not know what Smith had written to Homer, however his questions—and the limited criteria by which he apparently decided the merits of the painting—may be inferred from Homer's sardonic reply. There is no reference suggesting Smith made his inquiry on behalf of another buyer. *By the Sea Side* does not figure in the extensive records Smith kept on his art purchases.

By the 1930s the Misses Mills may have found it more pleasant to believe their father had acquired

their painting without becoming involved in sordid details of commerce. In fact, the use of an intermediary to purchase the painting from a Gill's annual exhibition would seem unnecessary, unless Mills had been out of the city when Gill's show opened and asked Smith to handle the purchase for him. However, it seems more reasonable that Smith had considered, but decided against purchasing the painting, or yielded to Mills's interest. Either way, he would have had no reason to keep Homer's letter, and would naturally have passed it on to Mills.

ABG: Having hung in the Mills family home virtually all its life, this painting was unknown before 1936 when it entered the Springfield Museum's collection, entitled *Promenade on the Beach*. Presumably, it had come to be known by that title in the Mills household, rather than by an identification of Homer's choice. Indeed, "Promenade" does not seem a term with which Homer would have been comfortable. Gordon Hendricks made one of his intuitive leaps in assuming the *By the Sea Side* in Gill's 1880 exhibition was the painting the Misses Mills had given to the Springfield Museum. (He lets his imagination overreach in assuming Homer offered the painting to George W. V. Smith, and in describing Smith as an art dealer.) But it was Martha Hoppin's research in 1991 that produced documentary proof of the connection—and thus, the original title of the painting—in the detailed description given in the Springfield *Daily Republican*'s review of Gill's exhibition.

> On the left hand of Mr. Shirlaw's large painting stands Winslow Homer's latest, one of his most peculiar motives, and like no one else in the world. It is a shore view in late afternoon, the skies nearly filled with violet clouds, through which patches of blue are seen, and rosy dots from the sinking sun vary their monotone. The sea is dully blue beneath, and fishing boats under full sail are scudding a little ways out, their sails gleaming strangely in the level sunlight. On the beach walk two women, both young, and looking out with such expressions in their faces as suggest romances. Mr. Homer probably painted the peculiar phase of nature first, but he has made a poem of it by introducing these figures. The painting of the whole is masterly; it is a Homer to be coveted.

The appearance of *By the Sea Side* early in 1880 is startling following on what appears to be approximately two years in which Homer was immersed in rustic, bucolic themes, using farm fields, pastures and orchards as setting for the figures of children and adolescents. It had been a decade since pretty young women at the seaside had been his subject for major oils: *Long Branch* (2:No. 356); *Low Tide* 2:No. 358 (and its surviving parts, No. 359 and No. 360); *Eagle Head, Manchester, Massachusetts* (2:No. 364);

No. 874. By the Sea Side

see color illustration, p. 453

Manners and Customs at the Sea Side (2:No. 361); and *Girl in the Surf* (2:No. 363) were all executed in 1869 and 1870. (The subject reappeared briefly in 1872 in *On the Beach at Marshfield* [2:No. 394]).

Homer's serious interest in the subject apparently revived in the late 1870s. The finished oils *Evening on the Beach* (No. 656) and *Woman on the Beach* (No. 658) are not dated, but in costume and association with the dated ceramic fireplace surround panel (No. 657-a) in which *Evening on the Beach* reappears, may be assigned to 1878. One of the two closely related watercolors known as *Startled* (No. 659 and No. 660) is inscribed with the date of 1878. The central image of *Sundown* (No. 775), one of Homer's three contributions to the National Academy of Design annual exhibition of 1879, was a young woman seated on a beach.

That *By the Sea Side* repeats the principal elements of *Evening on the Beach* is unmistakable: In both, two fashionably dressed young women stroll from viewers' right to left along a flat expanse of sand; strong raking light from the left causes their figures to cast dramatic shadows; sky and sea are dark, but calm; a bright accent is placed on the horizon at the far right. Although a finished composition, *Evening on the Beach* would seem to have served as the preliminary study for *By the Sea Side*.

However, the lost *Sundown*, in which Homer probably invested considerable pride and hopes, may also have had a telling influence on the creation and character of *By the Sea Side*. *Sundown* had been savaged by the New York critical press when shown in the 1879 *Annual*; it subsequently disappeared. From press descriptions it is clear that *Sundown* and *By the Sea Side* had more in common than just general theme: The *New York Herald* told its readers that in *Sundown*

A young girl sits on the seashore at sunset and watches the sparkle of the reflections of the sun's rays in a shell, which she holds. Behind her the waves break on to a lower level of the beach, which, though not seen, is finely suggested, and in the middle distance is a schooner. In golden sunset tone the picture is admirable; the cold blue of the wave rolling in is very true, and the effect of sunlight on the broken crests and the white sails of the vessel is very real.

The New York *Evening Post* described "an American girl in a dressing gown, seated on the beach alone. The waves roll up toward her, in deep blue . . . . Purplish clouds unwreath themselves, entwine and vanish above the sea, and a stately ship—a piece of significant invention, novel, bold and large in

handling." And *Appletons' Journal* wrote: "'Sundown'"
.... is a seashore scene, with sky and sea bathed in
deep indigo—a study of effect of light that may be
true, but which seems to us an excessive exaggeration."

By the Sea Side is not only exceptional for Homer's
departure from his overwhelming preoccupation
with land-locked subjects for the two years preceding
its date of execution; it is his only known oil painting
from the year 1880. It is reasonable to speculate
that—nettled by the negative reaction to *Sundown*—
Homer detached himself from his concentration
on the milieu of farm and pasture to address again
Sundown's true subject: the extraordinary quality
of the light from the last sun rays of the day falling
across the sand of an ocean beach.

PROVENANCE
(Gill's Art Galleries, Springfield, MA, 1880); Isaac
Mills, Springfield, MA, 1880; Emily Mills and Eliza-
beth Mills, Springfield, MA, his daughters, c. 1893

EXHIBITIONS
Gill's Art Galleries, Springfield, MA, *Third Annual
Artists' Exhibition*, opened 17 Feb. 1880, no. 41 (as *By
the Sea Side*); Whitney 1944; Worcester 1944, no. 15;
NGA 1958/MFA, Boston, 1959, no. 45/41; Mariners,
Norfolk, 1964, no. 16; Whitney 1973, no. 45 (Whitney,
only); Portland 1974; Whitney, Fairfield, 1984; NGA
1995, no. 103; Chrysler 2000

LITERATURE
"Fine Arts. Fifty-Fourth Annual Exhibition of the
Academy of Design—Important Pictures—First
Notice," *New York Herald*, 30 Mar. 1879; "The
Academy Exhibition. First Impression and a Hasty
Tour of the Galleries," *(NY) Evening Post*, 30 Mar.
1879; "The Academy Exhibition," *Appletons' Journal
of Literature, Science, and Art* 21 (6 May 1879): 471;
"Mr. Gill's Exhibition. Some of the Paintings to be
Seen This Evening," *Springfield (MA) Daily
Republican*, 17 Feb. 1880; Hendricks 1979, 140–41

875
Beach Scene
1880

Ceramic, 2¹⁵⁄₁₆ × 5¹⁵⁄₁₆ (7.463 × 15.083)
Inscribed ur: W. H.; vertically, along right side:
T. Sturgis. 1880

Addison Gallery of American Art, Phillips Academy,
Andover, MA, gift of Mrs. Reginald Sturgis, 1949.23

ABG: This tile is traditionally attributed to Winslow
Homer, and dated 1880. There are, however, impedi-
ments to full agreement in both propositions.

Although the subject is easily related to other works
by Homer, notably the central panel in a fireplace
surround (No. 657-a), its execution is less than skillful, and lacking in Homer's characteristic articulation.
The disparity in scale between the "W. H." at upper
left, and the vertically arranged "T. Sturgis. / 1889"
invites doubt as to which inscription refers to the
creator of the work. ("W. H." might be acknowledge-
ment of the source of the image.) If "W. H." is the
artist's signature, than what is the purpose of the
other inscription; and why is the date associated with
it rather than the "W. H."? The scale and dimensions
of the tile, itself, are inconsistent with the standard
8 inch square of the group of "Tilers" to which
Homer belonged.

The last digit of the inscribed date appears more
like a "9 than a "0." If this were a work of 1889,
than its creation occurred too long after Homer was
concerned with decorative ceramics for association
with him to be credible.

EXHIBITIONS
Addison 1980; Addison 1990

No. 875. Beach Scene

No. 876. Girl with Shell at Ear

876

Girl with Shell at Ear

1880

Girl on Dunes

Charcoal, watercolor, 11⅞ × 11¹³⁄₁₆ (30.163 × 30.005)
Inscribed lr: Homer / 1880; on mounting sheet, ul:
Granville H. Norcross / with compt's of / Winslow
Homer / Oct 12 1907

Worcester Art Museum, bequest of Grenville H.
Norcross, 1937.14

ABG: *Girl with Shell at Ear* may be considered
part of the group of highly finished drawings, and
watercolor paintings featuring prettily dressed
young ladies seated in the out of doors executed
by Homer in 1880. (See No. 885 through No. 893.)
This drawing, however, is exceptional in placing
the subject at the sea side rather than in a country
landscape. Although a later work than the lost oil
Sundown (No. 775), this image of a girl seated on
a sandy hillock and preoccupied with a shell echoes
the feature of that painting.

PROVENANCE
Grenville H. Norcross, Boston, 1907

EXHIBITIONS
IMA, Boston, 1941, no. d-1; Worcester 1944, no. 89;
Worcester 1987, no. 61

877

Charles Savage Homer, Jr.

1880

Watercolor, 21 × 15⅝ (53.340 × 39.688)
Inscribed l: W. H. 1880

Private collection

ABG: Homer apparently made this highly finished cabinet portrait of his elder brother for himself. It appears in the photographs of the interior of the apartment he shared with Samuel T. Preston in the early 1380s, and to which he returned late in 1882 when he came back from his extended stay in England. There Homer had hung it in the central location over a fireplace. That it is a watercolor—strangely, the medium in which Homer was more successful when essaying portraiture—rather than an oil is also an indication the work was not intended for an impersonal audience. A "proper" portrait would have been expected to be in the more permanent, serious oil medium.

As the portrait surely remained within the Homer family until long after both brothers' deaths, there is no way to know whether Winslow kept it throughout his lifetime, and it passed to Charles as Winslow's sole heir, or Winslow had given it to Charles some time between the 1880s and 1910.

PROVENANCE
Charles S. Homer, Jr., nd; Mrs. Charles S. Homer, Jr., by bequest, 1917; Charles L. Homer, by bequest, 1937; Alice Homer Willauer (Mrs. Osborn Willauer), Dedham, MA, probably 1955; Peter O. Willauer, Thomaston, ME, her son, by gift, 1974; (Coe Kerr Gallery, 1987); (John H. Surovek Gallery, Palm Beach, FL, 1987); private collection, 1988; (Spanierman Gallery, LLC, 1989)

EXHIBITIONS
Bowdoin/Colby 1954

No. 877. Charles Savage Homer, Jr.

878

Sketch of Mr. Marsh at the Tiller of His Sailboat Off Cape Ann

1880

Watercolor, 9¼ × 12½ (23.495 × 31.750)
Inscribed lr: Homer / 1880

Indianapolis Museum of Art, gift of Mrs. James Fesler, 29.76

George J. Marsh was treasurer of the Cape Ann Savings Bank in Gloucester, MA, and was described to LG by several sources as a friend whom Homer visited. Marsh's small pleasure craft, "The Kulinda," with himself at its tiller is presumably the subject of No. 879, No. 880, No. 881, and No. 882.

In 1940 LG showed a photograph of this watercolor to Conrad R. Hamon, who had a long career with the Cape Ann Savings Bank; Mr. Hamon thought it a very good portrait of Mr. Marsh.

PROVENANCE
George J. Marsh, Annisquan, MA, probably 1880; Cape Ann Savings Bank, Gloucester, MA, nd [?]; (Ernst Zimmerman, Boston, c. 1928); Mrs. James W. Fesler, 1929

see color illustration, p. 454

No. 878. Sketch of Mr. Marsh at the Tiller of His Sailboat Off Cape Ann

879

The Sloop Kulinda

[1880]

Watercolor, 16½ × 11⅝ (41.910 × 29.528)
Inscribed ll: Winslow Homer

The Carnegie Museum of Art, Pittsburgh, bequest
of Mr. and Mrs. James H. Beal, 93.189.35

LG wrote to the Cape Ann Savings Bank, of which
Mr. George J. Marsh had long been treasurer, to ask
whether the sailboat in this watercolor had belonged
to Marsh. Mr. Conrad R. Hamon, Assistant
Treasurer of the bank, replied by letter of 7 August
1940: "The writer recalls the painting as it was in
our banking rooms for years. It was a picture of Mr.
Marsh's boat 'Kulinda,' with someone, probably
Mr. Marsh, at the wheel. . . . It seems that Winslow
Homer was an intimate friend of Mr. Marsh, and
was with him a great deal at Mr. Marsh's summer
home at Annisquam and on his boat."

PROVENANCE
George J. Marsh, Annisquam, MA, probably 1880;
Cape Ann Savings Bank, Gloucester, MA, nd;
Morris Hall Pancoast, Rockport, ME, and Natchez,
MS, c. 1931; (Frank K. M. Rehn, by 1936); Mr. and
Mrs. James H. Beal, Pittsburgh, 1952

EXHIBITIONS
Maynard Walker 1953, no. 12

No. 879. The Sloop Kulinda

880

A Yacht

[1880]

Watercolor, 9½ × 13¾ (24.130 × 34.925) sight
Inscribed lr: Homer

Private collection

This work is rendered entirely in washes of opaque white and of black watercolor or ink; linear detailing is mostly in graphite, with some ink. It may be seen in the photographs of the interior of the Benedick building apartment Homer shared with Samuel T. Preston for part of 1880 and 1881, and again following his return in late 1882 from his extended stay in England.

PROVENANCE
Samuel Thorndyke Preston, New York, by gift of Homer, probably 1880; Mrs. Ames, Somerville, MA, his sister, by bequest, 1898; Charles T. Ames, Cleveland, her son, by gift, nd; Mrs. Robert J. Warner, Omaha, his daughter, by 1936; (Milch Galleries, nd); Mr. and Mrs. R. Frederick Woolworth, New York, 1956; (M. Knoedler & Co., 1962)

881

Yachting

1880

Watercolor, 13³⁄₁₆ × 18¾ (33.498 × 47.625) sight
Inscribed lr: Homer 1880

Private collection

ABG: The Danenberg Galleries assigned the title *Ipswich Bay* to this watercolor. While the subject is all but surely George J. Marsh sailing his boat, the "Kulinda," in the waters off Annisquam, the site cannot be specifically identified.

PROVENANCE
(Old Davis Homestead sale, Annisquam, MA, nd); Martha Rogers Harvey (Mrs. George Wainwright Harvey), Annisquam, MA, nd; Maud Vila, South Acton, MA, c. 1922; Herbert F. Vila, Sanford, SC, her brother, by bequest, c. 1968; (Bernard Danenberg Galleries, 1969)

EXHIBITIONS
Farnsworth 1970, no. 41 (as *Ipswich Bay*)

No. 880. A Yacht

882

Sailing Out of Gloucester

[1880]

Watercolor, 13¾ × 19¾ (34.925 × 50.165)
Inscribed lr: Homer

The Arkell Museum at Canajoharie (NY), 317111

Homer here repeats the central image of *A Yacht* (No. 880) and *Yachting* (No. 881) with the addition of the diminutive figure of a woman standing against the mast. The sailboat in these three works is in all probability the "Kulinda," owned by George J. Marsh. It may also be presumed that it is Marsh shown sailing the boat in the three. It is interesting to note the illusion Homer created through the contrast in scale of the figures and the boat, that the "Kulinda" was large enough to be worthy of the designation "yacht." His portrait sketch of Marsh at the tiller of his boat (No. 878) is probably the more accurate representation of the relative proportion of captain to vessel.

PROVENANCE
Edward C. Stedman, New York, nd; Dr. Alexander C. Humphreys, 1905; (American Art Association, 15 Feb. 1917, Humphreys sale, no. 117); (M. Knoedler & Co., 1917); Samuel A. Lewisohn, New York, 1917; (William Macbeth, Inc., 1938); Bartlett Arkell, New York, 1940

EXHIBITIONS
Philadelphia WC Club 1910, no. 154; Mount Holyoke 1940, no. 15; Vose 1940, no. 10; University of Arizona 1963, no. 22; Hamilton 1964, no. 18; Rockwell 1998; Farnsworth 2006

No. 881. Yachting

No. 882. Sailing Out of Gloucester

see color illustration, p. 455

No. 883-A. Yachting Girl

883-A

Yachting Girl

1880

Graphite, watercolor, 10 × 15⅞ (25.400 × 40.323)
Inscribed ll: copyright - 1880 - Winslow Homer

Collection of Mr. and Mrs. Paul Mellon

ABG: This elaborate drawing is composed like a musical fugue from the subject of No. 880, No. 881, and No. 882. The sail and rigging against which this adventurous young woman braces herself is an enlarged detail from the central image of those three works; the whole image may be seen just beyond her.

Homer's extensive use of opaque white, not only to represent sea foam and clouds, but in drawing fine lines, highlights, and his signature suggests he created this drawing expressly to be reproduced by "process;" that is, by photography. The reproductive print is No. 883-b.

PROVENANCE
(Doll & Richards, Boston, 1880); Mrs. Charles Fairchild, Boston, 1880; Sally Fairchild, Boston, nd; (Dickinson's Old Curiosity Shop, Boston, nd); (Otho Wiecker, Boston, by 1934); (Wildenstein & Co., by 1948)

EXHIBITIONS
Doll & Richards 1880; Wildenstein 1948, no. 15; Houston 1952, no. 34; NGA 1958, no. 202

883-B

Yachting Girl

1880

Photolithograph, watercolor, 7⅞ × 12½ (20.003 × 31.750) sheet

ABG: Homer contributed three works to the Century Association's monthly exhibition held in early April 1880. Each was identified only as "Fac simile," and the valuation of each was noted as two dollars.

It may be inferred that Homer had a project in hand to market a suite of inexpensive prints of his drawings mass-produced by photolithography. It is likely this *Yachting Girl*, a photographically reduced duplication of No. 883-a, was one of them, and that *Pretty Maiden* (No. 884-b) was another. The third is not identified.

Homer enhanced the interest—and value—of individual *Yachting Girl* prints by uniquely elaborating details in opaque white watercolor; no two of the known examples are exactly alike. No record of the production or distribution of these prints is known. Examples of the photolithograph *Yachting Girl* are held in the collections of the Bowdoin College Museum of Art, Brunswick, Maine; the Plainfield (New Jersey) Public Library; and the Clark Art Institute, Williamstown, Massachusetts. Others have been in the market, but as the sources of these are not identified, there is no way to make a reliable estimate of how many examples of the print survive.

EXHIBITIONS
Century Association, New York, 3 Apr. 1880, no. 48 (as *Fac simile*) [?]; Bowdoin 1966, no. 2 (Bowdoin

No. 883-B. Yachting Girl

No. 884-B. A Pretty Maiden

College Museum of Art impression); Clark AI 1986, no. 28 (Clark Art Institute impression); Knoedler 1986, no. 49 (Bowdoin College Museum of Art impression)

LITERATURE
"The New Process of Reproducing Fac-Similies of Paintings, Etchings, &C.," *New York Herald*, 23 Jan. 1876

884-A

A Pretty Maiden

1880

[Graphite, watercolor]
Inscribed ll: Winslow Homer / 1880

Unlocated

ABG: The original drawing necessary to making a photographic reproduction *A Pretty Maiden* (No. 884-b) is not known to survive.

An example of this reproduction of a Homer drawing was in Mrs. Charles S. Homer, Jr.'s estate, which she may be assumed to have inherited from her husband, who had been Homer's sole heir. Samuel Thorndyke Preston's niece, Mrs. William A. Preston, described another, which she had inherited from her mother, in a letter to LG of 20 April 1939. Mrs. Preston's print may be presumed to be the one that hung in the apartment Homer and Samuel Preston shared in the Benedick building for part of 1880 and 1881, and again following his return in late 1882 from his extended stay in England. It may be seen in the formal "portrait" photographs made of the apartment.

An example is held in the collection of the Deerfield (Massachusetts) Academy.

ABG: See Commentary No. 883-b.

EXHIBITIONS
Century Association, New York, 3 Apr. 1880, no. 47 or 49 (as *Fac simile*) [?]

884-B

A Pretty Maiden

1880

Photolithograph, watercolor, 9⅛ × 4½
(23.178 × 11.430)
Inscribed across bottom edge: Artotype. Copyright 1880, Louis R. Menger, Publisher, N. Y. Hardown & Bierstadt, N. Y.

885

Seated Girl with a Basket

[1880]

Chalk, watercolor, 15⅞ × 10³⁄₁₆ (40.323 × 25.878)
Inscribed lr: Winslow Homer

Cooper-Hewitt, National Design Museum,
Smithsonian Institution, gift of Charles Savage
Homer, Jr., 1912-12-79

ABG: No. 885 is one among a number of large
presentation drawings Homer executed in 1880.
Besides liberal dimensions, they have a subject in
common: well dressed, neatly shod, comely young
women. In No. 885, No. 886, No. 887, No. 888,
No. 889, and No. 891 the young woman is solitary
and seated; her mood is pensive. Two watercolors
specifically dependent on these drawings, No. 890

and No. 892, and a third, No. 893, for which no
such antecedent drawing is known, share the theme.
Three closely related watercolors of 1880 are known
which feature the same type of young woman, but
even more fashionably and elaborately dressed, and
brightened in temperament. No. 894 and No. 895
present pairs of young women; No. 896 shows a
figure alone.

These young women are frequently assigned to a
particular geographical location, inviting the corollary
that Homer, pencil and pad in hand, was seated in
front of each young woman, and thus passing time
in the same location. Despite the strong suggestion
of pasture or garden in the backgrounds of these
images, the site most often suggested is Gloucester,
Massachusetts, probably because that fishing port
is the one place Homer is known to have remained
for any length of time within the year 1880.

It is more likely that these drawings and watercolors
are constructions, and that Homer's subjects are
professional models posing in his New York studio.
These young women are all presented as idle
urbanites. The somewhat incongruous country scenes
behind them are generalized versions of the hills
and fields with which Homer had been preoccupied
for the past several summers, and would have been
supplied from his well-stocked imagination. He also
would have had no trouble in clothing these women
in the ruffles and flourishes of current fashion without
reference to the actual costumes of his models.

The group of drawings and watercolors is an
interesting counterpoint to the many country girls
in aprons and poke bonnets who naturally populate
the landscapes of many works of 1878 and 1879.

PROVENANCE
Charles S. Homer, Jr., by bequest, 1910

EXHIBITIONS
Carnegie 1937, no. 193; Cooper-Hewitt 1972, no. 40;
Lowe, Syracuse, 1979, no. 9; Greenville County 1986

No. 885. Seated Girl with a Basket

No. 886. Girl Seated

886

Girl Seated

[1880]

Charcoal, watercolor, $18\frac{3}{8} \times 14\frac{13}{16}$
(46.673×37.625)
Inscribed lr: Homer

Museum of Fine Arts, Boston, given anonymously
in memory of Phyllis S. Tuckerman, 1996.136

ABG: See commentary No. 885.

PROVENANCE
Francis Bartlett, Boston, nd; Phyllis Sears Tuckerman
(Mrs. Bayard Tuckerman), Beverly, MA, his
granddaughter, by 1940; private collection, c. 1965

EXHIBITIONS
Knoedler 1986, no. 48; New Britain 2003

No. 887. Portrait of a Woman

Portrait of a Woman

1880

Charcoal, watercolor, 19½ × 13⅞ (49.530 × 35.001)
Inscribed ll: Homer / 1880

The Carnegie Museum of Art, Pittsburgh, gift of
Mrs. Charles Homer, 18.33.1

ABG: See commentary No. 885.

PROVENANCE
Charles S. Homer, Jr., by bequest, 1910; Mrs.
Charles S. Homer, Jr., by bequest, 1917

888+

Woman Seated on a Bench

1880

Charcoal, watercolor, 17¾ × 13¾ (45.085 × 34.925)
Inscribed ll: Homer / 1880

Private collection

The widow of Charles Ames, Samuel Thorndyke
Preston's nephew, wrote LG on 8 June 1937 concerning several Homers she had received from her husband: "I have another picture by Winslow Homer
which is a sketch of a girl sitting on a log. It looks
like crayon and is in another city, impossible to get
at." LG apparently wrote Mrs. Ames again in hopes
of getting more detailed information on the drawing. Mrs. Ames's daughter replied by letter of 7
August 1939: "I vaguely remember such a picture but
it was put in storage with a few of our things years
ago . . . . my father was killed in an accident and we
never bothered to get the things in storage so I
assume they have been sold years ago." LG's record
of this work remained in a file he labeled "Up
Against a Blank Wall."

   Such a tenuous description of a lost work is not
enough to give this drawing a history of ownership
flowing from Samuel Preston without reservation.
The drawing assigned the title *Girl on a Rock* (No.
891) which also only recently came to light, is also
without a substantial history of ownership.
Certainly, neither this drawing nor No. 891 need be
the work Mrs. Ames recalled just because their early
ownership histories are undocumented. However, if
Mrs. Ames's memory of an image she hadn't seen in
some time has any credibility, then her description
of "a girl sitting on a log" is a reasonable blurring of
the rustic bench on which this girl sits.

ABG: See commentary No. 885.

PROVENANCE
Mrs. Shirley Goodman, New York, nd; private collection, c. 1990; (Sotheby's, 17 Mar. 1994, sale 6538,
no. 16)

No. 888. Woman Seated on a Bench

No. 889. Seated Girl

889

Seated Girl

[1880]

Chalk, watercolor, 19¾ × 14 (50.165 × 35.560)
Inscribed ll: Homer

Cooper-Hewitt, National Design Museum,
Smithsonian Institution, gift of Charles Savage
Homer, Jr., 1912-12-274

The figure in this fully developed drawing clearly
served—greatly reduced in scale—as the model for the
young woman sitting *On the Garden Wall* in No. 890.

ABG: See commentary No. 885.

PROVENANCE
Charles S. Homer, Jr., by bequest, 1910

EXHIBITIONS
Whitney 1936, no. 108; Carnegie 1937, no. 142;
Cooper-Hewitt 1972, no. 39; Columbia/Telfair 1974,
no. 14; Lowe, Syracuse, 1979, no. 7; Greenville
County 1986

890

The Garden Wall

1880

Girl on a Wall

Watercolor, 8¼ × 12⅛ (20.955 × 30.798)
Inscribed ll: Homer 1880

Huntington (WV) Museum of Art, gift of Ruth
Woods Dayton, 67.1.131

See No. 889, the large drawing of a young woman,
which served as the source for the figure in this
watercolor.

ABG: See commentary No. 885.

PROVENANCE
William Harris Arnold, Nutley, NJ, nd; Mrs.
William Harris Arnold, Cambridge, MA, nd; Weld
Arnold, Boston, her son, nd; (M. Knoedler & Co.,
c. 1950); (Martha Jackson Gallery, 1954); (William
Macbeth, Inc., by 1955); Ruth Woods Dayton
(Mrs. Arthur S. Dayton), Lewisburg, WV, 1955

EXHIBITIONS
Nelson-Atkins 2001

No. 890. The Garden Wall

No. 891. Girl Seated on a Rock

891+

Girl Seated on a Rock

[1880]

Charcoal, watercolor, 16 × 15¼ (40.640 × 38.735)
Inscribed ll: Homer

Private collection

ABG: The relationship of No. 889 and No. 890,
is repeated in No. 891 and No. 892: Homer reused
the figure from a large presentation drawing as
the subject focus in a smaller watercolor landscape
painting. In this instance, another detail is carried
from the drawing to the watercolor: the figure
of a shepherd takes the same position in the far
background of both.
    See commentary No. 885.

PROVENANCE
Mrs. Celia Salata, Peabody, MA, nd; (Joseph Boyle
auction management, 3 June 2003); (Kaminski
Auction, Beverly, MA, 2004); (Vose Galleries of
Boston, 2004)

No. 892. Waiting

892

Waiting

1880

Watercolor, 8⁵⁄₁₆ × 12⁵⁄₁₆ (21.115 × 31.275)
Inscribed lr: Homer 1880

Spanierman Gallery, LLC, New York

ABG: See No. 891, and commentary No. 885.

PROVENANCE
(American Art Association, 22 Feb. 1919, Montross
sale, no. 30); (Milch Galleries, 1919); William
Tierney, New York, 1919; (Babcock Galleries, 1954);
Dr. Thomas Edward Hanley, Bradford, PA, 1959; (E.
V. Thaw, Inc., by 1966); Dr. Theodore Leshner, New
York, by 1970; CIGNA Museum and Art Collection,
Philadelphia, 1985; (Sotheby's, 18 May 2005, sale
8096, no. 134)

No. 893. Lady at Houghton Farm

893
Lady at Houghton Farm
[1880]

The Black Hat

Watercolor, 9 × 13 (22.860 × 33.020)

Berger Collection, Denver Art Museum, TL-17487

In 1976 when this watercolor came to light and was brought to LG for examination, he recorded the following inscription on its reverse: "Painted and presented by Winslow Homer to me as a wedding gift. May 19th, 1880. Josephine M. Hamline."

Mrs. Donald Ford shared with LG the results of her research on the recipient of Homer's wedding gift: Josephine Meade Hamline was the daughter of Henry Meade of Norwich, New York. She married John Hamline on May 19, 1880. Mr. Hamline had graduated from Northwestern University in Chicago in 1875, and Columbia College of Law in 1877. He returned to Chicago to make his career in the practice of law. He also was an alderman for the third ward of that city. The connection to the Homer family remains unexplained.

Mrs. Ford adopted EHG's suggested title, *The Black Hat*, for this otherwise unnamed painting. The present titling is a more recent owner's preference.

ABG: See commentary No. 885.

PROVENANCE
Josephine Meade Hamline (Mrs. John Henry Hamline), Chicago, by gift of Homer, 1880; Mrs. Uri Grannis, Lake Forest, IL, her daughter, nd; (Grannis estate auction, Lake Forest, IL, 1973); Mrs. Donald J. Ford, Lake Forest, IL, 1973; (Sotheby's, 25 Apr. 1980, sale 4365, no. 56); Duane B. Garrett, Tiburon, CA, nd; James K. Devlin Trust, Dallas, nd; (Spanierman Gallery, LLC, 1986); private collection, c. 1987; (Spanierman Gallery, LLC, 1992)

EXHIBITIONS
Portland 1998

894
Two Girls
[1880]

Watercolor, 9½ × 6⅜ (24.130 × 16.192)
Inscribed ll: Homer

Private collection

ABG: See commentary No. 885.

PROVENANCE
Mr. and Mrs. William Crary Brownell, New York, probably c. 1880; William Crary Brownell, New York, nd; the second Mrs. William Crary Brownell, New York, 1928

292

895

Two Girls Reading a Letter

[1880]

Watercolor, 9¾ × 7¼ (24.765 × 18.415)
Inscribed lr: W. H.

Private collection

Mrs. Otho Wiecker told LG in 1940 that a New York couple, whose name she could not recall, had consigned this watercolor to Mr. Wiecker after it had languished several years in the hands of the Macbeth gallery in New York.

Mr. and Mrs. Nathan Pulsifer lent a number of works to the Brooklyn museum's 1915 exhibition of Homer watercolors. Among them was *Reading a Letter*, catalogued as 9¾ inches by 7⅜ inches. By the 1930s no work appropriate to that title and of that size was in the collections of either of the Pulsifer sons. Harold Pulsifer told LG that the family had sold at auction two Homer watercolors which they considered less good than their others. He could not recall the subjects of either, or where they had been auctioned, but did know the family regretted disposing of the paintings. It seems likely *Two Girls Reading a Letter* was one of the two.

ABG: See commentary No. 885.

PROVENANCE
Lawson Valentine, New York, nd [?]; Lucy Houghton Valentine (Mrs. Lawson Valentine), 1891 [?]; Almira Valentine Pulsifer (Mrs. Nathan Trowbridge Pulsifer), her daughter, 1911 [?]; (Otho Wiecker, Boston, nd); Edwin S. Webster, Boston, before 1939

EXHIBITIONS
Brooklyn 1915, no. 30 (as *Reading a Letter*) [?]; Worcester 1944, no. 30; MFA, Boston, 1959, no. 90

No. 894. Two Girls

No. 895. Two Girls Reading a Letter

No. 896. Girl in Autumn Landscape

896

Girl in Autumn Landscape

[1880]

A Flock of Blackbirds

Watercolor, 11¼ × 7⅝ (28.575 × 19.368)
Inscribed ll: Homer

Private collection

ABG: See commentary No. 885.

PROVENANCE
Mr. and Mrs. William Crary Brownell, New York,
probably c. 1880; William Crary Brownell, New
York, nd; Virginia Swinburne Hale, Carmel, CA,
Mrs. Brownell's niece, by bequest, 1928; (Weyhe
Gallery, 1941); (Grand Central Art Gallery, 1955);
Thomas J. Watson, New York, 1955; Helen Watson
Buckner, New York, his daughter, c. 1956

897

Two Ladies

1880

Watercolor, 6¹⁵⁄₁₆ × 7¹⁵⁄₁₆ (17.623 × 20.163)
Inscribed lr: Homer / 1880

The Metropolitan Museum of Art, given in memory
of Florence Baird Meyer, 18.123.3

PROVENANCE
Florence Baird Meyer, New York, nd

EXHIBITIONS
Metropolitan 1972, no. 28

898

The Music Lesson

1880

Ink, watercolor, 10 × 14½ (25.400 × 36.830)
Inscribed lr: Homer / 1880

Private collection

PROVENANCE
(Sotheby Parke-Bernet, 19 June 1981, sale 4650M,
no. 132); private collection, 1981; (Hirschl & Adler
Galleries, 1988); private collection, 1988; (Christie's,
23 May 1990, sale 7082, no. 23); (Hirschl & Adler
Galleries, 1990)

No. 897. Two Ladies

No. 898. The Music Lesson

Illustration: "The Shepherdess. From a Sketch by Winslow Homer."
[George William Sheldon], "Sketches and Studies VII. From the
Portfolios of R. Swain Gifford, Winslow Homer, Arthur Quartley,
A. T. Britcher," (NY) Art Journal 6 (Nov.. 1880): 326

899
The Shepherdess
[1880]

[drawing]

Unlocated

Like No. 788 and No. 851, the two Homers which
illustrated George Sheldon's article, "Sketches and
Studies. II" in the April 1880 issue of the *Art Journal*,
the single image by Homer which accompanied
"Sketches and Studies. VII" in the November 1880
issue may be presumed to have been made by photographic transfer to the engraver's block, rather than
the, by then, obsolete method of the artist drawing
directly on the block.

ABG: See commentary No. 756.
    The November 1880 *Art Journal* illustration was
captioned: "Shepherdess. From a Sketch by Winslow
Homer." The original rendering should have survived,
as did the two photographer's models for the April
Art Journal illustrations. This invites the question:
Was that sketch the very rough oil study, No. 756,
which so closely resembles the illustration, or was
it a near duplicate image in a graphic medium?
Certainly there is a marked difference between the
illustrations with Sheldon's April 1880 article and the
one published in November. The latter were clearly
made from linear drawings, where the strong masses
of this shepherdess suggest a medium applied with a
brush. However, would No. 756, a very loosely
brushed, color image, be provided to the *Art Journal*
for photographic transcription into a linear, colorless
form, especially by an artist so accustomed and
accomplished in the demands of illustration?
Homer's sketch in oil might have served as his own
model for a drawing provided to the magazine, and
now lost.

LITERATURE
[George William Sheldon], "Sketches and Studies
VII. From the Portfolios of R. Swain Gifford,
Winslow Homer, Arthur Quartley, A. T. Britcher,"
(NY) Art Journal 6 (Nov. 1880): 326. Reprinted in,
G. W. Sheldon, *Hours with Art and Artists* (New
York: D. Appleton and Company, 1882), 138

No. 900. Young Woman

see color illustration, p. 456

900

Young Woman

1880

Watercolor, 9⁷⁄₁₆ × 13³⁄₈ (23.973 × 33.973)
Inscribed lr: Homer 1880

Berry-Hill Galleries, New York

ABG: Homer passed much of the summer of 1880 in Gloucester, Massachusetts, and, thus, his paintings and drawings of that year which involve the sea (with and without sailboats) are commonly assumed to be scenes of Gloucester, and are awarded titles to reinforce the supposed identification. However, there is a small group of summer seaside subjects dating from 1880 which are quite distinct from the acknowledged Gloucester subjects. Among the more pronounced differences are a gentler shoreline, where grassy banks blend into shallow water, and a brighter palette dominated by blues and greens. Among the titles of the many paintings Homer contributed to the American Water Color Society annual exhibition of 1881 was "Field Point, Greenwich, Conn." That association with a coastal town in western Connecticut infers Gloucester was not Homer's only working base in the summer of 1880. The placid water, sloping lawns and groves

seen in the watercolors No. 900 through No. 911 are surely more appropriate to the terrain of Long Island Sound than to the forbidding, rocky coastline of Massachusetts' North Shore. The presence of a slender young woman dressed in black in the landscape setting of No. 900 through No. 909 further links these paintings into a suite associated with a particular place and passage of time.

The siting of a few more works from this summer are more ambiguous. The boys swimming in what probably was a fresh water pond (No. 912, No. 913, and No. 914), or young people playing in shallows around a boat dock (No. 915 and No. 916) could as well be children of Connecticut or Massachusetts.

PROVENANCE
Mrs. Walter E. Swift, New York, nd; (Kennedy Galleries, 1950); (Charles D. Childs Gallery, Boston, c. 1950); Mr. and Mrs. Homer Strong, Rochester, NY, 1951; Strong Museum, Rochester, NY, 1969; (Christie's, 4 Dec. 2003, sale 1309, no. 26)

EXHIBITIONS
Everson 1983, no. 2; Whitney, Fairfield, 1984; NGA 1986, no. 55

LITERATURE
Helen A. Cooper, *Winslow Homer Watercolors* (Washington, DC, 1986), 66, 69

No. 901. Woman with Flower

901

Woman with Flower

1880

Watercolor, 8⅞ × 11¼ (22.543 × 28.575)
Inscribed lr: Homer 1880

Private collection

ABG: See commentary No. 900.

PROVENANCE
Charles S. Homer, Jr., by bequest, 1910; Mrs.
Charles S. Homer, Jr., by bequest, 1917; Maria W.
Blanchard, New York, by gift, before 1937; Elizabeth
Cooper, Westchester, NY, by bequest, c. 1944;
(William Macbeth, Inc., 1949); (James Graham and
Sons, 1949); Arthur G. Altschul, New York, 1949

EXHIBITIONS
NGA 1958, no. 98; University of Arizona 1963, no. 6;
Whitney 1973, no. 93; NGA 1986, no. 54

902

Girl at Gloucester

1880

Watercolor, 9⅞ × 13⅝ (25.083 × 34.608)
Inscribed lr: Homer 1880

Private collection

The Vose Galleries told the Babcock Galleries that the Sylvia Pettys from whom they purchsed this watercolor had "inherited it from her father, who had inherited it from his father, N. T. Pulsifer." There has to have been some confusion in this history of ownership, as Almira Valentine Pulsifer and her husband, Nathan Trowbridge Pulsifer's only grandchildren were the sisters, Natalie and Alice Pulsifer.

ABG: See commentary No. 900.

PROVENANCE
Mrs. Sylvia Pettys, Newtonville, MA, nd; (Robert C. Vose Galleries of Boston, 1944); (E. C. Babcock Art Galleries, 1944); Joseph Katz, Baltimore, 1945; (Victor Spark, nd); (Wildenstein & Co., 1954)

EXHIBITIONS
Whitney 1944; Worcester 1944, no. 31; Whitney 1973, no. 92 (Whitney, only)

No. 902. Girl at Gloucester

No. 903. Young Woman with a Parasol

see color illustration, p. 457

903

Young Woman with a Parasol
1880

Watercolor, 9½ × 13¼ (24.130 × 33.655)
Inscribed lr: Homer 1880

Private collection

Knoedler gallery records include reference to this watercolor, under the title *Waverly Oaks*, apparently as having been received in February 1913 from Allan A. Morrill. The painting was not necessarily there on consignment; no notation of sale is in Knoedler record. The mistaken identification of its setting as Belmont, Massachusetts, could have been Knoedler's invention. However, the origin is more likely Charles S. Homer, Jr., who gave the watercolor to his business associate, Allan A. Morrill. The grove known as

Waverley Oaks, which Charles would have remembered from the time his parents lived in Belmont, was probably the only experience of such a stand of trees he shared with his brother. It is impossible to know whether the inscription, "Waverly Oaks" (using the late spelling) on the reverse of the sheet is the source of the early titling, or its result.

ABG: See commentary No. 900.

PROVENANCE
Charles S. Homer, Jr., by bequest, 1910; Allan A. Morrill, Chicago, by gift, c. 1912; Allan D. Morrill, East Kingston, NH, his son, nd; (Charles D. Childs Gallery, Boston, and, Old Print Shop, New York, by 1946); H. B. Harris, New York, c. 1946; (Wildenstein & Co., nd); Mr. and Mrs. Benjamin M. Reeves, 1952; (Sotheby's, 27 May 1992, sale 6305, no. 20)

EXHIBITIONS
Wildenstein 1947, no. 51 (as *Waverly Oaks*); Wildenstein 1949, no. 8 (as *Waverly Oaks*)

904

The Rendezvous

1880

Watercolor, 8½ × 11⅜ (21.590 × 28.893)
Inscribed ll: Homer 1880

Private collection

ABG: See commentary No. 900.

PROVENANCE
(Arlington Art Gallery, nd); (American Art
Association/Anderson Galleries, 11–12 Nov. 1926,
Arlington Gallery sale, no. 223); (Newhouse
Galleries, 1926); (Gustave Wiegand, 1928); (Ainslie
Galleries, nd); (William Macbeth, Inc., 1930);
Elizabeth Ball, Muncie, IN, 1936; (William
Macbeth, Inc., 1937); Mr. and Mrs. Thomas N.
Metcalf, Boston, 1937; (William Macbeth, Inc., nd);
Millicent Rogers (Mrs. H. Huddleston Rogers),
Washington, DC, 1952

EXHIBITIONS
Mount Holyoke 1940, no. 19; University of Arizona
1963, no. 105

No. 904. The Rendezvous

No. 905. Girl Seated in a Grove

905
Girl Seated in a Grove
1880

Watercolor, 9¾ × 13½ (24.765 × 34.290)
Inscribed lr: Winslow Homer / 1880

Private collection

ABG: See commentary No. 900.

PROVENANCE
Grace Barrett Valentine (Mrs. Henry C. Valentine),
Darien, CT, c. 1880; Susie Valentine Brown (Mrs.
Lewis B. Brown), Darien, CT, her daughter, nd;
Valentine M. Brown and Manning B. Brown,
Darien, CT, her sons, by 1940; (William Macbeth,
Inc., 1940); Mr. and Mrs. Thomas N. Metcalf,
Boston, 1940

906

Young Girl in Woods

1880

Watercolor, 8¹¹⁄₁₆ × 11⁵⁄₁₆ (22.068 × 28.735)
Inscribed ll: Homer 1880

Unlocated

ABG: See commentary No. 900.

PROVENANCE
(The Clipper Ship, 1966); (Charles Auction
Gallery, Flushing, NY, spring 1966 sale); Adolf
Loewenstein, North Miami, FL, 1966; (William J.
Fischer [auction] Gallery, Nov. 1966 sale); (Sally
Turner, Plainfield, NJ, 1966); (Coe Kerr Gallery,
nd); The Hunter Museum, Chattanooga, TN, 1971;
(Sotheby's, 4 Dec. 1987, sale 6512, no. 50); (Taggart
& Jorgensen Gallery, Washington, DC, 1987);
private collection, 1987; (Taggart & Jorgensen
Gallery, Washington, DC, 1990)

No. 906. Young Girl in Woods

No. 907. A Girl in a Punt

907
A Girl in a Punt
[1880]

Watercolor, 8⅝ × 11⁷⁄₁₆ (21.908 × 29.053)
Inscribed lr: Homer

Farnsworth Art Museum, Rockland, ME, 45.534

ABG: See commentary No. 900.

PROVENANCE
Alexander Wadsworth Longfellow, Portland, ME,
nd [?]; Mary Longfellow, Portland, ME, his sister,
nd; Alexander Bower, Portland, ME, 1943

EXHIBITIONS
University of Arizona 1963, no. 50; Farnsworth 1970,
no. 31; South Texas 1978, no. 9; Terra 1990, no. 20;
Parthenon 2000; Farnsworth 2006

908
Girl on a Beach
[1880]

Watercolor, 9 × 7 (22.860 × 17.780)
Inscribed ll: W. H.

Private collection

Boyer Gonzales, Jr., wrote LG in January 1939 to
inform him of a watercolor and an etching by Homer
which his mother still owned; several other works
Homer had given to his father had been lost in the
great hurricane that devastated Galveston, Texas,
in 1900. Mrs. Gonzales, Sr., wrote LG in March
1939 that "when we were married in September 1907
Winslow Homer sent this small watercolor as a
wedding gift." Later that year Mrs. Gonzales sent
along a small black and white photograph of the
painting, identifying it by writing the following
on the reverse: "watercolor 9 × 7 painted in 1879
by Winslow Homer. Presented by him to Boyer
Gonzales and Eleanor Hertford, as a wedding gift
September 1907."

ABG: Boyer Gonzales (1864–1934) was the son of Thomas Gonzales, a cotton broker and prominent citizen of Galveston. The family wealth was such that Boyer could lead a life primarily devoted to travel (favoring the established spas and resorts) and painting in watercolors. The Gonzales were well acquainted with the Arthur B. Homer family, who summered at Prout's Neck. Arthur facilitated Boyer Gonzales's introduction to Winslow, at Prout's Neck in the summer of 1887. Thereafter Gonzales made a summer visit to Homer almost annually through 1900.

Gonzales had to take responsibility for the family business following his father's death in 1896, but he was not adept at the work and the business was rapidly diminishing when the 1900 hurricane destroyed it—along with most of Galveston's economic structure. Gonzales then turned his pursuit of watercolor painting from an avocation to a profession. He enjoyed a minor career in the 1920s, being particularly recognized for his views of coastal sea- and landscapes, which were strongly reminiscent of Homer in style.

Homer and Gonzales had a sporadic correspondence through the 1890s, but it seems to have ceased as Gonzales became more preoccupied with business and problems of health. Then Homer wrote on 4 October 1907, clearly in reply to news from Gonzales: "My dear Mr. Gonzales, It is a great pleasure to hear from you again. I certainly congratulate you on your happy life —- & also on your recent marriage — How happy both of you must be. I am about to hunt up some sketch to send with this for a wedding present — something that can go in the bottom of your trunk."

Homer squeezed a post script along the right edge and across the top of the sheet: "Just found a sketch of a girl that would not go to the Little Church Around the Corner made in 1879 — sent by this mail to you."*

Girl on a Beach is undated, but in subject details, particularly the elegant young lady dressed in black, it seems to belong in company with a number of works inscribed with a date of 1880. Homer was reaching back more than twenty-five years in dating the watercolor to 1879; his memory may not have been perfectly accurate.

See commentary No. 900.

*The information on Boyer Gonzales's life and career provided above is wholly derived from Edward Simmen's 1997 biography *With Bold Strokes: Boyer Gonzales, 1864–1934*. Simmen quotes part of Homer's 1907 letter. The letter is held by the Galveston and Texas History Center, Rosenberg Library, Galveston, Texas.

The "Little Church Around the Corner" on 29th Street near Fifth Avenue in New York enjoyed a considerable reputation for romantic weddings, particularly as a destination for eloping couples.

PROVENANCE
Mr. and Mrs. Boyer Gonzales, Galveston, TX, by gift of Homer, 1907; Eleanor Hertford Gonzales (Mrs. Boyer Gonzales), Woodstock, NY, 1934

LITERATURE
Edward Simmen, *With Bold Strokes: Boyer Gonzales, 1864–1934* College Station, TX: Texas A & M University Press, 1997)

No. 908. Girl on a Beach

No. 909. Girl on Beach

909

Girl on Beach

1880

Watching the Bathers

Watercolor, 8⅛ × 12³⁄₁₆ (20.638 × 30.958)
Inscribed lr: Homer 1880

Private collection

William Howe Downes, the Boston *Evening Transcript*'s art critic, completed one of LG's information-gathering questionnaires on this painting. Although Downes did not date it, he probably wrote this account of his acquisition in early 1938.

> I refused to accept this watercolor at first, for two reasons, I did not wish to put myself under any obligation to Kabatznick, and I had some doubts as to the authenticity of the work. However, Kabatznick sent it to my house in spite of my refusal. So I asked my friend Fergus Turner, of Doll & Richards (who dealt in Homer's pictures for many years), to give me his opinion as to its genuineness. He came to my house, examined the picture carefully, and said that it was undoubtedly a Homer.

LG wrote Benjamin Kabatznick in May 1938 to ask where he had gotten the painting, but Mr. Kabatznick could not recall his source beyond that it had been "a New York dealer."

ABG: The years which had passed between Downes having accepted the gift of this watercolor and writing his account for LG may explain his imperfect memory of circumstances related to the gift. It probably was offered not long after Downes had reviewed a group of three Homer watercolors at Kabatznick's gallery, and thus presented a more acute ethical dilemma than Downes recalled. Also, as he had not questioned this watercolor when he wrote about it in his column, he presumably did not then question its authenticity.

> The third example is a single figure piece. On a rock in the foreground, close by the seaside, a young women is sitting. She wears a black silk gown, of the style of 1880 with flounced skirt and rather close-fitting basque. In the distance is a bathing beach with a row of bathing-houses and the faintly indicated figures of a group of bathers in the water and on the sands.

Downes's review is known from an unidentified clipping. It may be presumed to have appeared in the *Transcript*, and no later than 1922, the year Downes retired from the paper.

See commentary No. 900.

PROVENANCE
(Kabatznick Gallery, Boston, c. 1920); William
Howe Downes, Boston, by gift, nd

EXHIBITIONS
Nelson-Atkins 2001

LITERATURE
W[illiam] H[owe] D[ownes], "The Fine Arts.
Watercolors by Homer. Three Early Works . . . on
View at Kabatznick's Gallery," [*(Boston) Daily
Evening Transcript*], clipped

910+

Sailing Calm Water

1880

Watercolor, 9⅜ × 13¾ (23.813 × 34.925)
Inscribed lr: Homer 1880

Private collection

ABG: See commentary No. 900.

   A clipping, which may be presumed to have been
cut from an issue of the Boston *Evening Transcript*,
has been kept with this watercolor painting. It is a

review by William Howe Downes of three watercolors
by Homer which were then at the Kabatznick
Gallery in Boston. The association of article and
painting is doubtless because Downes's description
of one of the works at Kabatznick's so closely
corresponds to this painting:

> In another of the pictures we have a sunny bit
> of cove somewhere on Cape Ann, with soft blue
> water, and a sloop yacht lying at anchor near the
> farther shore, which forms an undulating line of
> low grassy hills against the horizon. The mainsail
> of the sloop is up, and the jib down, lying loose
> along the bowsprit. The wavering reflection of the
> blue water makes a very interesting note near the
> centre of the design.

   This article may also be presumed to date from
no later than 1922, the year Downes retired from the
Transcript.

PROVENANCE
(Kabatznick Gallery, Boston, c. 1920); private
collection, nd

LITERATURE
W[illiam] H[owe] D[ownes], "The Fine Arts.
Watercolors by Homer. Three Early Works . . . on
View at Kabatznick's Gallery," [*(Boston) Daily
Evening Transcript*], clipped

No. 910. Sailing Calm Water

No. 911. Yacht in a Cove, Gloucester

see color illustration, p. 458

911

Yacht in a Cove, Gloucester

1880

Watercolor, 10 × 13¾ (25.400 × 34.925)
Inscribed ll: Homer 1880

A. Alfred Taubman, Bloomfield Hills, MI

ABG: See commentary No. 900.

PROVENANCE
(Doll & Richards, Boston, 1880); (William Postar,
Boston, 1971); private collection, 1971; (Kennedy
Galleries, by 1972)

EXHIBITIONS
Doll & Richards 1880

912

The Swimming Hole

[1880]

Graphite, 7½ × 9¾ (19.050 × 24.765)
Inscribed lr: W. H.

Brooklyn Museum, Frederick Loeser Fund, 28.209

ABG: See commentary No. 900.

PROVENANCE
(Andre Rueff, Brooklyn, nd)

913

Boys Swimming

[1880]

Graphite, 8 × 13⅜ (20.320 × 33.973)
Inscribed lr: Homer

Private collection

LG examined and recorded this drawing in the home
of Mrs. Margaret Chapin Osgood in April 1937.
Mrs. Osgood told him that like all her Homers it had

308

No. 912. The Swimming Hole

No. 913. Boys Swimming

come to her by gift. In the Boston tradition of aristocratic restraint, she did not name the giver, however, it was undoubtedly her uncle, Horace D. Chapin.

The precise history of the drawing before it came to Mrs. Osgood is somewhat ambiguous. Horace Chapin was Edward Hooper's brother-in-law, and executor of his estate, and, thus, official or unofficial guardian of those of Hooper's five daughters who were unmarried at their father's death. Chapin was also a collector in his own right. It is easy to understand that establishing the distribution of Homers among members of the Hooper and Chapin families was complicated. In the course of researching for his 1911 biography of Homer, William Howe Downes posed the question squarely to Chapin in a letter of 2 May 1911: "Which of the Homers from your house and from your sister's house are to be set down as belonging to you, and which are to be credited to the Hooper estate?" Chapin responded by naming five watercolors then in his home as belonging to his brother-in-law's estate, but that one drawing—which he did not name or describe—was his own. He named as his property two watercolors and two drawings then in the home of one of his sisters, neither of those drawings was *Boys Swimming*.

It would seem that the unnamed drawing Chapin said was his property was *Boys Swimming*. However, Downes illustrated it in his book, captioned "[photographed] From the drawing belonging to the Edward W. Hooper estate, Boston." Then in his appendix list of the Boston Museum of Fine Arts' Homer memorial exhibition, Downes notes Chapin as having lent the drawing—which he might have done on behalf of the estate. On the other hand, Museum of Fine Arts records also name Chapin as the lender, without qualification.

ABG: See commentary No. 900.

PROVENANCE
Horace D. Chapin, Boston, nd [?]; Margaret Chapin Osgood (Mrs. Robert B. Osgood), Boston, his sister, c. 1936

EXHIBITIONS
MFA, Boston, 1911

LITERATURE
Downes 1911, op. 60

No. 914. Four Boys Bathing

see color illustration, p. 459

No. 915. Boys Bathing

see color illustration, p. 460

914

Four Boys Bathing

1880

Watercolor, 9½ × 13½ (24.130 × 34.290)
Inscribed ll: Homer 1880

Williams College Museum of Art, Williamstown,
MA, gift of Mrs. William C. Brownell, 58.15

ABG: See commentary No. 900.

PROVENANCE
Mr. and Mrs. William Crary Brownell, New York,
probably c. 1880; William Crary Brownell, New
York, nd; the second Mrs. William Crary Brownell,
New York, 1928

EXHIBITIONS
University of Arizona 1963, no. 136; Hamilton 1964,
no. 9; Whitney 1973, no. 91; Whitney, Fairfield, 1984

915

Boys Bathing

1880

Watercolor, 5¾ × 13¼ (14.605 × 33.655)
Inscribed ll, on boat stern: Homer / 1880

Hood Museum of Art, Dartmouth College, Hanover,
NH, from the estate of Tatiana Ruzicka (1915–1995),
presented by Edward Connery Lathem, in memory
of Rudolph Ruzicka (1883–1978), w.996.47

ABG: See commentary No. 900.

PROVENANCE
Charles S. Homer, Jr., by bequest, 1910; Dr. and
Mrs. William S. Dennett, New York, by gift, c. 1912;
Marie Beck Dennett (Mrs. William S. Dennett),
New York, by bequest, nd; Rudolph Ruzicka,
Hanover, NH, by bequest, 1943; Tatiana Ruzicka,
his daughter, by bequest, 1978; Edward C. Latham,
Hanover, NH, by bequest, 1995

EXHIBITIONS
Doll & Richards 1880 [?]

916

A Sloop at a Wharf

[1880]

Watercolor, 9 × 13 (22.860 × 33.020)
Inscribed ll: Homer

Private collection

ABG: See commentary No. 900.

PROVENANCE
Charles S. Homer, Jr., by bequest, 1910; Mrs. Charles
S. Homer, Jr., by bequest, 1917; Dr. and Mrs. James
D. Farr, New York, by gift, nd; Jocelyn Farr, Prout's
Neck, ME, by bequest, 1953; (Barridorff Galleries,
Portland, ME, 22 Sept. 1984, no. 15); (Shephard
Gallery, Newport, RI, 1984); private collection, c.
1984; Leon Black, New York, nd; (Berry-Hill Galleries,
Inc., 1999); private collection, 1999; (Sotheby's, 24
May 2000, sale 7480, no. 59); (Godel & Co., 2000)

No. 916. A Sloop at a Wharf

No. 917. Children Playing under a Gloucester Wharf

see color illustration, p. 461

917
Children Playing under a Gloucester Wharf

1880

Watercolor, 8⅟₁₆ × 13½ (20.480 × 34.290)
Inscribed lr: Homer 1880

Museum of Fine Arts, Boston, Hayden Collection,
Charles Henry Hayden Fund, 21.2554

The distinguished Boston watercolorist and teacher,
Ross Turner (1847–1915) recounted to William
Howe Downes an August day passed with Homer in
Prout's Neck as one among several unnamed guests.
Turner told Downes this occasion occurred in about
1896. By his account Homer was a congenial—and
generous host. Turner came away from the visit
with this painting, as he described: "This charming
day at last came to an end, and we strolled down the
hillside, and finding a conveyance ready, we bade
our host farewell, hugging to ourselves a delightful
study, one of the earlier Gloucester subjects, depicting
some girls in gayly colored sunbonnets, wading
in the shallow water, with just a touch of a white
cloud beyond, and a deep rich shade of a hillside
in sunlight across the bay."

PROVENANCE
Ross Turner, Salem, MA, by gift of Homer, c. 1896;
Sterling B. Turner, Salem, MA, his son, nd

EXHIBITIONS
Doll & Richards 1880; MFA, Boston, 1936; Mount
Holyoke 1940, no. 6; MFA, Boston, 1941; Colorado
Springs 1947, no. 8; Ogunquit 1954, no. p-2; NGA
1958/MFA, Boston, 1959, no. 100/91; Wellesley
(Massachusetts) College Museum of Art, *The
Gloucester Watercolors of Winslow Homer*, 2–31 Mar.
1976; MFA, Boston, 1977, no. 52; MFA, Boston,
1993/1996, no. 50/11

LITERATURE
Downes 1911, 196–97

No. 918. Ten Pound Island

918

Ten Pound Island

[1880]

Watercolor, 3¾ × 5⅝ (9.525 × 14.288)
Inscribed ll: W. H.

Private collection

This painting is seen to the left of a doorway in one of the two formal "portrait" photographs made of the rooms occupied for part of 1880 and 1881, and later, by Homer and Samuel T. Preston in the Benedict building on New York's Washington Square.

ABG: This diminutive painting could as easily have been done by Homer during his 1873 stay in Gloucester, or that of 1880. Its small size and opacity in watercolor technique would seem to favor an 1873 date, but the fact that it hung in the cooperative residence Homer and Samuel Preston established in 1880 gives priority to that date. Homer's stay with the Ten Pound Island light house keeper apparently was arranged through the Preston family who were cousins of his sister-in-law, Martha French Homer. Mrs. Preston was also related to Mrs. Octavious A. Merrill, the light house keeper's wife. It is easy to imagine Homer sending or giving this postcard-sized view of the island and its light to Preston as a momento of the place he was living during the summer-long absence from New York.

PROVENANCE
Samuel Thorndyke Preston, New York, by gift of Homer, nd; Mrs. Ames, Somerville, MA, his sister, by bequest, 1898; Mrs. William A. Preston, New Ipswich, NH, her daughter, nd; John Preston, New Ipswich, NH, her son, by gift, before 1941

EXHIBITIONS
Vermont Art Center 1964, no. 20; Terra 1990, no. 9

919

Boy in Boat, Gloucester

[1880]

Man in a Boat, Coast of Maine

Watercolor, 9⅛ × 13¾ (23.178 × 34.925)
Inscribed lr: Sketch W. H.

The Art Institute of Chicago, Mr. and Mrs. Martin A. Ryerson Collection, 1933.1243

PROVENANCE
Charles S. Homer, Jr., by bequest, 1910 [?]; Charles W. Gould, New York, nd; (M. Knoedler & Co., 1915); Martin A. Ryerson, Chicago, 1915

EXHIBITIONS
Doll & Richards 1880; Brooklyn 1915, no. 46 (as *Man in Boat, Coast of Maine*); AI Chicago 1916; AI Chicago 1920; Hackley 1921; Omaha 1924; AI Chicago 1926; Albright 1929, no. 22; Saint Louis 1932; AI Chicago 1936, no. 2; Herron 1936; Century 1951, no. 6; Terra 1990, no. 28; AI Chicago 2008

920

Boys Sitting on a Dock

[1880]

Watercolor, 6⅞ × 10⅞ (17.463 × 27.623)
Inscribed lr: W. H.

Private collection

PROVENANCE
(M. Knoedler & Co., by 1932); Dr. and Mrs. George Woodward, Chestnut Hill, PA, 1932; (M. Knoedler & Co., 1934); Andrew V. Stout, New York, 1944; Mrs. Andrew V. Stout, New York, nd; (Hirschl & Adler Galleries, 1968); private collection, by 1972; (Hirschl & Adler Galleries, 1973); (Peterson Galleries, Los Angeles, c. 1978); (Stephen Straw Company, Inc., Newburyport, MA, c. 1979); (Phillips, Boston, 2 May 1980, sale 289, no. 40); private collection, 1980

No. 919. Boy in Boat, Gloucester

see color illustration, p. 462

No. 920. Boys Sitting on a Dock

No. 922. Children and Sail Boat

921

Children Wading at Gloucester

1880

Watercolor, 9⅝ × 13⅝ (24.448 × 34.608)
Inscribed ll: Homer 1880

Private collection

PROVENANCE
(Doll & Richards, Boston, 1880); Edward W. Hooper, Boston, 1880; Ellen Sturgis Hooper Potter (Mrs. John Briggs Potter), Boston, his daughter, by bequest, 1901; Mary Hooper Warner (Mrs. Roger Sherman Warner), Boston, her sister, by 1917; Sturgis Warner, Washington, DC, her son, by bequest, 1972

EXHIBITIONS
Doll & Richards 1880; Saint Botolph Club, Boston, *Regular Water-Color Exhibition*, 17–29 Mar. 1890, no. 11 or 14 (as *Children at Gloucester*); MFA, Boston, 1911; Boston Symphony 1937

922

Children and Sail Boat

1880

Boys Beaching a Boat

Watercolor, 9¾ × 13¾ (24.765 × 34.925)
Inscribed lr: Homer 1880

Smithsonian American Art Museum, Smithsonian Institution, Washington, DC, partial and promised gift of Sam Rose and Julie Walters, 2004.30.1

PROVENANCE
(Doll & Richards, Boston, 1880); Edward W. Hooper, Boston, 1880; Fanny Hooper Curtis (Mrs. Greely S. Curtis), Boston, his daughter, by bequest, 1901; Estate of Fanny Hooper Curtis, 1963; (Hirschl & Adler Galleries, 1964); Dr. and Mrs. Fletcher H. McDowell, New York, 1964; (Gerald Peters Gallery, 1995); Samuel G. Walters, Washington, DC, c. 1995

EXHIBITIONS
Doll & Richards 1880; MFA, Boston, 1911 (as *Children and Sail-boat*); Fogg 1932, no. 3 (as *Children and Sail-boat*)

923
The Green Dory
[1880]

Watercolor, 13¾ × 19⅝ (34.925 × 49.848)
Inscribed lr: Homer

Museum of Fine Arts, Boston, bequest of Dr. Arthur
Tracy Cabot, 42.538

PROVENANCE
(Doll & Richards, Boston, 1880); Dr. Samuel Cabot,
Boston, 1880; Dr. Arthur Tracy Cabot, Boston,
his son, nd; Mrs. Arthur Tracy Cabot, Boston, in
trust, 1912

EXHIBITIONS
Doll & Richards 1880; MFA, Boston, 1911; Paris
1923, no. 1; Carnegie 1923, no. 19; Worcester 1944,
no. 32; Colorado Springs 1947, no. 5; NGA
1958/MFA, Boston, 1959, no. 103/92; Mariners,
Norfolk, 1964, no. 15; Farnsworth 1970, no. 30;
MFA, Boston, 1977, no. 53

No. 923. The Green Dory

see color illustration, p. 463

No. 924. Pulling the Dory

924

Pulling the Dory

[1880]

Watercolor, 8⁷⁄₁₆ × 13¼ (21.433 × 33.655)

The Farnsworth Art Museum, Rockland, ME, bequest of Mrs. Elizabeth B. Noyce, 97.3.19

The Homer family assumed this watercolor was a work of 1873, and labeled it as such in the 1936 Prout's Neck Association Homer exhibition drawn almost entirely from the Mrs. Charles S. Homer, Jr.'s holdings. That erroneous dating—occasionally stretched to "1873–75"—remained attached to the work until it entered the Farnsworth Art Museum collection.

PROVENANCE
Charles S. Homer, Jr., by bequest, 1910; Mrs. Charles S. Homer, Jr., by bequest, 1917; Alice Homer Willauer (Mrs. Osborn Willauer), Dedham, MA, her grandniece, by gift, before 1936; (Christie's, 25 May 1989, sale 6838, no. 56); The November Collection, Maine, c. 1989

EXHIBITIONS
Prout's Neck 1936, no. 3 (dated 1873); Macbeth 1936, no. 41 (dated c. 1873); Portland 1989; Portland 1991; Parthenon 2000; Farnsworth 2006

LITERATURE
The Farnsworth Art Museum, "An Eye for Maine," by Donelson Hoopes, in *An Eye for Maine: Paintings from a Private Collection* (Rockland, Maine, 1994), 12–13

925

Boy with Blue Dory

1880

Watercolor, 9¼ × 17¹⁄₁₆ (23.495 × 43.340)
Inscribed lr: Winslow Homer '80

Private collection

Mary Hamilton, the first owner of this painting, was a sometime member of the Homer family household. Her place may only be inferred from occasional references in family correspondence. She apparently served as a companion to Mrs. Charles S. Homer, Sr. in her later years. Miss Hamilton probably accompanied the senior Homers on their summer visits to Prout's Neck, presumably including that of 1883, their first in a home of their own, The Ark, and last before Mrs. Homer's death in the spring of 1884. Thereafter Charles S. Homer, Sr. passed the winters in a residential hotel in Boston, returning to The Ark for the summer month. Miss Hamilton then also returned to The Ark in the role of housekeeper, probably annually, at least through 1891. She is thought to have died in the mid-1890s.

John P. Adams told LG that his aunt, Miss Chapman, said the boy in the painting was one Sam Sloan, as if she had known him. Such an identification is almost surely apocryphal, however. Miss Chapman is not known to have had any direct association with Homer or his family, so her naming of the subject would have been second-hand from Miss Hamilton, or her own invention. Miss Hamilton, in turn, is unlikely to have been acquainted with the Gloucester boys who came under Homer's gaze in the summer of 1880.

PROVENANCE
Mary Hamilton, [Brooklyn, NY ?], by gift of Homer, c. 1890; Jane Chapman, Brooklyn, NY, her niece, by bequest, c. 1900; John P. Adams III, Cos Cob, CT, her nephew, by c. 1936; Hamiton Adams, Stamford, CT, his son, c. 1960; (Sotheby's, 3 Dec. 2003, sale 7950, no. 26)

No. 925. Boy with Blue Dory

see color illustration, p. 464

926

Boys Beaching a Dory

1880

Watercolor, 9½ × 13⁷⁄₁₆ (24.130 × 34.133)
Inscribed ll: Homer 1880

Toledo (OH) Museum of Art, purchased with funds
from the Florence Scott Libbey Bequest, 1950.274

PROVENANCE
Osborn McArthur, West Yarmouth, MA, nd;
Horace D. Chapin, Boston, c. 1935; Mary Chapin
White (Mrs. Joseph L. White), Upper Montclair,
NJ, his niece, by bequest, c. 1936

EXHIBITIONS
University of Arizona 1963, no. 128; Whitney,
Fairfield, 1984

No. 926. Boys Beaching a Dory

No. 927. Boys in a Dory

927

Boys in a Dory

1880

Watercolor, 13¾ × 19½ (34.925 × 49.530)
Inscribed lr: Homer / 1880

Addison Gallery of American Art, Phillips Academy,
Andover, MA, given anonymously, 1931.6

PROVENANCE
John Elderkin, New York, by 1904; (William
Macbeth, Inc., 1904); Dr. George Seasler [or
Gessler], Philadelphia, 1905; (John Levy Galleries,
1931); (William Macbeth, Inc., 1931); Thomas
Cochran, New York, 1931

EXHIBITIONS
Art Club of Philadelphia, *Fourteenth Annual
Exhibition of Water Colors and Pastels*, 20 Mar.–
16 Apr. 1905, no. 156; Fogg 1932, no. 10; NE
Museums 1936; Whitney 1936, no. 49; New Britain
1942; Addison 1980; Bowdoin 1983, no. 7; NGA
1986, no. 50; Addison 1990; Terra 1990, no. 29

No. 928. Boys in a Dory

928

Boys in a Dory

1880

Watercolor, 9⅛ × 13⅜ (23.178 × 33.973)
Inscribed lr: Homer 1880

Private collection

PROVENANCE
James Fitzsimmons, Boston, by gift of Homer, nd;
Florence A. Fitzsimmons, Roxbury, MA, his daughter,
before 1936; Mary Evelyn Fitzsimmons Douglass
(Mrs. Aubrey Douglass), Sacramento, CA, her sister,
by 1948; Malcolm Douglass, New York, her son, by
1987; (Steppingstone Gallery, 1987)

EXHIBITIONS
MFA, Boston, 1936

929

Boys in a Dory

1880

Watercolor, 9⅞ × 13⅞ (25.083 × 35.243)
Inscribed lr: Homer 1880

Smithsonian American Art Museum, Smithsonian
Institution, Washington, DC, partial and promised
gift of Sam Rose and Julie Walters, 2004.30.2

The name "Fairchilde" is written in pencil on the
reverse of this watercolor, suggesting it is one of the
two works Mrs. Charles Fairchild purchased from
the Doll & Richards Homer exhibition of 1880. The
other was No. 1008. Doll & Richards records only
note the date of sale (both on 16 December), and their
stock numbers (25 and 42) and prices ($60 and $150).

ABG: The owner of this work in the 1990s called
it "Waiting for Dad," a title long assigned to a
watercolor and related oil of 1873 (No. 2:475 and
No.2:476).

No. 929. Boys in a Dory

No. 930. Two Dories

930
Two Dories
1880

Watercolor, 8⅛ × 13¼ (20.638 × 33.655) sight
Inscribed lr: Homer 1880

Private collection

ABG: The likely first owner of this watercolor and
of No. 991, Rebecca Valentine, was born in 1834, the
younger sister of Lawson and Henry Valentine. She
married Mr. Fairbanks in 1855, and was nearing fifty
years of age in 1880, when Homer executed the two
watercolors associated with her.

PROVENANCE
Rebecca Valentine Fairbanks (Mrs. Leland Fairbanks,
Jr.), nd [?]; Mrs. Walter Gates Richardson, her
daughter, nd; Walter Gates Richardson, by bequest,
nd; Robert Richardson, Clarcona, FL, his son, by
1948; (Milch Galleries, 1954)

931

Gloucester Harbor

1880

Watercolor, 13⁹⁄₁₆ × 19⅜ (34.450 × 49.213)
Inscribed ll: Winslow Homer 1880

Museum of Fine Arts, Boston, given in memory of
Edward William Hooper, Trustee of the Museum
1879–1901, from a grandson, 1996.458

PROVENANCE
Edward W. Hooper, Boston, nd; Louisa Chapin
Hooper Thoron (Mrs. Ward Thoron), Boston, his
daughter, by bequest, 1901; private collection, 1975

EXHIBITIONS
MFA, Boston, 1911; MFA, Boston, 1924

LITERATURE
Downes 1911, op. 56

No. 931. Gloucester Harbor

see color illustration, p. 465

No. 932. Landing on a Rock

932

Landing on a Rock

1880

The Clam Diggers

Watercolor, 8 × 13 (20.320 × 33.020)
Inscribed lr: Homer 1880

Unlocated

In the 1920s this watercolor was occasionally lent to general exhibitions of American art under a title probably assigned by the Ainslie Gallery: "The Clam Diggers." Clams are not taken from solid rock; these boys may be presumed to be occupied in securing their little boat.

PROVENANCE
(Ainslie Galleries, by 1911); (William Macbeth, Inc., 1911); William H. Childs, New York, 1913; (E. C. Babcock Art Galleries, 1947); (Milch Galleries, by 1954); Mr. and Mrs. Frank W. Spencer, New York, 1954; (Kennedy Galleries, 1972)

933+

At Gloucester

[1880]

Watercolor, 9³⁄₁₆ × 14 (23.338 × 35.560)

Private collection

ABG: *At Gloucester* and *Boys Fishing, Gloucester* (No. 934) present a rare, but not unique demonstration of Homer replicating an image. (See No. 944 and No. 945 for another example.) A first impulse on seeing two so nearly identical works is to assume one is a copy by someone other than Homer. However, the stylistic character of the two paintings belies that explanation. The documented history of ownership of both works is shallow. Mrs. Harriet Appleton Curtis's daughter believed this watercolor had come into her family's possession from someone in the family of Homer St. Gaudens. Both families were long-standing pillars of Boston's cultural and social aristocracy. *Boys Fishing, Gloucester* was said to have been found in the attic of the house in Wolfeboro, New Hampshire, lived in by successive generations of the same family. It is difficult to conceive an opportunity for a copyist to have created one of these two. On the other hand, it is at just this period that Homer was exploring ways to amplify his output by unconventional methods, such as the use of carbon paper to get two sketched compositions for the work and time of creating one.

PROVENANCE

Mrs. Harriet Appleton Curtis, Boston, nd; Estate of Harriet Appleton Curtis, 1975; private collection, 1975; (Hirschl & Adler Galleries, 1992); (Hollis Taggart Galleries, 1993)

No. 933. At Gloucester

No. 934. Boys Fishing, Gloucester

934
Boys Fishing, Gloucester
1880

Watercolor, 9 × 13¾ (22.860 × 34.925)
Inscribed ll: Winslow Homer N. A. 1880

Private collection

ABG: See commentary No. 933.

PROVENANCE
Sylvia G. Reade, Wolfeboro, NH, by 1974; (Vose
Galleries of Boston, 1974); Memorial Art Gallery,
University of Rochester, Rochester, NY, 1974; (Vose
Galleries of Boston, nd); Mr. and Mrs. William
Maxion, New York, nd; William Maxion, Jr., New
York, by bequest, nd; (Chad Anyan Fine Arts
Acquisitions, Los Angeles, c. 1996); private collection,
1996; (Christie's, 23 May 2001, sale 9654, no. 41)

935

Four Rowboats with Children

[1880]

Watercolor, 9¾ × 13⅝ (24.765 × 34.608)

Cooper-Hewitt, National Design Museum, Smithsonian Institution, gift of Charles Savage Homer, Jr., 1912-12-13

PROVENANCE
Charles S. Homer, Jr., by bequest, 1910

EXHIBITIONS
Carnegie 1937, no. 151; Cooper-Hewitt 1972, no. 49; Columbia/Telfair 1974, no. 23; South Texas 1978, no. 7; Greenville County 1986; Terra 1990, no. 26

No. 935. Four Rowboats with Children

936

Boy and Girl in a Rowboat

[1880]

Two Boys Fishing

Watercolor, 9¹⁵⁄₁₆ × 14 (25.243 × 35.560)

Cooper-Hewitt, National Design Museum, Smithsonian Institution, gift of Charles Savage Homer, Jr., 1912-12-222

PROVENANCE
Charles S. Homer, Jr., by bequest, 1910

EXHIBITIONS
Carnegie 1937, no. 169; Cooper-Hewitt 1972, no. 47; Columbia/Telfair 1974, no. 21; South Texas 1978, no. 2; Greenville County 1986; Terra 1990, no. 24

No. 936. Boy and Girl in a Rowboat

No. 937. Two Girls in a Rowboat

937
Two Girls in a Rowboat
[1880]

Watercolor, 9⁹⁄₁₆ × 13 (24.290 × 33.020)

Cooper-Hewitt, National Design Museum,
Smithsonian Institution, gift of Charles Savage
Homer, Jr., 1912-12-223

PROVENANCE
Charles S. Homer, Jr., by bequest, 1910

EXHIBITIONS
Carnegie 1937, no. 171; Cooper-Hewitt 1972, no. 48;
Columbia/Telfair 1974, no. 22; South Texas 1978,
no. 18; Everson 1983, no. 1; Terra 1990, no. 25

938

Two Boys Rowing

[1880]

Watercolor, 10 × 13¾ (25.400 × 34.925)
Inscribed lr: Homer

Private collection

PROVENANCE
(Doll & Richards, Boston, 1880); Gen. Francis W.
Palfrey, Boston, 1880; Hope Gardner (Mrs. Paul
Gardner), New York, his granddaughter, nd; (Sotheby
Parke-Bernet, 20 Apr. 1979, sale 4236, no. 51)

EXHIBITIONS
Doll & Richards 1880

No. 938. Two Boys Rowing

939

Rowboat

1880

Watercolor, 9⅞ × 13¹⁵⁄₁₆ (25.083 × 35.403)
Inscribed lr: Homer / 1880

Bowdoin College Museum of Art, Brunswick, ME,
Henry Hill Pierce, Jr., in memory of William John
Curtis, Class of 1875, 1991.45

PROVENANCE
(Doll & Richards, Boston, 1880) [?]; (Montross
Gallery, nd); William J. Curtis, New York, nd;
Mrs. William J. Curtis, New York, by bequest,
1927; Henry Hill Pierce, Jr., New Haven, CT, her
grandson, by bequest, 1941

EXHIBITIONS
Doll & Richards 1880

No. 939. Rowboat

No. 940. Two Boys Rowing

940

Two Boys Rowing

1880

Watercolor, 9⅞ × 14 (25.083 × 35.560)
Inscribed lr: Homer 1880

Museum of Fine Arts, Boston, gift of James J.
Minot, 1974.588

PROVENANCE
(Doll & Richards, Boston, 1880); Alexander
Cochrane, Boston, 1880; Hugh Cochrane, Boston,
his brother, by gift, nd; Eleanor M. Cochrane Sears
(Mrs. Richard D. Sears), Boston, his daughter, by
bequest, by 1938; Miriam Sears Minot (Mrs. James J.
Minot), Beverly, MA, her daughter, by 1965

EXHIBITIONS
Doll & Richards 1880; MFA, Boston, 1977, no. 51

No. 941. Off Gloucester Harbor

941

Off Gloucester Harbor

[1880]

Watercolor, 9¼ × 13½ (23.495 × 34.290) sight
Inscribed lr: Homer

Private collection

ABG: This work was stolen from its owner's home
in 1969. It was reclaimed in 1995, having remained
in the sphere of the thief or thieves throughout
the previous twenty-six years. At some time in that
period minor details were added to its background:
several sails on the horizon line at the far left, and
a scattering of flying birds. Presumably these changes
were made in hope of disguising the painting for
possible introduction into the art market. They were
so easily removed, it appeared that whoever did
the "retouching" took care to use a medium which
would not intrude below the surface of the painting.
Consequently, the work has been returned to its
original character.

PROVENANCE
(Doll & Richards, Boston, 1880) [?]; Dr. Henry C.
Angell, Boston, by 1911; (F. W. Bayley & Son,
Boston, nd) [?]; Horace D. Chapin, Boston, nd;
Margaret Chapin Osgood (Mrs. Robert B. Osgood),
Boston, his sister, c. 1936; private collection, 1957

EXHIBITIONS
Doll & Richards 1880; MFA, Boston, 1959, no. 93

LITERATURE
Ralph Blumenthal, "A Stolen Homer Returns
Home, But Less Authentic Than Before," *New York
Times*, 15 Feb. 1995

942

Boating Boys at Gloucester

1880

Fishermen in Boats; Lobster Men

Watercolor, 10 × 13½ (25.400 × 34.290)
Inscribed lr: Homer 1880

Private collection

This watercolor is visible in one of the two photographs of the apartment in the Benedict building Homer shared with Samuel T. Preston for part of 1880 and 1881, and again following his return in late 1882 from his extended stay in England.

PROVENANCE
Charles S. Homer, Jr., by bequest, 1910; Walter H. Crittenden, Brooklyn, by gift, c. 1911; Mrs. William Allen Putnam, Jr., Cornwall, NY, his niece, by gift, after 1937; (Hirschl & Adler Galleries, 1964); Sally Semple Aall, nd; private collection, 1998; (Christie's, 29 Nov. 2007, sale 1911, no. 71)

EXHIBITIONS
Brooklyn 1915, no. 58 (as *Fishermen in Boats*); Katonah 1963, no. 11 (as *Maine Fishermen*)

No. 942. Boating Boys at Gloucester

No. 943. Boy Fishing from a Boat

943
Boy Fishing from a Boat
1880

Watercolor, 8½ × 12¾ (21.590 × 32.385) sight
Inscribed lr: Homer 1880

Private collection

PROVENANCE
(William Macbeth, Inc., nd); William Harris
Arnold, Nutley, NJ, before 1910; Mrs. William
Harris Arnold, Cambridge, MA, by 1938;
(Wildenstein & Co., c. 1946)

EXHIBITIONS
Wildenstein 1948, no. 11; Wildenstein 1949, no. 12;
Wildenstein 1947, no. 53

944
Boy in a Dory
1880

Watercolor, 9¾ × 13¾ (24.765 × 34.925)
Inscribed lr: Homer 1880

Wadsworth Atheneum, Hartford, bequest of Charles
C. Cunningham, 1980.6

ABG: Like No. 933 and No. 934, *Boy in a Dory*
and *Boy in a Small Boat* (No. 945) are examples of
Homer replicating an image. Two so nearly identical
paintings invite an assumption that one is a copy
by a hand other than Homer's. However, the stylistic
character of the two paintings belies that explanation.
The widely disparate histories of the two also suggest
their independence.

The perception of these two watercolors may be
clouded by the existence of a third rendering of the
image which was created at approximately the same
time as they, but is a documented copy of No. 944.

In 1936 LG wrote William Minot (apparently the
third of that name), the son of William Minot, Jr.,
who had purchased a work from the December 1880
Doll & Richards exhibition and sale of Homer's

Gloucester works. The inquiry was referred to the eldest of Mr. Minot, Jr.'s four children, Mrs. Henry M. Channing. She responded that she knew nothing of any Homer held in the family. (LG's inquiry may have occasioned No. 944—which is surely the work purchased in 1880 by Mr. Minot, Jr.—becoming available for purchase in 1936.)

Mrs. Channing did not forget LG's inquiry, and in February 1954 wrote him the following.

My attic has yielded a water color 8 by 11½ of a boy in a sailing skiff which he steers with an oar. It is unsigned and therefore I hesitated about writing to you until I found my father's sketching notebook of 1880. My father led an active business life, but painted for relaxation. Though totally untaught he was interested in the subject and kept a book in which he put down his observations or results of talks with those who knew more of the subject than he. In 1880 under *Homer* he has jotted down the following: "first light wash of Y[ellow] O[chre]. let dry. Then sky & water Prussian Blue. Take up edges with dry brush - let dry - Repeat. let dry. R[ose] M[adder] Sep[ia]

light wash - let dry. Shade up with 2nd light wash of same. For sail R[aw] S[ienna] - afterward R[aw] S[ienna] & L[ight] R[ed] Boat Sep[ia] Ind[igo] & Cr[imson] L[ake] and L. R. on mast & oar. Ven[etian] Red in shadow of sail. Br[own] madder added for boy's face. Shadows in water same as boat, but Y[ellow] O[chre] first. (They are green)

LG understood this account of pigments used to render features corresponding to those of No. 944 to be Mr. Minot's record of having made a copy of the painting he had just purchased to see how Homer had done it. (Copying was a long-recognized training exercise.) Apparently it did not occur to Mrs. Channing that the work she had found in her attic could be something other than the object LG had been seeking in 1936, and as she did not request his opinion, he did not disabuse her of the idea.

Nearly a decade later Mrs. Channing's discovery appeared in the art market, accompanied by copies of LG's initial inquiries after the work her father had purchased in 1880. The watercolor discovered in Mrs. Channing's attic passed through the hands of several dealers; by 1970 it had acquired a "signature"

No. 944. Boy in a Dory

and inscribed dating of 1880 at lower left—and the company of two additional, but completely fabricated letters. One, dated to 1936, purports to be from LG to Mrs. Channing praising the watercolor which she had in her possession, and had let him examine; the other is dated to 1954, is supposedly from Mrs. Channing to LG, and tells him only that she has "finally found the picture in question."

The Homer catalogue raisonné last knew of the whereabouts of this copy in 1991.

PROVENANCE
(Doll & Richards, Boston, 1880); William Minot, Boston, 1880; (Peter Caras, Boston, c. 1936); Charles C. Cunningham, Brookline, MA, 1936

EXHIBITIONS
Doll & Richards 1880; Vermont Art Center 1957, no. 17; Katonah 1963, no. 19

945+
Boy in a Small Boat
[1880]

Watercolor, 9¼ × 13½ (23.495 × 34.290)

Private collection

ABG: See commentary No. 944.

PROVENANCE
private collection, c. 1935; (Maggie Milgrim, 2002); (A. J. Kollar Fine Paintings, Seattle, 2004)

No. 945. Boy in a Small Boat

No. 946. Sailing a Dory

946

Sailing a Dory

[1880]

Watercolor, 9¼ × 13¼ (23.495 × 33.655)

Private collection

ABG: LG recognized this work as a Gloucester subject but had not committed to dating it to Homer's visit of 1873 or 1880. Albert Ten Eyck Gardner assigned it to 1873. I believe that in style it bears a greater affinity to Homer's Gloucester watercolors of 1880.

PROVENANCE
Charles S. Homer, Jr., by bequest, 1910; Mrs. Charles S. Homer, Jr., by bequest, 1917; Maria W. Blanchard, New York, by gift, by 1936; Ralph Whittier, Bangor, ME, by gift, c. 1945; Ralph Whittier Estate, 1950; (Maynard Walker Galleries, 1950); private collection, 1952; (Christie's, 26 May 1999, sale 9156, no. 11); a corporate collection, 1999; (Christie's, 2 Dec. 2004, sale 1440, no. 65)

EXHIBITIONS
Maynard Walker 1953, no. 13; NGA 1958/MFA, Boston, 1959, no. 86/79

LITERATURE
Gardner 1961, 71

947

Boy in a Sailing Skiff

[1880]

Graphite, watercolor, 8¾ × 6⅛
(22.225 × 15.558) sight

Unlocated

PROVENANCE
Charles S. Homer, Jr., by bequest, 1910; Mrs.
Charles S. Homer, Jr., by bequest, 1917; J. Hartley
Merrick, Prout's Neck, ME, by gift, 1931; Lucy M.
Bostwick, Haverford, PA, his niece, by bequest,
1946; Mortimer W. Pratt, Prout's Neck, ME, by gift,
1971; (Frank S. Schwarz & Son, Philadelphia, 1980)

No. 948. Sailing

No. 947. Boy in a Sailing Skiff

948

Sailing

[1880]

Graphite, watercolor, 9¹³⁄₁₆ × 7⅝ (24.925 × 19.368)

Private collection

Arthur P. Homer consigned this drawing to the
Macbeth gallery in New York, in 1940, just a few
months before he died. Homer's nephews had a
predilection for embellishing the remains of the
Homer estate in their possession with stories of personal associations. Arthur told Robert McIntyre of
the Macbeth gallery that the subject of this drawing
was himself in his very first sailboat, and thus, on
water in the vicinity of Prout's Neck, Maine, where
his parents summered. Arthur Patch Homer was born
in 1876. The style and use of media in this drawing
characterize it clearly as a work of Homer's 1880
summer spent in Gloucester, Massachusetts—nowhere
near his younger brother's family. Nor is it likely a

child of four years of age would have been out sailing alone, either in Gloucester harbor or off Prout's Neck.

The Macbeth gallery returned the drawing unsold, probably in consequence of Arthur's death and the settling of his estate. Mrs. David Williams told LG she had purchased it in about 1951 from a benefit sale for a New York music school held annually in Prout's Neck and organized by several of her fellow summer residents. Apparently the drawing had reverted to Arthur's brother, Charles L. Homer, as he had donated it to the sale. Charles had his own story to dress up the drawing: he told Mrs. Williams it had recently come back to the family after having been lost in a Boston framers shop for thirty years.

PROVENANCE
Charles S. Homer, Jr., by bequest, 1910; Mrs. Charles S. Homer, Jr., by bequest, 1917; Arthur P. and Charles L. Homer, by bequest, 1937; Alice Redfield Grimm Williams (Mrs. David E. Williams), Bryn Mawr, PA, c. 1951; Sara Grimm, her daughter, 1961; Sonia Grimm Villalba, Santa Fe, NM, her daughter, 2002; (Menconi & Schoelkopf Fine Art, 2004)

949+
Sailing by Moonlight
1880

Watercolor, 9⅝ × 13¾ (24.448 × 34.925)
Inscribed ll: W. H. / 1880

Private collection

PROVENANCE
Elizabeth McKean, Boston area, nd; (Sotheby's, 1 Dec. 1988, sale 5787, no. 67)

No. 949. Sailing by Moonlight

No. 950. Sailing Dories

950
Sailing Dories
1880

Watercolor, 9¼ × 13⅛ (23.495 × 33.338)
Inscribed ll: Homer 1880

Unlocated

PROVENANCE
(Doll & Richards, Boston, 1880); Edward W. Hooper,
Boston, 1880; Ellen Sturgis Hooper Potter (Mrs. John
Briggs Potter), Boston, his daughter, by bequest, 1901;
Mary Potter Swann (Mrs. George Cushing Swann),
her daughter, by 1977; Nicholas Hubby, Boston, by
1983; (Vose Galleries of Boston, 1984); (R. M. Light
& Co., Inc., Sacramento, CA, 1984); (Christopher
Middendorf, Washington, DC, 1984)

EXHIBITIONS
Doll & Richards 1880; MFA, Boston, 1911; Copley
Society 1921, no. 16; MFA, Boston, 1924; MFA,
Boston, 1936; MFA, Boston, 1959, no. 95

No. 951. Boy and Sailboat

951
Boy and Sailboat
1880

Watercolor, 8¾ × 13¾ (22.225 × 34.925)
Inscribed lr: Homer 188[0]

Private collection

952+

Boys in Boats
1880

Watercolor, 9½ × 13¾ (24.130 × 34.925)
Inscribed ll: Homer 1880

Private collection

ABG: When this watercolor came to light in 2004 it was said to have come into Mrs. Howard Swinney's possession through the Valentine family, because she was related to the Valentines. Such an assumption has merit but is unsupported.

PROVENANCE
Gladys Swinney (Mrs. Howard Swinney), nd; Carmelita Hopkins Kingsley, Harwich, MA, her niece, by gift, 1997; (Sotheby's, 1 Dec. 2004, sale 8032, no. 106)

EXHIBITIONS
Doll & Richards 1880

No. 952. Boys in Boats

953
Schooner and Three Dinghies
[1880]

Graphite, 14 × 10 (35.560 × 25.400)

Cooper-Hewitt, National Design Museum, Smithsonian Institution, gift of Charles Savage Homer, Jr., 1912-12-11

PROVENANCE
Charles S. Homer, Jr., by bequest, 1910

954
Sketches of Sailing Craft
[1880]

Graphite, 8⅜ × 9⅝ (21.273 × 24.448)

Cooper-Hewitt, National Design Museum, Smithsonian Institution, gift of Charles Savage Homer, Jr., 1912-12-192

PROVENANCE
Charles S. Homer, Jr., by bequest, 1910

No. 953. Schooner and Three Dinghies

No. 955. Sketches of Sailing Boats

No. 956. Four Sketches of Sloops

955

Sketches of Sailing Boats

[1880]

Graphite, 10 × 14 (25.400 × 35.560)

Cooper-Hewitt, National Design Museum,
Smithsonian Institution, gift of Charles Savage
Homer, Jr., 1912-12-194

PROVENANCE
Charles S. Homer, Jr., by bequest, 1910

956

Four Sketches of Sloops

[1880]

Graphite, watercolor, 9⁹⁄₁₆ × 5⅝ (24.290 × 14.288)

Cooper-Hewitt, National Design Museum,
Smithsonian Institution, gift of Charles Savage
Homer, Jr., 1912-12-10

PROVENANCE
Charles S. Homer, Jr., by bequest, 1910

957

Two-masted Schooner

[1880]

Graphite, 5 × 7⅞ (12.700 × 20.003)

Cooper-Hewitt, National Design Museum, Smithsonian Institution, gift of Charles Savage Homer, Jr., 1912-12-190

PROVENANCE
Charles S. Homer, Jr., by bequest, 1910

No. 957. Two-masted Schooner

958

Three Sketches of Schooners

[1880]

Graphite, 9⅞ × 8¼ (25.083 × 20.955)

Cooper-Hewitt, National Design Museum, Smithsonian Institution, gift of Charles Savage Homer, Jr., 1912-12-9

PROVENANCE
Charles S. Homer, Jr., by bequest, 1910

EXHIBITIONS
Terra 1990, no. 23

959

Four Schooners

[1880]

Graphite, 7¾ × 14 (19.685 × 35.560)

Cooper-Hewitt, National Design Museum, Smithsonian Institution, gift of Charles Savage Homer, Jr., 1912-12-7

PROVENANCE
Charles S. Homer, Jr., by bequest, 1910

No. 959. Four Schooners

960

Two Schooners and Dories

[1880]

Graphite, 5¹³⁄₁₆ × 13¾ (14.765 × 34.925)

Cooper-Hewitt, National Design Museum, Smithsonian Institution, gift of Charles Savage Homer, Jr., 1912-12-5

PROVENANCE
Charles S. Homer, Jr., by bequest, 1910

EXHIBITIONS
Academy of Arts & Letters 1953, no. 171c; Ogunquit 1954, no. 30b; Ithaca 1971, no. 25b; Cooper-Hewitt 1972, no. 51

961

Schooner with Dinghy

[1880]

Graphite, 9⅝ × 13⅝ (24.448 × 34.608)

Cooper-Hewitt, National Design Museum, Smithsonian Institution, gift of Charles Savage Homer, Jr., 1912-12-191

PROVENANCE
Charles S. Homer, Jr., by bequest, 1910

EXHIBITIONS
University Club 1938, no. 14; Ithaca 1971, no. 26; Terra 1990, no. 37

962

Six Studies of Sailboats

[1880]

Graphite, 8¼ × 11 (20.955 × 27.940)

Cooper-Hewitt, National Design Museum, Smithsonian Institution, gift of Charles Savage Homer, Jr., 1912-12-6

PROVENANCE
Charles S. Homer, Jr., by bequest, 1910

963

Point of Land with Lighthouse

[1880]

Graphite, 9⅝ × 13¾ (24.448 × 34.925)

Cooper-Hewitt, National Design Museum, Smithsonian Institution, gift of Charles Savage Homer, Jr., 1912-12-195

PROVENANCE
Charles S. Homer, Jr., by bequest, 1910

No. 960. Two Schooners and Dories

No. 961. Schooner with Dinghy

964
Two Schooners
[1880]

Graphite, watercolor, 9⅜ × 13¼ (23.813 × 33.655)

Cooper-Hewitt, National Design Museum, Smithsonian Institution, gift of Charles Savage Homer, Jr., 1912-12-193

PROVENANCE
Charles S. Homer, Jr., by bequest, 1910

EXHIBITIONS
Carnegie 1937, no. 180; University Club 1938, no. 15

965
Schooner with Three Dories
1880

Graphite, watercolor, 5⅛ × 9⅜ (13.018 × 23.813)
Inscribed lr: Winslow Homer 1880

Cooper-Hewitt, National Design Museum, Smithsonian Institution, gift of Charles Savage Homer, Jr., 1912-12-12

PROVENANCE
Charles S. Homer, Jr., by bequest, 1910

EXHIBITIONS
Academy of Arts & Letters 1953, no. 171b; Ogunquit 1954, no. 30c; Ithaca 1971, no. 25c; Cooper-Hewitt 1972, no. 52; Terra 1990, no. 38

No. 966. Fishing Fleet at Gloucester

966+

Fishing Fleet at Gloucester

1880

Graphite, watercolor, 5⅝ × 13⅛ (14.288 × 33.338)
Inscribed lr: Homer 1880

Colby College Museum of Art, Waterville, ME,
The Lunder Collection

PROVENANCE
(Doll & Richards, Boston, 1880); Edward W.
Hooper, Boston, 1880; Robert F. Balfour, Balbirnie,
Scotland, his godson, by gift, 1892; Alice Balfour,
Balbirnie, Scotland, his sister, by bequest, 1914;
Alan John Balfour, her great-nephew, by gift, nd;
(Christie's, 27 Sept. 1996, sale 8478, no. 41);
(Thomas Colville Fine Art, LLC, New Haven, 1996)

EXHIBITIONS
Doll & Richards 1880

967

Mackerel Fleet at Gloucester

1880

Graphite, watercolor, 9⅞ × 14 (25.083 × 35.560)
Inscribed ll: W. H. 1880

Peabody Essex Museum, bequest of Julia Bird, M20241

PROVENANCE
Charles S. Homer, Jr., by bequest, 1910; Mrs. Charles
S. Homer, Jr., by bequest, 1917; Charles L. Homer, by
bequest, 1937; (William Macbeth, Inc., 1938); (David
B. Findlay Galleries, 1943); Julia Bird, before 1984

EXHIBITIONS
Prout's Neck 1936, no. 18

968

Sailboats

[1880]

Graphite, watercolor, 8¼ × 13¾
(20.955 × 34.925) sight
Inscribed lr: W. H.

Private collection

PROVENANCE
(William Macbeth, Inc., 1902/07) [?]; (Thompson,
Detroit, 1943); (E. C. Babcock Art Galleries, 1943);
(Ivan Podgoursky, nd)

No. 967. Mackerel Fleet at Gloucester

No. 968. Sailboats

No. 969. Schooners in Gloucester Harbor

969

Schooners in Gloucester Harbor

[1880]

Graphite, watercolor, 9½ × 13½
(24.130 × 34.290) sight
Inscribed lr: Winslow Homer N. A.

Private collection

PROVENANCE
Jacob Otis Wardwell, Haverhill, MA, nd; Sheldon E.
Wardwell, Brookline, MA, his son, by bequest, 1940;
(Charles D. Childs Gallery, Boston, 1941); Donald
B. Willson, Medford, MA, 1941; Caroline Robie,
Hill, NH, his widow, by 1962; (M. Knoedler &
Co., 1963); Mr. and Mrs. Charles C. Cunningham,
Jr., Brookline, MA, 1963; (Hirschl & Adler Galleries,
by 1987)

EXHIBITIONS
Whitney 1973, no. 170; Knoedler 1986, no. 55

970

New England Coast— Sailing Ships in Harbor

1880

Graphite, watercolor, 7¼ × 13⅜ (18.415 × 33.973)
Inscribed ur: Homer / 1880

Farnsworth Art Museum, Rockland, ME, 46.649

PROVENANCE
Larchmont Yacht Club, Larchmont, NY, nd; (Kende
Galleries at Gimbel Brothers, 5–6 Dec. 1941, sale 36,
no. 200); Thomas E. Finger, 1941; (Plaza Galleries,
Mar. 1943, Finger estate sale); Leroy Ireland, 1943;
(William Macbeth, Inc., 1943); (David B. Findlay
Galleries, 1943)

EXHIBITIONS
University of Arizona 1963, no. 49; Farnsworth 1970,
no. 28; South Texas 1978, no. 14; Terra 1990, no. 34;
Farnsworth 2006

No. 970. New England Coast—Sailing Ships in Harbor

No. 971. Schooners Off Shore

971

Schooners Off Shore

1880

Graphite, watercolor, 8½ × 13¾ (21.590 × 34.925)
Inscribed lr: Winslow Homer 1880

Private collection

PROVENANCE
(Doll & Richards, Boston, 1880); Charles W.
Seabury, Boston, 1880; Dr. and Mrs. Henry A.
Christian, Boston, his daughter and son-in-law, nd;
(Wildenstein & Co., c. 1950); Frederick Warburg,
New York, 1954; Mrs. Frederick Warburg, New York,
nd; (Sotheby's, 20 May 1998, sale 7135, no. 99)

EXHIBITIONS
Doll & Richards 1880

No. 972. Seascape with Boats

972
Seascape with Boats
1880

Harbor

Graphite, watercolor, 4¹⁵⁄₁₆ × 9¹³⁄₁₆ (12.543 × 24.925)
Inscribed ll: Homer 1880

Harvard University Art Museums, Fogg Art
Museum, Cambridge, MA, bequest of Aimée and
Rosamond Lamb, 1993.51

PROVENANCE
(Doll & Richards, Boston, 1880); Andrew C.
Wheelwright, Boston, 1880; Mary C. Wheelwright,
Majorca, Spain, his daughter, nd; (Giovanni
Castano, Boston, c. 1937); Aimée Lamb, Milton,
MA, nd

EXHIBITIONS
Doll & Richards 1880; MFA, Boston, 1959, no. 159

973
Three Boys
1880

Watercolor, 7 × 13¼ (17.780 × 33.655) sight
Inscribed lr: W. H. 1880

Private collection

PROVENANCE
C. J. McDonough, nd; (William Macbeth, Inc., nd);
(Milch Galleries, 1919); Horatio S. Rubens, New
York, 1919; Joan Rubens Rogers, his daughter, c. 1940;
(E. C. Babcock Art Galleries, c. 1944); (Wildenstein
& Co., c. 1944); Mr. and Mrs. Dunbar Bostwick,
New York, 1956

EXHIBITIONS
Wildenstein 1947, no. 52; Wildenstein 1948, no. 10;
Wildenstein 1949, no. 11; Houston 1952, no. 20

No. 973. Three Boys

No. 974. Gloucester Boys

974

Gloucester Boys

1880

Watercolor, 5⅞ × 12⅞ (14.923 × 32.703) sight
Inscribed lr: Winslow Homer 1880

Private collection

PROVENANCE
C. J. McDonough, nd; (William Macbeth, Inc., nd);
(Milch Galleries, 1919); Horatio S. Rubens, New
York, 1919; Joan Rubens Rogers, his daughter, c. 1940;
(E. C. Babcock Art Galleries, c. 1944); (Wildenstein
& Co., c. 1944); Arthur Sachs, Paris, 1955; James H.
Sachs, his son, c. 1975; (Sotheby's, 29 Nov. 1995, sale
6782, no. 103)

EXHIBITIONS
Wildenstein 1948, no. 9; Wildenstein 1949, no. 10;
Houston 1952, no. 19

975
Clear Sailing
[1880]

Watercolor, 7⅝ × 11⅛ (19.368 × 28.258)
Inscribed lr: Homer

Philadelphia Museum of Art, gift of Dr. and Mrs.
George Woodward, 1939.7.8

PROVENANCE
(Ainslie Galleries, by 1911); (William Macbeth,
Inc., 1911); William H. Childs, New York, 1913;
(William Macbeth, Inc., 1920); Dr. and Mrs.
George Woodward, Chestnut Hill, PA, 1920

EXHIBITIONS
Alliance, Philadelphia 1923, no. 15

No. 975. Clear Sailing

No. 976. Boys Watching A Steamboat

976+

Boys Watching A Steamboat

1880

Watercolor, 9½ × 13½ (24.130 × 34.290)
Inscribed lr: Winslow Homer 1880

Private collection

EXHIBITIONS
Doll & Richards 1880

977
Two Boys Watching Schooners
1880

Marblehead

Watercolor, 8½ × 13 (21.590 × 33.020)
Inscribed ll: Homer / 1880; lr, on boat: Homer

The Art Institute of Chicago, Mr. and Mrs. Martin
A. Ryerson Collection, 1933.1244

PROVENANCE
Charles S. Homer, Jr., by bequest, 1910 [?]; Charles
W. Gould, New York, nd; (M. Knoedler & Co.,
1915); Martin A. Ryerson, Chicago, 1915

EXHIBITIONS
Brooklyn 1915, no. 48; AI Chicago 1916; Carnegie 1917,
no. 9; AI Chicago 1920; Hackley 1921; Omaha 1924;
AI Chicago 1926; Albright 1929, no. 21; Saint Louis
1932; Pennsylvania 1936, no. 56; AI Chicago 1936,
no. 12; Herron 1936; Carnegie 1937, no. 51; Century
1951, no. 7; Terra 1990, no. 33; AI Chicago 2008

No. 977. Two Boys Watching Schooners

978

Boy Hailing Schooners

1880

Watercolor, 9⅝ × 8⁵⁄₁₆ (24.448 × 21.115)
Inscribed ll: 1880 / Homer

Private collection

PROVENANCE
Unidentified dealer, c. 1984; Edward H. Jenove,
Parlin, NJ, c. 1984; (Christie's, 7 Dec. 1984, sale
5794, no. 65)

No. 978. Boy Hailing Schooners

979

Boys Hailing a Sloop

1880

Two Figures and Sailboat

Watercolor, 8⅞ × 7 (22.543 × 17.780) sight
Inscribed ll: Winslow Homer 1880

Private collection

ABG: This may be presumed to have been one of the three watercolors by Homer on offer, and on view, at the Kabatznick Gallery in Boston in the early 1920s. (The others were No. 909 and No. 910). William Howe Downes described the three in his review for the Boston *Evening Transcript*; he wrote the following about these *Boys Hailing a Sloop*.

> One of the most characteristic examples [of Homer's Gloucester watercolors of 1880] is the little upright composition showing two barefoot boys standing in the shallow water near the edge of the sand beach, waving their hats energetically as if signalling to some friends in a distant sloop yacht. The moist sand in the foreground, a gray sea, and a sky in which warmish gray clouds form a thin veil, admitting the faint sunlight here and there, are all observed with Homer's characteristic keenness for naturalism. The placing of the two boys' figures, their attitudes and movements, and their organic relationship to the landscape scene, are no less convincing. While the drawing of these tiny figures is undeniably far from academic, it is highly expressive and vital.

Downes's article may be presumed to date from no later than 1922, the year he retired from the *Transcript*.

PROVENANCE
Louis Kronberg, nd; (Doll & Richards, Boston, 1918); Mrs. Roland Nickerson, 1918; (Kabatznick Gallery, Boston, c. 1920); unidentified private collection, nd; Dr. Hugh Williams, Boston, by gift, c. 1926; (Giovanni Castano, Boston, 1946); (Ivan Podgoursky, 1946); Dr. George H. A. Clowes, Indianapolis, c. 1946; (Newhouse Galleries, 1959); Mr. and Mrs. Julius H. Cohn, South Orange, NJ, by 1963; (Hirschl & Adler Galleries, 1973); private collection, 1976

LITERATURE
W[illiam] H[owe] D[ownes], "The Fine Arts. Watercolors by Homer. Three Early Works . . . on View at Kabatznick's Gallery," [*(Boston) Daily Evening Transcript*], clipped

No. 979. Boys Hailing a Sloop

No. 980. Gloucester, Group of Boats

980

Gloucester, Group of Boats

[1880]

Watercolor, 7 × 13½ (17.780 × 34.290)
Inscribed ll: Winslow Homer

Unlocated

PROVENANCE
Charles S. Homer, Jr., by bequest, 1910; (M.
Knoedler & Co., 1913); W. H. Dicks, Chicago, 1913

981

Gloucester Fishing Fleet

1880

Watercolor, 13 × 19 (33.020 × 48.260)
Inscribed lr: Winslow Homer / 1880

Private collection

PROVENANCE
(Doll & Richards, Boston, 1880); Francis Bartlett,
Boston, 1880; Herbert M. Sears, Boston, his son-in-
law, by bequest, 1914; Phyllis Sears Tuckerman (Mrs.
Bayard Tuckerman), Beverly, MA, Francis Bartlett's
granddaughter, c. 1942

EXHIBITIONS
Doll & Richards 1880

No. 981. Gloucester Fishing Fleet

982

Gloucester Harbor, Fishing Fleet

1880

Moonlight Schooners, Gloucester

Watercolor, 12¼ × 19¼ (31.115 × 48.895)
Inscribed lr; Winslow Homer 1880

Private collection

PROVENANCE
Charles S. Homer, Jr., by bequest, 1910; Mrs. Charles
S. Homer, Jr., by bequest, 1917; Charles L. Homer, by
bequest, 1937; (Giovanni Castano, Boston, by 1950);
International Business Machines Corporation, New
York, 1950; (Sotheby's, 25 May 1995, sale 6713, no. 53)

EXHIBITIONS
Sweat Museum [Portland Museum of Art], Portland,
Maine, [loan collection of paintings by Winslow
Homer], Oct. 1922 [?]; Ogunquit 1954, no. p-3 (as
Moonlight Schooners, Gloucester); Bowdoin/Colby
1954 (as *Moonlight Schooners, Gloucester*); NGA 1958,
no. 101; Miami 1991

No. 982. Gloucester Harbor, Fishing Fleet

see color illustration, p. 466

No. 983. Gloucester Fleet at Night

983
Gloucester Fleet at Night
[1880]

Watercolor, 10½ × 19¾ (26.670 × 50.165)
Inscribed lr: Winslow Homer / by C. S. H. Executor

Private collection

PROVENANCE
Charles S. Homer, Jr., by bequest, 1910; Mrs.
Charles S. Homer, Jr., by bequest, 1917; Arthur P.
and Charles L. Homer, by bequest, 1937; (Milch
Galleries, 1956); Mr. and Mrs. Solton Engel, New
York, 1956; Mr. and Mrs. R. Frederick Woolworth,
New York, c. 1960; Elizabeth, Dowager Duchess
of Manchester, Pebble Beach, CA, Mrs. Woolworth's
mother, by gift, nd; Marilyn Karos, Milwaukee,
WI, 1995

EXHIBITIONS
Sweat Museum [Portland Museum of Art], Portland,
Maine, [loan collection of paintings by Winslow
Homer], Oct. 1922 [?]; Behn-Moore 1953

984
Schooners at Anchor
1880

Watercolor, 9⅛ × 13¼ (23.178 × 33.655)
Inscribed ll: Winslow Homer 1880

Private collection

PROVENANCE
Mrs. Samuel Fleet Speir, before 1911; Genevieve
A. Rounds (Mrs. Wellington Rounds), her grand-
daughter, nd; (Milch Galleries, 1957); George W.
Volkel, Westfield, NJ, 1957; (Swain's Art Store,
Plainfield, NJ, c. 1966)

No. 984. Schooners at Anchor

No. 985. Sailboats at Gloucester

985
Sailboats at Gloucester
[1880]

Watercolor, 8 × 13¼ (20.320 × 33.655) sight

Private collection

No. 986. Schooner at Gloucester

986

Schooner at Gloucester

[1880]

Schooner on Saco Bay

Watercolor, 9¼ × 13¼ (23.495 × 33.655) sight

Private collection

When LG examined this work in 1936 it bore no signature; at that time it belonged to Mrs. Charles S. Homer, Jr. Following Mrs. Homer's death the following year it came into the possession of her nephew, Charles L. Homer, who sold it probably not long after to the person who was its owner at the time it was photographed in about 1961. That photograph clearly shows an attached strip of paper bearing the inscription "Winslow Homer." in genuine script. This was probably cut from a letter or other document, and added to the water-color by Charles L. Homer, thinking it would enhance the value of the work.

Although the bond between this watercolor and its signature is artificial, both are surely the product of Homer's hand.

ABG: The Homer family favored assigning Prout's Neck locations to those among the paintings they inherited which showed substantial expanses of water. Thus Mrs. Charles S. Homer, Jr. gave this watercolor a title identifying it with Saco Bay. The mistaken titling—which implied a much later dating for the work—prevailed until LG recognized it as part of the body of watercolors Homer produced in Gloucester in the summer of 1880.

PROVENANCE
Charles S. Homer, Jr., by bequest, 1910; Mrs. Charles S. Homer, Jr., by bequest, 1917; Charles L. Homer, by bequest, 1937

EXHIBITIONS
Prout's Neck 1936, no. 14 (as *Schooner on Saco Bay*); Macbeth 1936, no. 53 (as *Schooner on Saco Bay*); Macbeth 1938, no. 7 (as *Schooner on Saco Bay*)

987
Small Sloop
[1880]

Small Sloop, Saco Bay

Watercolor, 9½ × 13½ (24.130 × 34.290)
Inscribed lr: Homer

Private collection

ABG: Like No. 986, the setting of this watercolor was mistakenly accepted as the Maine coast near Prout's Neck because of a title assigned to it in the mid-1930s by the Homer family.

PROVENANCE
Charles S. Homer, Jr., by bequest, 1910; Mrs. Charles S. Homer, Jr., by bequest, 1917; (William Macbeth, Inc., by exchange, 1937); Mabel Brady Garvan (Mrs. Francis P. Garvan), New York, 1937; (Wildenstein & Co., c. 1946); Ernest G. Vietor, Greenwich, CT, 1951; (Christie's, 30 May 1986, sale 6142, no. 32); (David Findlay, Jr., Inc., 1986); private collection, nd; (Gerald Peters Gallery, Santa Fe, NM, nd); AOL Time Warner, New York, by 2003; (Christie's, 22 May 2003, sale 1236, no. 60)

EXHIBITIONS
Prout's Neck 1936, no. 11 (as *Small Sloop, Saco Bay*); Macbeth 1936, no. 54 (as *Small Sloop—Saco Bay*, c. 1879); Wildenstein 1948, no. 13 (as *Small Sloop, Saco Bay*); Wildenstein 1949, no. 9 (as *Small Sloop, Saco Bay*)

No. 987. Small Sloop

see color illustration, p. 467

No. 988. Seascape, Sunset

988

Seascape, Sunset

[1880]

Watercolor, 11⅞ × 21⅜ (30.163 × 54.293)

Private collection

Cameron Turner wrote LG in 1970, confirming that an inscription on the brown-paper covering over the back of this watercolor had been written by his father, the distinguished Boston watercolorist and teacher, Ross Turner (1847–1915). The text of this inscription was: "This picture was given to me by Mr. Winslow Homer at his studio at Prout's Neck Maine in the month of July 1888. [signed] Ross Turner."

Ross Turner told William Howe Downes he had received a watercolor painting from Homer as a gift on the occasion of a day-long visit in Prout's Neck on an August day in about 1896. Turner gave Downes a clear, detailed description of *Children Playing under a Gloucester Wharf* (No. 917) as that work.

Turner surely owned both works, which were distributed to his two sons following his death, and it is reasonable that his recollection of receiving both as gifts from Homer is accurate.

PROVENANCE
Ross Turner, Salem, MA, by gift of Homer, 1888; Cameron Turner, Beverly, MA, his son, 1915; Howard J. Jackman, Lynnfield, MA, c. 1971; (Berry-Hill Galleries, Inc., c. 1981); private collection, 1981; (Sotheby's, 29 Nov. 1995, sale 6782, no. 129)

EXHIBITIONS
Knoedler 1986, no. 56; Terra 1990, no. 22

LITERATURE
Downes 1911, 196–97

989
Coasters at Anchor
[1880]

Watercolor, 9¾ × 13⅝ (24.765 × 34.608)
Inscribed lr: Homer

Private collection

PROVENANCE
(Doll & Richards, Boston, 1880) [?]; Dr. Amos
Lawrence Mason, Boston, probably 1880; Marian
Steedman Mason Wilson (Mrs. Richard T. Wilson),
New York, his daughter, nd; Marian Mason Wilson
Jurgens (Mrs. C. H. H. Jurgens), Newport, RI, her
daughter, by bequest, by 1947; (Kennedy Galleries,
1968); private collection, 1968

EXHIBITIONS
Doll & Richards 1880

No. 989. Coasters at Anchor

990

Two Sailboats

1880

Watercolor, 8¼ × 16¹¹⁄₁₆ (20.955 × 42.388)
Inscribed lr: Homer 1880

Philadelphia Museum of Art, gift of Dr. and Mrs.
George Woodward, 1939.7.11

PROVENANCE
(M. Knoedler & Co., nd); (William Macbeth, Inc.,
1914); Dr. and Mrs. George Woodward, Chestnut
Hill, PA, 1916

EXHIBITIONS
Alliance, Philadelphia 1923, no. 2; Philadelphia 1953,
no. 5

No. 990. Two Sailboats

see color illustration, p. 468

No. 991. Schooners, Gloucester

991
Schooners, Gloucester
1880

Watercolor, 8¼ × 13⅛ (20.955 × 33.338) sight
Inscribed lr: Winslow Homer 1880

Private collection

ABG: The likely first owner of this watercolor and
of No. 930, Rebecca Valentine, was born in 1834, the
younger sister of Lawson and Henry Valentine. She
married Mr. Fairbanks in 1855, and was nearing fifty
years of age in 1880, when Homer executed the two
watercolors associated with her.

PROVENANCE
Rebecca Valentine Fairbanks (Mrs. Leland Fairbanks,
Jr.), nd [?]; Mrs. Walter Gates Richardson, her
daughter, nd; Walter Gates Richardson, by bequest,
nd; Robert Richardson, Clarcona, FL, his son, by
1948; (E. C. Babcock Art Galleries, 1948); F. L. P.
Fund, Summit, NJ, nd; (Kennedy Galleries, c. 1969);
private collection, 1983; (Kennedy Galleries, 1991)

EXHIBITIONS
Wellesley (Massachusetts) College Museum of
Art, *The Gloucester Watercolors of Winslow Homer*,
2–31 Mar. 1976

992

Lone Boat with Schooner

[1880]

Watercolor, 8¾ × 12¾ (22.225 × 32.385)
Inscribed lr: *Winslow Homer / by C. S. H. Executor*

Private collection

ABG: A near-duplicate of this painting exists, the circumstantial history of which indicates it is a copy made some time between 1918 and 1933, rather than a replication by Homer.

The Knoedler gallery recorded the sale of this watercolor, under the name *Lone Boat and Schooner* to the Macbeth gallery in February 1911. The painting was among those Knoedler was dispersing from the Winslow Homer estate for Charles S. Homer, Jr., executor and heir. The Macbeth gallery recorded its sale of the painting to Charles Wharton Stork of Philadelphia on 27 December 1918.

In 1976 Mrs. A. Thomas Richie brought *Lone Boat with Schooner* to LG for confirmation of its attribution. She told him she had received it as a gift from her father, Arthur Edwin Bye. Her father had told her nothing of its history, or how it came into his possession. However, LG had record of what he reasonably presumed were the whereabouts of *Lone Boat with Schooner* from 1933 to what now appeared to be its—undated—acquisition by Arthur Bye.

The Macbeth gallery recorded having represented Mr. Stork in selling his *Lone Boat with Schooner* on 20 October 1933 to a private collector who lived in Maine. The Macbeth gallery provided this 1933 buyer with a seamless provenance for the work, beginning with Macbeth's 1911 acquisition from Knoedler. LG's latest correspondence with the Maine owner had been in January 1940; he could

only assume the watercolor had passed from his Maine correspondent's possession to that of Mr. Bye some time after 1940.

Then in the mid-1990s the watercolor which very closely resembles *Lone Boat with Schooner* was put into the market by descendants of the Maine collector, under the title *At Sundown, Gloucester*; it was accompanied by the Macbeth gallery's 1933 account of its provenance. Two nearly identical paintings whose provenances diverge probably in about 1930 present an obvious problem. It seems equally obvious to look to Philadelphia, where a convergence of Charles Wharton Stork and Arthur Edwin Bye is highly likely to have occurred—especially considering Bye's professions.

Arthur Edwin Bye (1885–1969) enjoyed considerable celebrity in Philadelphia and nearby Bucks County. He was respected equally as a painter and as an art historian. In the latter character he was affiliated with the faculties of Lafayette College; Vassar College; and the University of North Carolina; and he held an appointment as a curator at the Philadelphia Museum. Not surprisingly, Bye was also active as an art dealer, and maintained a studio on Philadelphia's prestigious Rittenhouse Square for his business as a restorer of paintings. It is reasonable to speculate that Stork put his Homer watercolor in Bye's hands for some attention, such as treatment of the paper, or matting and framing. Bye—who had the skill—would thereby also have had the opportunity to execute a copy.

There are discrepancies between text markings on the reverse of this watercolor, No. 992, and on the reverse of its near-twin. Several of those on No. 992—but missing from its near-twin—link No. 992 to the period in 1911 when the Knoedler gallery had the painting in hand for Charles S. Homer, Jr. This fact supports acceptance that it was the original watercolor Arthur Bye passed on to his daughter. Just how Bye came into possession of the painting is not likely ever to be surely known.

As the work lent to the Museum of Modern Art by Mr. Stork for its 1930 exhibition on Homer, Albert P. Ryder and Thomas Eakins was not illustrated in the exhibition catalogue, it is not possible to know for sure which of the two hung on MOMA's wall.

No. 992. Lone Boat with Schooner

Charles S. Homer, Jr., by bequest, 1910; (M.
Knoedler & Co., 1911); (William Macbeth, Inc.,
1911); Charles Wharton Stork, Philadelphia, 1918;
Arthur Edwin Bye, Philadelphia, before 1933;
Margaret Bye Richie (Mrs. Thomas A. Richie),
Holicong, PA, his daughter, by gift, 1957; (William
Edward O'Reilly, Inc., 1976); (Hirschl & Adler
Galleries, 1976)

EXHIBITIONS
MOMA 1930, no. 24 (as *Sundown*) [?]

993
William B. Astor's Yacht
1880

The "Ambassadress" in Gloucester Harbor

Graphite, watercolor, 9 × 13 (22.860 × 33.020)
Inscribed ll: Gloucester Aug 25th 1880 / Winslow
Homer; lr: Wm B. Astors yacht

Cape Ann Historical Association, Gloucester, MA,
gift of Margaret Farrell Lynch, 1972, 2069

PROVENANCE
(William Macbeth, Inc., nd); Hoyt L. Warner, Sr.,
Cleveland, nd; Hoyt L. Warner, Jr., Cambridge,
MA, c. 1941

EXHIBITIONS
Terra 1990, no. 27

No. 993. William B. Astor's Yacht

No. 994. Sunset at Gloucester

994
Sunset at Gloucester
1880

Watercolor, 13 × 23¾ (33.020 × 60.325)
Inscribed ll: Winslow Homer Aug 25th 1880

Addison Gallery of American Art, Phillips Academy,
Andover, MA, given anonymously, 1930.11

PROVENANCE
Charles S. Homer, Jr., by bequest, 1910; Mrs. Charles
S. Homer, Jr., by bequest, 1917; (William Macbeth,
Inc., 1918); Thomas Cochran, New York, 1929

EXHIBITIONS
Brooklyn 1915, no. 2; Carnegie 1923, no. 20; Fogg
1932, no. 8; NE Museums 1936 (Smith College,
only, not in catalogue); Boston Symphony 1937;
Ogunquit 1954, no. p-15; Katonah 1963, no. 16;
Vermont Art Center 1964, no. 3; Wellesley
(Massachusetts) College Museum of Art, *The
Gloucester Watercolors of Winslow Homer*, 2–31 Mar.
1976; Addison 1980; Addison 1990; Terra 1990,
no. 39; Nelson-Atkins 2001 (Nelson-Atkins and
High, only); Addison 2004; AI Chicago 2008

No. 995. Sailboats Off the Coast of Ten Pound Island

see color illustration, p. 470

995+
Sailboats Off the Coast of Ten Pound Island

1880

Watercolor, 9⅜ × 13¼ (23.813 × 33.655)
Inscribed ll: Winslow Homer 1880

The Warner Collection of Gulf States Paper Corporation, Tuscaloosa, AL

Robert Macbeth passed along to LG in 1939 that he had been told Mrs. Walter Hodges of Brookline, Massachusetts, owned "a picture" by Homer. Although Mrs. Hodges acknowledged she had such an object, she rebuffed LG's several requests to see the work and refused to divulge its history. It had had two owners following Mrs. Hodges when it appeared in the market in 1990. By that time it had the company of an incongruous tale that Homer had painted it in 1880 as a gift for Mrs. Hodges.

ABG: The title *Sailboats Off the Coast of Ten Pound Island* was awarded to this painting in 1990. Ten Pound Island is so small and situated so closely to the waterfront of the city of Gloucester, it can hardly be said to have a coast.

PROVENANCE
(Doll & Richards, Boston, 1880); Edith MacKillop Hodges (Mrs. Walter W. Hodges), Brookline, MA, by 1939; Samuel Robinson MacKillop, her son, 1945; unidentified private collection, Boston, nd; (Vose Galleries of Boston, 1990); (Spanierman Gallery, LLC, 1990)

EXHIBITIONS
Doll & Richards 1880; Terra 1990, no. 36

996
Two Schooners
1880

Two Sailboats

Watercolor, 10 × 14 (25.400 × 35.560)
Inscribed lr: Homer 1880

Private collection

ABG: William Macbeth opened his gallery in April 1892. That August he approached Homer to let him have some things for an exhibition in his new establishment in the upcoming November. Homer agreed to send "one or more watercolors" in his reply of August 3, but it was 20 November when he sent off ten watercolors to Macbeth, numbered and priced (at from $25 to $75) but not titled. Macbeth gave them descriptive titles in order to enter them into gallery records; most were Gloucester subjects from 1880. Markings on the reverse of this watercolor reliably identify it as the fifth item on Homer's list, which Macbeth titled "Two Schooners." Macbeth gallery records note that it was eventually returned to Homer, unsold.

An unidentified newspaper clipping pasted—amidst others dated to the early 1890s—into one of Thomas B. Clarke's scrapbooks notes that "William Macbeth has a very attractive exhibition of water colors and pastels by American artists at his little gallery, 237 Fifth Avenue, including three or four seashore pieces by Winslow Homer."

PROVENANCE
Burton Mansfield, New York and New Haven, CT, probably 1903; (American Art Association/Anderson Galleries, 7 Apr. 1933, Mansfield estate sale 4035, no. 101); Mrs. Harlow Brooks, New York, 1933; (Wildenstein & Co., c. 1950); Kenneth Franzheim, Houston, 1953; Lillie Franzheim Webb, his sister, nd; (Sotheby's, 20 May 1998, sale 7135, no. 97)

EXHIBITIONS
Doll & Richards 1880; Macbeth Gallery, New York, [watercolors and pastels by American artists], c. Nov.–Dec. 1892 [?]; Houston 1952, no. 17 (as *Two Sailboats*)

LITERATURE
Thomas B. Clarke scrapbooks, Archives of American Art, Smithsonian Institution, Washington, DC

No. 996. Two Schooners

see color illustration, p. 469

997
Schooner at Sunset
1880

Watercolor, 9¾ × 13¹³⁄₁₆ (24.765 × 35.085)
Inscribed lr: Homer 1880

Harvard University Art Museums, Fogg Art Museum, Cambridge, MA, bequest of Grenville L. Winthrop, 1943.298

ABG: Few of Homer's twenty-three submissions to the American Water Color Society's Fourteenth Annual Exhibition may be reliably identified. However, it seems probable that number 578, titled *Sunset*, was this *Schooner at Sunset*. Two works were catalogued as *Sunset*, but only the one hung in the Academy's Corridor gallery attracted attention; it was number 578.

"G. W. H." (presumably George W. Hows) delivered his critique of the Society's 1881 exhibition for the *New York Evening Express* in a series of five articles in which he consistently demonstrated his contempt for the new "impressionists," among whom he classed Homer. In the process of ridiculing this work, he provided some descriptive details.

> No. 578 by Winslow Homer, is called in the catalogue "Sunset." It is well to be told what things are, for as Capt. Corcoran parenthetically puts it, "things are seldom what they seem." This curious combination of red and black certainly looks as little like a sunset as Roscoe Conkling resembles the Apollo Belvedere. But as Roscoe probably believes he resembles the latter, on the same hypothesis Mr. Homer may be led to believe that this scene-painter's frenzy looks like a sunset.

The critic for the *New York Herald* saw things quite differently: "Winslow Homer's numerous exhibits like most of those of J. Frank Currier, are hung high, where some of them are very effective. The former's sanguinary sunset at sea, on the top line, in the southeast corner of the Corridor, is a very powerful piece of impressionism."

The *Art Journal*'s reflections on the 1881 *Annual* published after its close also highlighted number 578:

> Among Winslow Homer's contributions the most interesting were studies of atmospheric effects along the coast, and the most important and impressionist the study called "Sunset," which hung in the corridor; a brilliant sky reflected from the ridges of the darkening waves over which a fishing-smack is scudding under full sail away from the spectator. The difference between the red reflected from vaporous clouds and the same color reflected from the liquid water, was admirably rendered.

The *Journal* concluded with the happy thought that "Financially the exhibition has been the most successful that the society has ever held. Something over a third of the contributions were sold for $32,000. . . . Among the sales on buyer's day were . . . and Winslow Homer's 'Sunset,' above mentioned." In this apparent error the *Journal* was repeating reports of the sale of *Sunset* made in the New York *Herald*, *Evening Post*, and *Tribune*. However, *Sunset*—the only one of Homer's works not priced in the exhibition catalogue—remained in his possession.

PROVENANCE
Charles S. Homer, Jr., by bequest, 1910; Mrs. Charles S. Homer, Jr., by bequest, 1917; Arthur P. and Charles L. Homer, by bequest, 1937; (William Macbeth, Inc., 1940); Grenville L. Winthrop, New York, 1940

EXHIBITIONS
AWS 1881, no. 578 (as *Sunset*) [?]; Prout's Neck 1936, no. 7; Fogg 1944

No. 997. Schooner at Sunset

see color illustration, p. 471

LITERATURE

"Fine Arts. Buyers' Day at the Water Color Society,"
New York Herald, 23 Jan. 1881; "Fine Arts," *(NY)*
Evening Post, 28 Jan. 1881; G. W. H., "Fine Arts. The
Water-Color Exhibition. Concluding Article," *(NY)*
Evening Express, 12 Feb. 1881; "Fine Arts. Fourteenth
Annual Exhibition of the American Water Color
Society—Sixth Notice," *New York Herald*, 21 Feb.
1881; "The American Water-Color Society," *(NY)*
Art Journal 7 (Mar. 1881): 95–96

998
Sunset Fires
1880

Watercolor, 9¾ × 13⅝ (24.765 × 34.608)
Inscribed ur: Winslow Homer / 1880

The Westmoreland County Museum of Art,
Greensburg, PA, gift of William A. Coulter Fund,
1964.36

ABG: William Macbeth opened his gallery in April
1892. That August he approached Homer to let him
have some things for an exhibition in his new establishment in the upcoming November. Homer agreed
to send "one or more watercolors" in his reply of
August 3, but it was 20 November when he sent off
ten watercolors to Macbeth, numbered and priced
(at from $25 to $75) but not titled. Macbeth gave
them descriptive titles in order to enter them into
gallery records; most were Gloucester subjects from

1880. Markings on the reverse of this watercolor
identify it as the second item on Homer's list, titled
"Sunset Fire" by Macbeth.

An unidentified newspaper clipping pasted—
amidst others dated to the early 1890s—into one of
Thomas B. Clarke's scrapbooks notes that "William
Macbeth has a very attractive exhibition of water
colors and pastels by American artists at his little
gallery, 237 Fifth Avenue, including three or four
seashore pieces by Winslow Homer."

PROVENANCE
(William Macbeth, Inc., 1892); Dexter M. Dawes,
Englewood, NJ, 1901; (Gropper Art Gallery,
Cambridge, MA, c. 1960); (Kennedy Galleries, c. 1963)

EXHIBITIONS
Macbeth Gallery, New York, [watercolors and pastels
by American artists], c. Nov.–Dec. 1892 [?]; Everson
1983, no. 3; Whitney, Fairfield, 1984; NGA 1986,
no. 60; Terra 1990, no. 40; NGA 1995, no. 106;
Suzanne H. Arnold Art Gallery, Lebanon Valley
College, Annville, PA, *Winslow Homer: Graphic*

No. 998. Sunset Fires

see color illustration, p. 472

No. 999. Gloucester Sunset

see color illustration, p. 473

Expressions, 22 Oct.–11 Dec. 1998; Nelson-Atkins 2001 (Nelson-Atkins and High, only); Dulwich/Terra, Giverny 2006, no. 13; AI Chicago 2008

LITERATURE
Thomas B. Clarke scrapbooks, Archives of American Art, Smithsonian Institution, Washington, DC

999
Gloucester Sunset
[1880]

Watercolor, 9½ × 13½ (24.130 × 34.290) sight
Inscribed lr: Homer

Private collection

Charles Homer consigned this work to the Knoedler gallery in January 1911 under the title *Gloucester, Sunset*; it was returned to him in 1915. By 1928, when the Macbeth gallery sold it for Charles Homer's widow, the scene had been imaginatively relocated to Prout's Neck, Maine. Although not inscribed with a date, this watercolor is easily recognized by stylistic characteristics as a work of 1880, some years before Homer routinely painted at Prout's Neck.

PROVENANCE
Charles S. Homer, Jr., by bequest, 1910; Mrs. Charles S. Homer, Jr., by bequest, 1917; (William Macbeth, Inc., 1928); Ellen C. Dupont Meeds (Mrs. H. S. Meeds, later Mrs. Robert Wheelwright), Wilmington, DE, 1928; Mrs. Paulina Meeds Wellford, Wilmington, DE, by bequest, 1968; private collection, nd; (Hirschl & Adler Galleries, 1978)

EXHIBITIONS
MOMA 1930, no. 44 (as *Prout's Neck, Sunset*); NGA 1986, no. 62; Terra 1990, no. 32; NGA 1995, no. 105; Chrysler 2000; Nelson-Atkins 2001 (Los Angeles County, only); AI Chicago 2008

No. 1000. Eastern Point Light

see color illustration, p. 475

1000

Eastern Point Light

[1880]

Watercolor, 9¹¹⁄₁₆ × 13⁷⁄₁₆ (24.608 × 34.133)

Princeton University Art Museum, Princeton, NJ, gift of Alastair B. Martin, class of 1938, 1957.116

This watercolor was illustrated over the caption "7. Schooners [*sic*] at Sunset" in the catalogue of the Prout's Neck Association's Homer exhibition of 1936. In consequence *Eastern Point Light* has occasionally been called by the title which rightfully belongs to No. 997.

PROVENANCE

Charles S. Homer, Jr., by bequest, 1910; Mrs. Charles S. Homer, Jr., by bequest, 1917; Charles L. Homer, by bequest, 1937; Alastair Bradley Martin, Glen Head, NY, 1956

EXHIBITIONS

Doll & Richards 1880 [?]; AWS 1881, no. 540; Prout's Neck 1936 (not numbered); Behn-Moore 1953 (as *Schooners in the Moonlight*); Bowdoin/Colby 1954 (as *Schooners in the Moonlight, Saco Bay*); NGA 1958, no. 102; Wellesley (Massachusetts) College Museum of Art, *The Gloucester Watercolors of Winslow Homer*, 2–31 Mar. 1976; Whitney, Fairfield, 1984; NGA 1986, no. 59; Miami 1991; NGA 1995, no. 104; AI Chicago 2008

LITERATURE

American Art in the Princeton University Art Museum, Volume I: Drawings and Watercolors (New Haven: Yale University Press, 2004), 160–62

1001

Sailboat and Fourth of July Fireworks

1880

Watercolor, 9⅝ × 13¹¹⁄₁₆ (24.448 × 34.768)
Inscribed ll: July 4 1880; lr: W. H.

Harvard University Art Museums, Fogg Art Museum, Cambridge, MA, bequest of Grenville L. Winthrop, 1943.305

ABG: William Macbeth opened his gallery in April 1892. That August he approached Homer to let him have some things for an exhibition in his new establishment in the upcoming November. Homer agreed to send "one or more watercolors" in his reply of August 3, but it was 20 November when he sent off ten watercolors to Macbeth, numbered and priced (at from $25 to $75) but—with one exception—not titled. Macbeth gave the listed numbers 1 through 9 descriptive titles in order to enter them into gallery records; most were Gloucester subjects from 1880.

The number 10 is followed by a title written by Homer himself: "Bergen Point, N.J.." Someone of the Macbeth gallery staff noted in the margin to the left of "10:" "July 4th '80,." which, presumably, was copied from the inscribed dating on the painting. The gallery's own record of the ten paintings is phrased: "10. Bergen Point, July 4, 1880." Markings on the reverse of this watercolor reliably identify it as the tenth item on Homer's list.

Gordon Hendricks carelessly transformed Homer's notation on the list he sent to Macbeth into a statement that this watercolor is inscribed at "lower right W. H. Bergen Point, N.J." Based on the association of the painting and Bergen, Hendricks places Homer in New York at the beginning of July 1880; making an excursion to the Jersey shore to celebrate the Fourth of July holiday; and then remaining in the city for some time thereafter until going to Gloucester.

There is no documentation of just when Homer arrived in Gloucester. Yet for him to have remained in New York well into the summer would have been unusual, and probably, uncomfortable. However, there is also no question that the script "Bergen

No. 1001. Sailboat and Fourth of July Fireworks

see color illustration, p. 474

Point, N. J." written on the November 1892 list is
Homer's. It would seem that his memory of where
he found that subject on the Fourth of July in 1880
would not have entirely dimmed in twelve years.
Thus, his reference to the scene being set in New
Jersey waters, rather than Massachusetts, perhaps
should be believed. However, in theme and characteristics of style, this watercolor fits too seamlessly
with No. 997, No. 998, No. 999, No. 1000, and No.
1002, to be from a different context. And, although
the month of July runs for thirty-one days, Homer
having inscribed "Gloucester / July 1880" on the
drawing *Gloucester Harbor* (No. 1004) also tends to
contradict his allusion to Bergen.

PROVENANCE
Jacob Otis Wardwell, Haverhill, MA, after 1892;
Sheldon E. Wardwell, Brookline, MA, his son,
by bequest, 1940; (William Macbeth, Inc., 1941);
Grenville L. Winthrop, New York, 1941

EXHIBITIONS
Doll & Richards 1880; Fogg 1944

LITERATURE
Metropolitan Museum of Art, "Sailboat and
Fourth of July Fireworks," by Nicolai Cikovsky, Jr.,
in *A Private Passion: 19th-Century Paintings and
Drawings . . . Winthrop Collection, Harvard University*
(New York, 2003), 444–46

1002

The Sculpin

1880

Watercolor, 9¼ × 13¼ (23.495 × 33.655) sight
Inscribed lr: Homer [18]80

Berger Collection Educational Trust, Denver Art
Museum, PTL-3165

Gen. and Mrs. Merriam, the earliest owners of
this watercolor, had a summer residence in Prout's
Neck, Maine.

PROVENANCE
Gen. Henry Clay Merriam, New York, by gift of
Homer, 1907; Mrs. Henry Clay Merriam, New York,
by bequest, 1912; Maud Merriam Bradley (Mrs.
Henry T. Bradley), New York, her daughter, by 1938;
(M. Knoedler & Co., 1964); private collection, 1965;
(Sotheby's, 22 May 1996, sale 6854, no. 50)

EXHIBITIONS
Portland 1998; Parthenon 2000

No. 1002. The Sculpin

No. 1003. Two Men in a Rowboat

1003

Two Men in a Rowboat

1880

Foggy Morning

Watercolor, 9⅝ × 13½ (24.448 × 34.290)
Inscribed lr: Homer 1880

Unlocated

PROVENANCE
Alexander Bower, Portland, ME, by 1938; Robert C.
Vose Galleries of Boston, by 1945

1004

Gloucester Harbor

1880

Graphite, watercolor, 9¼ × 14 (23.495 × 35.560)
Inscribed ll: Gloucester / July 1880; lr: Winslow
Homer

Private collection

PROVENANCE
Mabel H. Chapin, Boston, nd; Horace D. Chapin,
Boston, her brother, nd; Margaret Chapin Osgood
(Mrs. Robert B. Osgood), Boston, his sister, c. 1936

EXHIBITIONS
Doll & Richards 1880; MFA, Boston, 1911

LITERATURE
Downes 1911, op. 56

No. 1004. Gloucester Harbor

No. 1005. Reflections, Gloucester

1005

Reflections, Gloucester

1880

Watercolor, 7¾ × 12¼ (19.685 × 31.115)
Inscribed lr: Homer 1880

Private collection

PROVENANCE
Mr. Kernan, nd; George W. H. Ritchie, New York,
nd; Mrs. George W. H. Ritchie, Providence, RI, nd;
Edwin D. Hague, Cleveland, nd; Florence B. Hague
(Mrs. Edwin D. Hague), Brookline, MA, nd;
(Wildenstein & Co., 1948); R. Frederick Woolworth,
New York, 1956; (Milch Galleries, c. 1958); private
collection, 1958; (Kennedy Galleries, 1976); Dr. and
Mrs. John E. Larkin, White Bear Lake, MN, 1982;
(Sotheby's, 2 June 1983, sale 5055, No. 70); Ron Hall,
Dallas, 1983; private collection, nd; (M. Knoedler &
Co., 1986); private collection, 1987; (Spanierman
Gallery, LLC, 1989)

EXHIBITIONS
RISD 1931, no. 28; Houston 1952, no. 18; Terra 1990,
no. 35; Chrysler 2000

1006

Sailing a Dory, Gloucester

1880

Watercolor, 9¹⁄₁₆ × 13¹⁄₁₆ (23.020 × 33.180)
Inscribed lr: Homer 1880

Philadelphia Museum of Art, gift of Dr. and Mrs.
George Woodward, 1939.7.14

PROVENANCE
P. H. Mahon, Brooklyn, nd; (M. Knoedler & Co.,
c. 1917); Dr. Thomas L. Bennett, New York, 1917;
(M. Knoedler & Co., 1922); Dr. and Mrs. George
Woodward, Chestnut Hill, PA, 1924

EXHIBITIONS
Macbeth 1938, no. 9

No. 1006. Sailing a Dory, Gloucester

No. 1007. The Lobster Pot

see color illustration, p. 476

1007

The Lobster Pot

[1880]

Watercolor, 9⅝ × 13¾ (24.448 × 34.925)
Inscribed lr: Homer

Private collection

PROVENANCE
(Doll & Richards, Boston, 1880); Frank Morison,
Boston, 1880; Mrs. Clifton L. Bremer, Milton, MA,
his daughter, by bequest, nd; Clifton L. Bremer,
Milton, MA, by bequest, 1959; (Charles D. Childs
Gallery, Boston, 1959); private collection, 1959;
(Martha Parrish & James Reinish, Inc., 2000)

EXHIBITIONS
Doll & Richards 1880; Terra 1990, no. 21

1008

Gloucester Harbor and Dory

[1880]

Watercolor, 13 11/16 × 19 5/8 (34.768 × 49.848)
Inscribed lr: Winslow Homer

Harvard University Art Museums, Fogg Art
Museum, Cambridge, MA, given anonymously,
1939.240

Mrs. Charles Fairchild purchased two watercolors
from the Doll & Richards Homer exhibition of
1880, this and No. 929. Doll & Richards records
only noted the date of sale (both on 16 December),
and their stock numbers (25 and 42) and prices
($60 and $150). Mrs. Fairchild's address was then
191 Commonwealth Avenue, in Boston.

Seventeen years later the Charles Fairchild who
consigned the watercolor for sale to a Boston dealer
did so from a business address on Wall Street in New
York. Mr. and Mrs. Fairchild may have removed to
New York, or the 1897 seller may have been their son.

PROVENANCE
(Doll & Richards, Boston, 1880); Mrs. Charles
Fairchild, Boston, 1880; Charles Fairchild, New
York, by 1897; (Doll & Richards, Boston, 1897);
Edward W. Hooper, Boston, 1899; Alexander H.
Higginson, before 1901; (Doll & Richards, Boston,
1920); Horace D. Chapin, Boston, 1920; Margaret
Chapin Osgood (Mrs. Robert B. Osgood), Boston,
his sister, c. 1936

EXHIBITIONS
Doll & Richards 1880; Copley Society 1921, no. 46;
Fogg 1932, no. 22; Fogg 1936, no. 34; Mount
Holyoke 1940, no. 11; Fogg 1944; Worcester 1944,
no. 33; Walker Art Center 1945; Terra 1990, no. 30;
Nelson-Atkins 2001 (Nelson-Atkins and Los Angeles
County, only); Dulwich/Terra, Giverny 2006, no. 11

No. 1008. Gloucester Harbor and Dory

see color illustration, p. 477

No. 1009. Two Schooners, Gloucester

1009

Two Schooners, Gloucester

[1880]

Watercolor, 9 11/16 × 13 11/16 (24.608 × 34.768)
Inscribed lr: W. H.

Philadelphia Museum of Art, gift of Dr. and Mrs.
George Woodward, 1939.7.4

PROVENANCE
Charles S. Homer, Jr., by bequest, 1910; (M.
Knoedler & Co., 1917); Dr. and Mrs. George
Woodward, Chestnut Hill, PA, 1920

EXHIBITIONS
Alliance, Philadelphia 1923, no. 18; Carnegie 1937,
no. 122 (as *Gloucester Harbor*); Philadelphia 1953,
no. 7; Albright-Knox 1966, no. 15

No. 1010. Two Schooners

1010

Two Schooners

1880

Graphite, watercolor, 5 × 9 (12.700 × 22.860)
Inscribed ll: Homer 1880

Private collection

PROVENANCE
Charles S. Homer, Jr., by bequest, 1910; (William Rolfe, Jr., Marblehead, MA, c, 1961); Steven Juvelis, Lynn, MA, c. 1961; Mr. and Mrs. Charles C. Cunningham, Jr., Brookline, MA, 1962; (Vose Galleries of Boston, nd); private collection, 1988; (Christie's, 5 June 1997, sale 8662, no. 26)

1011

Gloucester Schooners and Sloop

1880

Two Sailboats

Watercolor, 13¹³⁄₁₆ × 19¾ (35.085 × 50.165)
Inscribed lr: Winslow Homer 1880

Philadelphia Museum of Art, gift of Dr. and Mrs. George Woodward, 1939.7.9

PROVENANCE
Charles S. Homer, Jr., by bequest, 1910; (M. Knoedler & Co., nd); (William Macbeth, Inc., 1914); Dr. and Mrs. George Woodward, Chestnut Hill, PA, 1916

EXHIBITIONS
Alliance, Philadelphia 1923, no. 19 (as *Two Sailboats*); Philadelphia 1953, no. 6; NGA 1958/MFA, Boston, 1959, no. 104/94; University of Arizona 1963, no. 111; Mariners, Norfolk, 1964, no. 17; Terra 1990, no. 31; Nelson-Atkins 2001 (Los Angeles County and High, only); Dulwich/Terra, Giverny 2006, no. 12

No. 1011. Gloucester Schooners and Sloop

No. 1012. Schooner at Gloucester

1012

Schooner at Gloucester

1880

Gloucester Harbor

Watercolor, 9⅜ × 13⅜ (23.813 × 33.973) sight
Inscribed lr: Homer 1880

Private collection

PROVENANCE
Charles S. Homer, Jr., by bequest, 1910 [?]; Arthur
B. Homer, by gift, 1910 [?]; Arthur P. Homer,
before 1928; Dr. Ansel Kinney, Evanston, IL, 1929;
(Wildenstein & Co., by 1948); private collection, 1954

EXHIBITIONS
Wildenstein 1948, no. 12; Houston 1952, no. 21
(as *Gloucester Harbor*); NGA 1958, no. 99 (as
Gloucester Harbor)

1013

A Wreck near Gloucester

1880

Watercolor, 13¹³⁄₁₆ × 19⅝ (35.085 × 49.848)
Inscribed ll: Winslow Homer 1880

The Carnegie Museum of Art, Pittsburgh, 37.3.2

PROVENANCE
Edward C. Stedman, New York, nd; Dr. Alexander
C. Humphreys, 1905; (American Art Association, 15
Feb. 1917, Humphreys sale, no. 102); (M. Knoedler
& Co., 1917)

EXHIBITIONS
Philadelphia WC Club 1910, no. 155; Carnegie 1917,
no. 5; Carnegie 1923, no. 43; Carnegie 1937, no. 49;
Mariners, Norfolk, 1964, no. 18; Albright-Knox
1966, no. 14; Terra 1990, no. 41

No. 1013. A Wreck near Gloucester

see color illustration, p. 478

1014

Winding the Clock

1881

Watercolor, 19¾ × 11 (50.165 × 27.940)
Inscribed ur: Homer / 1881

Texas A & M University, Bill and Irma Runyon Art
Collection, College Station, TX

No. 1014. Winding the Clock

see color illustration, p. 479

ABG: Of the twenty-three paintings Homer
contributed to the American Water Color Society's
Fourteenth Annual Exhibition, twenty-two may be
presumed from their titles and critics' commentary
to have been subjects drawn from his travels and
sketches of the spring and summer of 1880. His
pensive ladies seated or strolling in landscape were
represented, but most of the works seem to have
been Gloucester scenes: ships at anchor in the
harbor; boys at play or at rest on the shore. Among
these were several of the kind a *New York Herald*
critic called "sanguinary sunsets at sea." Stylistically,
these would have ranged from the freely painted,
bright glimpses of nature to which Homer's audience
had become accustomed, to the radically fluid
impressions of evening light and atmosphere which
many found alarming.

The twenty-third painting was this *Winding the
Clock*. It stood in marked contrast to all the other
works Homer was showing. An interior scene, packed
with domestic detail, it is meticulously rendered to
the "high finish" considered the measure of excellence
when watercolor painting first challenged oil for
aesthetic respect. By this period in his work, the
narrative implications of the scene are also inconsistent with Homer's usually dispassionate presentation
of fashionable young ladies.

The Water Color Society's exhibition opened at
the end of January 1881; Homer's inscribed dating
on *Winding the Clock* implies it had been completed
just days earlier. Gen. Palfrey is acknowledged in the
catalogue as the owner of the painting. It is easy to
imagine that the conservative style Homer chose
for *Winding the Clock* may be accounted to it having
been made "to measure" for the General—even if
not exactly as a formal commission. A further speculation is that the subject is in fact a cabinet portrait
of one of the General's daughters shown in their
Boston home.

Winding the Clock is represented in an illustration
by Frederick S. Church reproduced in the catalogue
of the Water Color Society's 1881 *Annual*. Church's
drawing is a composite of the principle features of
six of the exhibited paintings.

See commentary No. 1015.

PROVENANCE
Gen. and Mrs. Francis W. Palfrey, Boston, 1881;
Louise C. Palfrey (Mrs. Francis W. Palfrey), Boston,
1889; the daughters of Gen. and Mrs. Palfrey, Boston,
by 1897; Hope Gardner (Mrs. Paul Gardner), New
York, the Palfrey's granddaughter, by 1936; (Sotheby
Parke-Bernet, 20 Apr. 1979, sale 4236, no. 46);
(Hirschl & Adler Galleries, 1979); Bill and Irma
Runyon, Texas, nd

EXHIBITIONS
AWS 1881, no. 74; Whitney 1944

No. 1015. Captain W. F. Bartlett and Lieutenant-Colonel F. W. Palfrey at Camp Benton, MD, November 1861

1015

Captain W. F. Bartlett and Lieutenant-Colonel F. W. Palfrey at Camp Benton, MD, November 1861
1881

Oil, 37⅞ × 23⅞ (96.203 × 60.643)
Inscribed ll: Winslow Homer 1881

Boston Public Library, Prints, 20th Regiment Collection

LG examined this painting at the Boston Public Library in 1936. At that time the image visible within the frame was somewhat less than the full painting because the canvas had been mounted on a smaller stretcher than Homer had used, probably to accommodate a favored frame. LG recorded that about⅞ inch at both the top and bottom of the painting had been wrapped over the stretcher, and—as seen from the front—the image was reduced by about ⅝ inch at right and 2½ inches at left. Homer's

signature and the dating inscription were on the wrap-around portion at the left, indicating that he had not, himself, reconfigured the composition. A late date for this act of minor vandalism may also be inferred from a supplementary inscription painted on the reverse of the canvas to compensate for the "disappearance" of the signature: "Signed on canvas / where turned in lower left / Winslow / Homer / 1881 / Attested by E. H. Garrett / 1922." Previous published illustrations of the painting have shown it within the elaborate frame into which it had been compressed.

Although the painting was long known simply as *Officers at Camp Benton, Maryland in 1861*, there seems never to have been any doubt that the figures at the center and at the left are portraits of Francis Winthrop Palfrey (1831–1889) and William Francis Bartlett (1840–1876). But which figure is which seems to have been open to interpretation. A label beneath the painting recorded by LG in 1936 implied Palfrey was at the left, and Bartlett in the center. Gordon Hendricks assumed Bartlett was at the left, and Palfrey held center stage. He was probably correct, in that it is likely Palfrey would be the focus of a commemorative portrait he had commissioned. Also, at the time represented in the painting, Palfrey held the rank of Lieutenant Colonel and commanded the 20th Regiment, while Bartlett was a Captain, and his subordinate.

In 1892 Gen. Palfrey's widow donated about 300 books and manuscripts on military history to the Boston Public Library, to initiate a special collection to be named for the 20th Regiment Massachusetts Volunteers of which her husband was a senior officer during the Civil War. Several years later surviving veterans of the 20th Regiment donated a substantial sum of money to augment this research collection, which at that time was kept in an area of the Library termed the Military Alcove. Then in 1897 two paintings were offered to serve as decoration for this alcove. One of these was *Officers at Camp Benton, Maryland* contributed by Gen. Palfrey's daughters.

The Library's Keeper of Rare Books, Zoltan Haraszti, wrote LG on 21 October 1936, enclosing a copy of a 25 January 1897 letter from Capt. Edward B. Robins, who presumably was a particularly dedicated survivor of the 20th, in which Robins names the junior officer standing at the right in the painting: "I have today asked Gen. Palfrey's family to present to the Alcove the oil painting of Palfrey, Bartlett and Abbott together."

ABG: Because of the coincidence that Homer made his first, very brief excursion to Civil War camps (those circling Washington, DC) at just the time Palfrey and Bartlett are documented as being at Camp Benton, Maryland, in October 1861, it is sometimes hopefully assumed that the artist drew this scene from immediate experience, and then completed the canvas twenty years later. However, the stilted character of the figures and composition strongly suggests otherwise. The Boston Public Library also has a photograph donated in 1977 by Gen. Palfrey's granddaughter which shows Palfrey, Bartlett, other members of the regiment, and a dark horse at Camp Benton late in 1861 or early 1862. The group stands in front of the same rustic building seen in Homer's painting. The awkward juxtaposition of the principal figures in a single frontal plane, and absence of enlivening detail in the foreground suggests Homer extrapolated his composition from one or more photographs. The photograph now in the Library's collection is likely to have been a source, and may have been the only record of the regiment's officers at Camp Benton available to him.

The inevitable question occasioned by this painting is why Homer would undertake such a work at a point in his career when he could decline offers of commissions without hesitation. A reply can only be speculative: it is possible the patronage of Palfrey, a member of a prominent Boston family, was worth overriding his antipathy to art-by-dictation. The watercolor *Winding the Clock* (No. 1014), apparently was Gen. Palfrey's property immediately on its completion, which suggests it was at least a *de facto*

commission. If Homer had a connection with the Palfrey family it may have been difficult to deny a request from the General to create this momento of Civil War comradeship. It may also be worth considering the impact the Civil War experience had had on virtually every American who lived through it—presumably, including Winslow Homer. Memories of the War were just beginning to turn from nightmare to nostalgia in the 1880s. Homer may have been more receptive to making to order such a scene than he would have been for any other subject.

A symptom of Gen. Palfrey's artistic partialities may be recognized in the fact that he owned Homer's drawing known as *Trooper Meditating beside a Grave* (2:No. 273), probably acquired in the early 1870s. However, he also owned *Two Boys Rowing* (No. 940), acquired from Doll & Richards' December 1880 exhibition and sale of Homer's drawings and watercolors done in Gloucester that summer.

Homer's sole contribution to the Century Association's March 1881 exhibition, which occurred just ten days before his departure for England, was identified as *Portrait Group*. The painting was noted in the Association's ledger with an insurance valuation of $1,000, indicating it was sizable and executed in oil. This painting is essentially the only surviving Homer which suits this information and the timing of the exhibition. Homer's 1877 portrait of Lawson Valentine's daughters (No. 628) is his only other such composition involving more than one figure, and it was probably the work shown at the Century in March 1878. On neither of these occasions when Homer showed a portrait was it associated with the name of a lender, who would presumably have had some immediate connection to the subjects depicted. An oversight in recording ownership by someone other than the artist is certainly possible, but would have been unusual. The void may denote that the paintings came to the Century directly from Homer's studio, and had not yet been formally accepted by their sponsors.

PROVENANCE
Gen. Francis W. Palfrey, Boston, probably 1881; Louise C. Palfrey (Mrs. Francis W. Palfrey), Boston, 1889; the daughters of Gen. and Mrs. Francis Winthrop Palfrey, Boston, by 1897

EXHIBITIONS
Century Association, New York, 5 Mar. 1881, no. 22 (as *Portrait Group*) [?]

LITERATURE
Hendricks 1979, 144–45

1016

Bob's Dilemma

[1881]

"The Mowers"

Ink, graphite, watercolor on cardboard,
6⅜ × 10 (16.192 × 25.400) image

Yale University Art Gallery, New Haven, gift of
Allen Evarts Foster, B. A. 1906, 1965.33.11

Although Homer had not been a substantial
contributor to the illustrated journals since 1874,
he returned to the field at isolated intervals well
into the 1880s. In the 1860s and earlier 1870s he had
executed his graphic designs in the then standard
technology: the image was drawn directly on the
block and was lost as skilled engravers cut away
the wood to make the surface relief fit the printing
press. This image, published with the caption
"Bob: 'Hallo! What's up now? Are your babies in
here?'" in the July 1881 issue of *St. Nicholas* was
created by a different method. Homer's drawing
was reproduced on the block by photo transfer thus
providing a basic guide for the engraver, while the
original drawing remained at his disposal as his
model in creating the illustration.

Homer's technique here is somewhat different
than that of *Pumpkins among the Corn* (No. 662)
and probably the lost original drawing for "The
Sower" (No. 661), both published in the *Scribner's
Monthly* of August 1878. Like *Pumpkins among the
Corn*, the support is cardboard coated on one side
with a white glazing, however the drawing is created
in a combination of conventional linear elements and
light washes, and lines made by scratching through
dense washes to reveal the white background.

The size of the illustration on the magazine page
is 3½ inches by 5½ inches. The overall size of the
drawing's support is 10½ inches by 14 inches. LG
recorded the following notation in the margin:

On block 3½ × 5½
The Mowers. St. Nich.
2 cols.
O. K.
W. F. C.

A rubber-stamped form is on the reverse:

This Picture is presented to
by the Century Co.   18 . It has been engraved,
published and copyrighted by the Century Co.,
New York, and must not be reproduced or
published without consent.

The name supplied to fill in the blank following
"presented to" was W. F. Clarke.

A further inscription on the reverse was written
by Rodman Gilder, on Allen Foster's request after

No. 1016. Bob's Dilemma

Foster had acquired this drawing. (Rodman Gilder
was the son of Richard Watson Gilder, editor of
Scribner's Monthly and its successor, *The Century
Magazine*.)

W. Fayal Clarke was associate editor and later
editor of *St. Nicholas*, and a stock-holder in the
Century Co., publishers of St. N. Each year,
illustrations owned by the Co. were divided
among the stock-holders.

R. G.

ABG: From the beginning of his career through
the 1870s Homer frequently represented scythers at
work in their fields; he would have had no need for
a specific model on which to base his composition
of "Bob's Dilemma." However, the drawing *Man
Reaping* (No. 786) has conspicuous similarities to
this illustration, despite the fact the two works are
mirror images of each other.

Homer had departed New York for his extended
stay in England more than three months before the
illustration based on this drawing appeared in print.
It may be assumed he had made and sold his drawing
before he left the city, and possibly quite some time
before; that is, there is no way to be sure this is a
work done after 1 January 1881.

PROVENANCE
The Century Company, New York, 1881; W. Fayal
Clarke, New York, 1881; (Coleman Galleries,
8 Apr. 1938, general sale); Allen Evarts Foster,
New York, 1938

EXHIBITIONS
AI Chicago 2008

LITERATURE
St. Nicholas 8 (July 1881): 664

Color Illustrations

THE PAINTINGS illustrated in color in this volume are a liberal selection of the works known, or highly likely, to have been submitted by Homer, himself, to major exhibition venues. The illustrations are arranged to suggest the experience of Homer's art had by his contemporaries. Those which may be reasonably identified as having been included in a particular principal exhibition or exhibitions are captioned accordingly.

612

The New Novel

American Society of Painters in Water Colors,
New York, *Tenth Annual Exhibition*, 1877;
Century Association, New York, 1877

613

Blackboard

American Society of Painters in Water Colors,
New York, *Tenth Annual Exhibition*, 1877

614
Backgammon

American Society of Painters in Water Colors,
New York, *Tenth Annual Exhibition*, 1877;
Century Association, New York, 1877

619
Dressing for the Carnival

Century Association, New York, 1877

620

Sunday Morning in Virginia

Century Association, New York, 1877;
National Academy of Design, New York,
Fifty-fifth Annual Exhibition, 1880

627
Camp Fire

Century Association, New York, 1877; National
Academy of Design, New York, *Fifty-fifth Annual
Exhibition*, 1880

622

In the Mountains (or) A Fresh Morning

National Academy of Design, New York, *Fifty-third Annual Exhibition*, 1878

625
Two Guides

National Academy of Design, New York, *Fifty-third
Annual Exhibition*, 1878

628

Almira Houghton Valentine and Mary Chamberlain Valentine

Century Association, New York, 1878

637
Gathering Autumn Leaves

Century Association, New York, 1878

640
Autumn

Century Association, New York, 1877

641
Summer (or) Butterflies

643
Peach Blossoms

645
A Littoral Tile

651
Resting Shepherdess

Art Students' League, New York, 1878

654
Fireplace Surround:
Shepherd and Shepherdess

Century Association, New York, 1878

672
The Milk Maid

Century Association, New York, 1879

674

Pond and Willows, Houghton Farm

American Water Color Society, New York,
Twelfth Annual Exhibition, 1879

677
On the Hill

American Water Color Society, New York,
Twelfth Annual Exhibition, 1879

678
Girl Seated on Hillside Overlooking the Water

705

Girl Picking Clover

Wm. A. Butters & Co., Chicago, *Original Water Color and Charcoal Sketches from Nature by Winslow Homer, N. A.*, 1879

708
Apple Picking

American Water Color Society, New York,
Twelfth Annual Exhibition, 1879

716
Fishing

722

Girl with Hay Rake

American Water Color Society, New York,
Twelfth Annual Exhibition, 1879

721

On the Fence

American Water Color Society, New York,
Twelfth Annual Exhibition, 1879

723
Spring

American Water Color Society, New York,
Twelfth Annual Exhibition, 1879

724
On the Stile

727

Woman Seated on Bench

American Water Color Society, New York,
Twelfth Annual Exhibition, 1879

728

The Flock of Sheep, Houghton Farm

American Water Color Society, New York,
Twelfth Annual Exhibition, 1879

732
Bo-Peep

American Water Color Society, New York,
Twelfth Annual Exhibition, 1879

734
Tending Sheep, Houghton Farm

743
Autumn, Mountainville, New York

American Water Color Society, New York,
Twelfth Annual Exhibition, 1879

735
Fresh Air

American Water Color Society, New York,
Twelfth Annual Exhibition, 1879

736
The Reaper

745
Autumn Trees

Century Association, New York, 1879;
American Water Color Society, New York,
Twelfth Annual Exhibition, 1879

748

The Pumpkin Patch

American Water Color Society, New York,
Twelfth Annual Exhibition, 1879

759
Shepherdesses Resting

Wm. A. Butters & Co., Chicago, *Original Water
Color and Charcoal Sketches from Nature by Winslow
Homer*, N. A., 1879

765
The Yellow Jacket

766
Woman Reading under Oaks

767

Peach Blossoms

Gill's Art Galleries, and Springfield Art Association,
Springfield, Massachusetts *Fourth Annual Artists'
Exhibition*, 1881

771
Woman Driving Geese

769
Girl with Laurel

772

Spring: The Shepherdess of
Houghton Farm

National Academy of Design, New York,
Fifty-fourth Annual Exhibition, 1879

789

Man and Plow Horse

Wm. A. Butters & Co., Chicago, *Original Water
Color and Charcoal Sketches from Nature by Winslow
Homer*, N. A., 1879

808
Youth of S. T. Preston

832

Girl on a Swing

Daniel A. Mathews Art Gallery, New York, 1880

863
Girl with a Letter

864
Houses on Hill

869
The Shepherdess

874
By the Sea Side

Gill's Art Galleries, Springfield, Massachutts, 1880

877
Charles Savage Homer, Jr.

882
Sailing Out of Gloucester

900
Young Woman

903
Young Woman with a Parasol

911

Yacht in a Cove, Gloucester

Doll & Richards, Boston, 1880

914
Four Boys Bathing

915
Boys Bathing

Doll & Richards, Boston, 1880

917

Children Playing under a Gloucester Wharf

Doll & Richards, Boston, 1880

919
Boy in Boat, Gloucester

Doll & Richards, Boston, 1880

923

The Green Dory

Doll & Richards, Boston, 1880

925
Boy with Blue Dory

931
Gloucester Harbor

982
Gloucester Harbor, Fishing Fleet

987
Small Sloop

990
Two Sailboats

996
Two Schooners

Doll & Richards, Boston, 1880

995
Sailboats Off the Coast of Ten Pound Island

Doll & Richards, Boston, 1880

997
Schooner at Sunset

American Water Color Society, New York,
Fourteenth Annual Exhibition, 1881

998
Sunset Fires

999
Gloucester Sunset

1001

Sailboat and Fourth of July Fireworks

Doll & Richards, Boston, 1880

1000

Eastern Point Light

Doll & Richards, Boston, 1880; American
Water Color Society, New York, *Fourteenth
Annual Exhibition*, 1881

1007

The Lobster Pot

Doll & Richards, Boston, 1880

1008

Gloucester Harbor and Dory

Doll & Richards, Boston, 1880

1013
A Wreck near Gloucester

1014

Winding the Clock

American Water Color Society, New York,
Fourteenth Annual Exhibition, 1881

Record of Works by Winslow Homer
VOLUME III: 1877 TO MARCH 1881

was designed by Marcus Ratliff.
2,000 copies were printed in fall 2008
by Meridian Printing in East Greenwich, Rhode Island.